In the Dark of the Night

Women's Voices in Ukrainian Literature

In the Dark of the Night

Selected Prose Fiction

by

Dniprova Chayka

and

Lyubov Yanovska

Translated by Roma Franko
Edited by Sonia Morris

Language Lanterns Publications
1998

Canadian Cataloguing in Publication Data

Main entry under title:

Women's voices in Ukrainian literature

Contents: v. 1. The spirit of the times : selected
prose fiction / by Olena Pchilka and Nataliya
Kobrynska. - v. 2. In the dark of the night : selected
prose fiction / by Dniprova Chayka and Lyubov Yanovska.
ISBN 0-9683899-0-2 (v. 1) . - ISBN 0-9683899-1-0 (v. 2) .

1. Short stories, Ukrainian--Women authors--
Translations into English. 2. Ukrainian fiction--
19th century--Translations into English. 3. Ukrainian
fiction--20th century--Translations into English.
I. Franko, Roma Z. II. Morris, Sonia V.

PG3932.5.W65 W65 1998   891.7'93'01089287   C98-920168-6

Series design concept: © Roma Franko and Sonia Morris
Translations: © Roma Franko
Portrait sketches: © Raissa Sonia Choi
Editorial assistance: Paul Cipywnyk
Cover production and technical assistance: Mike Kaweski

© 1998 Language Lanterns Publications
   321-4th Ave. N., Saskatoon, SK, S7K 2L9
   Web site: www.languagelanterns.com

Printed and bound in Canada by
Hignell Printing Ltd., Winnipeg

Women's Voices in Ukrainian Literature

Lovingly dedicated to
our mother
Sonia Melnyk Stratychuk
whose indomitable spirit inspired this series

Titles in Print

The Spirit of the Times, 1998
In the Dark of the Night, 1998

Forthcoming Titles in the Series

But the Lord is Silent, 1999
From Heart to Heart, 1999
Warm the Children, O Sun, 1999

Introduction to the Series

The turn of a century marks a pause in time—a pause that impels us to take stock, assess the extent and significance of societal changes, and make sense of our individual and collective experiences. When the end of a century coincides with the millennium, this need to engage in retrospective analyses is intensified.

The purpose of this series is to make accessible to English readers the selected works of Ukrainian women writers, most of whom have not been previously translated into English, and, in so doing, enhance our understanding of women's slow, difficult, and ongoing trek to political, economic and social equality—a trek on which women in Ukraine embarked over a century ago.

The works selected range from vignettes and sketches to novelettes and novels. Together they constitute an unsystematic but compelling social history of an era during which the mortar of social mores, religious beliefs, and gender distinctions began to crumble as successive political and ideological cataclysms wreaked havoc with time-honoured personal and societal relations.

The authors are not equally talented or skilled. What they have in common is an appreciation of the power of literature, be it as an avenue of self-actualisation or a vehicle of social activism. In addition to national, political, and educational issues, they address matters of gender which cut across ethnic and social divisions, and explore the power and often devastating consequences of social conditioning.

They do not, of course, speak with one voice. For some, women's concerns are overshadowed by larger issues of political freedom, cultural autonomy, and socio-economic reform. Their goals range from group emancipation to individual freedom, with many initially defining their emerging status in terms of a synthesis of traditional female roles, immediate community responsibilities, and more general humanitarian imperatives.

More importantly, whatever the subject matter, they observe and interpret experience from a female perspective. They intuitively understand that women forge their identities in the context of relationships, appreciate the power inherent in this need for connectedness and emotional wholeness, and demonstrate a keen sensitivity to both the promise and the human cost of change.

Their voices are loud and strong, what they have to say is worth hearing, and their impact should not be confined to one time or place. Translating their stories into English permits their message to transcend temporal and geographical boundaries.

The difficulties inherent in the process of translation were compounded by textual variations and vexing problems of transliteration. In the case of the earlier works, there were two other problems: archaic and dialectal language, and nineteenth century stylistic conventions. Ultimately, it was the criterion of readability that informed the many difficult decisions that had to be made.

A biographical note about each author anchors her writings in a social and historical context. No other analyses are provided; the works are allowed to speak for themselves.

Sonia Morris, Editor
Former Assistant Dean of the College of Education,
Former Head of the Department of Educational Psychology,
College of Education, University of Saskatchewan

Roma Franko, Translator
Former Head of the Department of Slavic Studies
and the Department of Modern Languages and Literatures,
College of Arts and Science, University of Saskatchewan

Contents

Contents

Dniprova Chayka

1861-1927

Biographical Sketch

Lyudmyla Berezyna-Vasylevska was born in southern Ukraine near the estuary of the Dnipro River. Her father was a severe and autocratic Russian village priest who made life very difficult for his family, and it was her kind and loving Ukrainian mother who protected her and nurtured her innate love of beauty.

As the family moved from village to village, Lyudmyla developed an intuitive appreciation of the rich and varied customs, beliefs, folk songs, and folk tales of her people. She received a good formal education and, after completing her schooling in a private gymnasium in Odessa, worked as a private tutor, a teacher in a village school, and a high school instructor in Odessa.

It was during this period in her life that Lyudmyla embarked on her lifelong labour of love—collecting Ukrainian folk songs and folklore materials. Her youthful enthusiasm for the oral tradition of the peasants led to her participation in an archaeological-ethnographical conference held in Odesa in 1884; at this conference the aspiring young writer presented three notebooks containing an impressive collection of folk songs.

In 1885, Lyudmyla married Feofan Vasylevsky, a Ukrainian historian and publicist, who worked as a statistician. An ardent Ukrainian patriot, he actively opposed the tsarist decrees that severely restricted the use of the Ukrainian language and impeded the development of Ukrainian literature and culture within the Russian Empire. Because of his involvement in Ukrainian organizations, he was released from his position, and the young couple fell upon hard times.

There were periods when both Lyudmyla and her husband found themselves under police surveillance because of their participation in subversive political movements. Her publications aroused the ire of the authorities; in 1905, she was arrested briefly for her writings, and her manuscripts were confiscated.

Lyudmyla Berezyna-Vasylevska, a modest and unassuming woman who wanted to protect her privacy, chose to write under the pseudonym of "Dniprova Chayka" ("The Seagull of the Dnipro"). This nom de plume was a most fitting one for a writer of a romantic bent, for not only was she born near the Dnipro River, but, in Ukrainian poetry and folk songs, the image of a lamenting seagull symbolizes a mother weeping for her children, or Ukraine bemoaning the sad fate of her people.

Dniprova Chayka published her first works—lyrical poetry, prose poems, and short stories—in journals and newspapers in both Eastern and Western Ukraine. She was strongly encouraged in her literary efforts by Ivan Franko, the leading writer and critic of the day, who held her talent in high regard. Warmly welcomed into the ranks of the literati, she counted many prominent Ukrainian writers, including the women authors featured in this series, among her friends and acquaintances.

In addition to her poetical works and short stories, Dniprova Chayka wrote poetry and fairy tales for children, and her great love of music led her to write the libretto for several children's operettas that have become Ukrainian classics, such as *Koza dereza (The Roguish Goat), Pan Kotsky (Sir Cat)* and *Zymova kralya (The Snow Queen).* The scores for these operettas were written by Mykola Lysenko, a famous Ukrainian composer, who also set several of her lyrical poems to music and collaborated with her in transcribing the melodies of the folk songs from her collection.

Following the birth of her three children, ill health and material circumstances forced Lyudmyla Berezyna-Vasylevska to abandon her writing and devote her time and energy to the demands of motherhood. She ensured that all her children had the best possible education: her older daughter studied medicine in France, while her son and younger daughter graduated from specialized post-secondary institutes in Kyiv.

In an entry made in her personal journal in the early 1880s, the young Lyudmyla wrote: "I feel like a chrysalis that is being transformed into a butterfly. But a butterfly's wings unfold in response to the sun, warmth, and the spring air, while my wings grow in response to the love of those who surround me."

Unfortunately, although her husband was very fond of her, he did not understand her creative nature; therefore, after their children were grown, they separated and, until her death in 1927, she lived with her older daughter in Kyiv.

In addition to writing in Ukrainian, Dniprova Chayka wrote lyrical poetry in Russian and translated Russian and Swedish literature into Ukrainian. Many of her works were published posthumously on the basis of archival materials that have since been lost.

Dniprova Chayka was one of the first writers to introduce into Ukrainian literature the new literary movement of Symbolism which, by the 1890s, was spreading from France through all of Europe, and her lyrical poems and prose poems contributed to the development of Ukrainian Modernism. Her short stories, however, written under the influence of populism, belong to the ethnographic-realistic school of literature.

The Voltairian
(1896)

"Madam! Oh, madam! Are you as uncomfortable in this carriage as I am? I told that scoundrel Levko, 'pack it well with straw and make a nice hollow in the middle'—but he didn't! And now, I swear to God, my insides are all shaken up. But then, I'm a man, praise the Lord; I'm stronger and healthier and, after all, I'm a peasant, praise God. But for a lady, well . . . Ladies are delicate, unaccustomed to the likes of this!"

This is what Stepan, my driver—with whom I often had the occasion to travel—said when he turned around to address me. Stepan hated to travel in silence, and he felt that the best way of initiating a conversation with me was to ask me how comfortable I was. It was like a preamble.

In actual fact, however, he really did sympathise with me, for he himself was scrawny and sickly. The servants did not think of him as a man, and they all teased him, calling him "Chicken."

The jolting of the old carriage bothered him as much as it bothered me. No matter how carefully Stepan drove, all the hay and straw—notwithstanding how well it had been packed— invariably fell apart whenever the carriage crossed small dams and went up inclines, and he had more trouble than enough trying to repack it.

I had to travel with Stepan in all kinds of weather, and there was only one difference: in dry weather, Stepan berated Levko for not packing the carriage properly and railed about the dust that covered us and made it difficult to breathe; in bad weather, he upbraided the steward for not providing enough fodder for the horses, and the lord for allowing a tender young lady to go out in such a "shaker" in bad weather. And he complained about the rain and the sun, and admonished the wind.

And when Stepan got good and angry, even God got a good raking over.

In order to divert his conversation to other topics, I would say laughingly: "But Stepan, what if Father Pymen could hear you now? He'd certainly make you do penance!"

"Oh, who gives a fig about Father Pymen! What penance do I need other than the one I already do all day long, every day? My father-in-law, my mother-in-law, my wife—they're all at me, all the time. And that's not all; the wretched women have taught the children to give me the finger, as if to say 'let's give it to the son of a bitch' . . . Do you believe it? I swear to God it's true!

"Well, you were just saying: sin and penance . . .

"What kind of sin was I born with that I've been doing penance from the day of my birth?

"How did I harm anyone while I was still a child? Just by virtue of the fact that I was born? But I didn't will it—I did not ask to be born!

"And when I was growing up, didn't I work? Didn't I hire myself out? Didn't I do as I was told? Did I squander away everything in drink, or did I steal anything? Didn't I go to live with my in-laws when my wife Hannah wanted me to? And you know what it's like to live with your in-laws; it's like falling head first into a kneading bowl full of dough—you would gladly pull away from it, but the dough just sticks to you.

"So why am I being punished both by God and by people? And why don't I get any sympathy from anybody—why? And yet they say that He's just and merciful, that He sees everything and knows everything. But if He sees everything, why does He allow ill fortune to befall a person?

"I once was on a pilgrimage in Kyiv, and I went to confession, and asked a monk about this—they said he was blessed and had the gift of prophesy.

"And he said to me: 'My child, you are falling into temptation.'

"But, I thought: what does this temptation matter to God? For He knows everything—not only what a person has done and what he will do, but even what he's thinking, and what he will think and do, whether he's been tempted or not!

"So does He just sit up there in the sky and watch people as they crawl around on the earth like worms and go into convulsions and writhe when they are struck down by ill fortune? So are we just His toys, or what?

"I've asked people about this many a time, and they just say: 'You're a fool, but you want to be smarter than everyone.'

"And they say that it's not the business of peasants to try to understand things like that!

"But if it isn't my business, then why did God give me this head? Why has He crammed it full of ideas like that?

"Did they come from the devil? But it was God Himself who created the devil, as well.

"And then again—of what use is the devil to God?

"Why does He need all that trouble with him? Why does God need to have that horned, vile beast tormenting people—His children—for all eternity?"

I would listen for a long time, and then ask: "Where did you get infected with such ideas, Stepan? Did you come up with them yourself, or are there others among your countrymen who are saying the same thing? And do they agree with you?"

"Well, you see, my lady, most of my ideas just come to me, and then I raise these questions with others. There are some who understand me, like Arkhyp and Serhiy, for example.

"But—how can I explain it to you?—this idea of mine, this train of thought, never stops, never goes to sleep. It keeps gnawing and gnawing away at me like a termite. But as for the others, it's as if their ideas are dozing; once in a while they blink their eyes, and then they drowse off again.

"It's probably because they're fatter than I am!" Stepan added with a smile, turning to me his gaunt, pointed little face with its bushy eyebrows, uneasy grey eyes, and thin lips under a sparse, blond moustache.

His lively and sensitive face, and his entire figure, which was scrawny and nervous, made him different from the other servants. It was not surprising that the other servants laughed at him and said he was "not a man but a chicken, or the devil knows what."

Stepan's life at home was bad.

The family that he joined was quite large: three women—his wife, his mother-in-law, and the mother-in-law's mother-in-law—two girls, and his father-in-law. And even though the father-in-law was healthy, he was lazy, and a drunkard as well, and so Stepan had to work on behalf of everyone to support everyone.

They say he was on the thin side even as a young man, but after ten years in such a family he had become as skinny as a rake. He began to grow weak in the chest, and when he did not have the strength to work, the women would torment him almost to death, and his drunken father-in-law would try to pick a fight with him. It was then that Stepan would abandon everything and go someplace to hire himself out. His family did not try to stop him; they simply took all his earnings away from him.

When Stepan worked for hire, he was fed better, and no one tormented him, and so his health would gradually begin to improve. But, as soon as he began to feel better, he would begin to think more and more, and he would share his wild ideas with other people, scaring them with his provocative questions.

He worked for lords, in factories, and on estates. He did not, however, like to live for any length of time in priests' homes, so as soon as he was well-nourished, he would leave them.

"It's boring," he said. "You eat and eat like a hog, and sleep until your eyes swell, and sit all alone, as if you were cursed. There's no singing, and no talking; you just sit alone, day after day, like a screech owl."

"What do you mean, there's no one to talk with there? Why, *batushky [Russian Orthodox priests]* are ever so eloquent and knowledgeable."

"Oh, don't talk to me about priests. They talk sweetly to you until they have you in their grasp, and then, you better look out—they either snort and scoff at you or yell at you about the work, and it's no use even asking what they're yelling about.

"Take Father Pymen, he made fun of me in such a strange way for what I was saying that it's almost impossible to explain."

"What was it he said?"

"Well! He said: 'You're a devil's Voltairian!' Now, what exactly is a 'Voltairian'? I understand what 'a devil's' means, but the other word is something very strange . . . And it's very hard when all kinds of ignorant people pick it up and taunt you with it!"

Stepan often worked at the factory or the sugar refinery, but he could not keep up for long with the healthy strapping men who worked there. Moreover, he took issue with the fact that workers were not treated like people, but like objects or " numbers," which he pronounced "lumbers."

He worked most frequently for lords, because peasants could not bring him back to health. He liked our rather small estate the best, because the people here were his own fellow peasants, and he had his favourite spot in the niche between the stove and the wall in the small, warm bunkhouse.

Most of all, however, he liked the fact that in our small household it was easy to go from one job to another; he could be a shepherd or a herdsman for a while, and then he could move to the barn and tend to the cattle and horses. There he felt right at home. The old horses recognised and welcomed him, and the young ones quickly became accustomed to him; he knew exactly what to do there, and everyone knew him as an excellent and caring groom.

In time, Stepan came to regard me as a friend, because even though I travelled quite frequently, I did not put on airs.

And travelling was what Stepan liked to do best; he would amble along, letting the horses graze wherever he could. He would water them, slow them down going into ravines, and not rush them going uphill. And he had his fill of talking with me; and if I fell silent, he pretended to talk to the horses.

Wherever we went, he immediately made friends with the other grooms, drivers, and servants. He would get the latest news from them, and then we would be on the road again. And, on the road, he would weave the news, like yarn, into the warp of his strange vignettes.

Once, on Holy Thursday—the dough for the *paska [braided circular Easter bread]* was just being started—the chambermaid, white with fear, called me out and said that Stepan had come from the village (he was not in service at our place just then).

I went out and looked—an apparition stood before me! Stepan's pointed face had become still sharper, he was pale as death, his hands and feet were trembling, and his hair was standing on end.

"What's wrong?"

"Vva-vva. . . ." his lips were trembling so badly that he could not say anything else.

"God help you! What happened?"

They gave him some water to drink and then splashed him with it three times.

He began to come to, as if awakening from a bad dream, and shouted insanely: "Lady! Give me your rifle! I'll shoot the whole devil's brood and wipe their stench off the face of the earth, damn them all to hell!"

It took all my efforts to soothe him and persuade him to sit and calm down a little. Then I asked him to wait while I checked the *paska* dough, for he was almost out of his mind, and I could see that it was impossible to talk to him.

A half hour went by.

I came out and began questioning him—he was a little calmer now.

It turned out that the women in his house had tormented him because they had no finely ground wheat flour for the *paska*, and when he replied that he was not working anywhere at the time and had no means of earning money, they jumped him and beat him up. Now he was ashamed to look even his own children in the face, let alone other people.

He took away a sack of flour on credit, carried it home, began to work for us again, and did not even visit his family at Easter to exchange traditional holiday greetings and kisses.

And so we resumed our joint trips and, along with them, our conversations.

One fine day we were driving to the station.

It was the first Sunday after Easter, the day when graves are blessed.

The air was fresh, the birds were chirping, the fragrant birch trees appeared to be covered in a fine green down, and the clear azure sky above the glade was boundlessly high. The oaks were still barren, but near their roots the grass was a thick carpet of green, speckled with tiny flowers. It was so pleasant and cheery that one was moved to laugh, and talk, and sing.

This mood was reflected in everyone who met or overtook us as they made their way to the noonday liturgy or returned home from early matins.

Both to the left and the right of the road, little groups of young women, men, and older women were brightly outlined against the green backdrop of the grass.

Throngs of children were running around among the tree trunks and the bushes on both sides of the road. The young women, decked out in dark blue, brightly flowered kerchiefs, carried small bundles and packages, and many clasped infants to their bosoms. The girls, bedecked with ribbons or flowers, wore poppy-red skirts, embroidered blouses, and coral beads.

The young men, in new vests, green and checkered sashes, and cherry red caps flashed by in a happy, boisterous throng.

All that was missing was the customary singing, for it was a Sunday morning, and there was a service in the church. And it was only Stepan's gloomy figure in his light wool grey cloak that marred the happy scene, and not only because he swayed slowly and uncertainly before me like a dark blot, but because I sensed, under his exterior, an even darker and more troubling blemish on his soul.

"Oh, just look!" Stepan turned to me as he pointed his whip handle at the women folk. "Do you see how sad they are? They were just having masses said for their deceased parents. May you be cursed with your loud jabbering! Giddy-yap!"

Stepan took his anger out on the horses, lashing them with his whip with all his strength. The horses tore off, raced through the glade without pausing, and rushed up to the dam; the carriage bounced up and down, all its iron parts clattered, and I had to hang on with both hands in order not to tumble out.

Stepan began hissing and sharply drew in the reins.

"May evil times damn you! If one has to drive like this in the next world as well, then may the devil take it!"

In the meantime, the horses slowed to a trot, and farther on, in some sand, they came to a complete stop.

"Why are you so angry, Stepan? You almost shook the living daylights out of me! What have I done to annoy you?" I asked laughingly.

Stepan scowled and snorted; then he slung the reins over the corner of the coach-box, put the whip to one side, and threw one foot over the coach bow, so that he was facing me. This was a sign that the conversation was to be a long one.

"Well, what would you think? Nothing pains me more than that kind of ignorance. Now then, tell me, you're educated, enlightened, so do these superstitions have such power over you as well? I haven't noticed that somehow, but then again, I don't know . . . perhaps I'm mistaken . . . and I'd like to know how you look at it."

"At what, exactly?"

"At these masses for the dead. You see, what I'm saying is that a man lives, suffers, sins, repents, and then once again he forgets about God, treats people badly, sins even more, and then dies. This time, he hasn't repented of his sins.

"Immediately, his wife, mother, and father begin crying and beseeching God: 'O God, cleanse him of his sins! O God, forgive him! O God, accept him into Your heavenly kingdom. And we, so to say, will pay you for it!'—a peasant has to pay for everything everywhere!

"Well, it goes without saying that people feel sorry for their own! And the priests are listening to it all: 'Yes, indeed, your Kuzma—or Sydir—was a sinner! He won't see the heavenly kingdom; he'll fall under Lucifer's rule if his blood relatives don't buy him out with prayer and offerings.'

"And they tell you about such a lot of things: the fiery Gehenna, and the gnashing of teeth, and the unending wailing, and the abyss of the nether world!

"And the little old women strive to do their utmost, because in their own terror and ignorance they paint the scenes for themselves as vividly as if they could actually see them: the huge cauldrons filled with boiling tar, the hooks for hanging people, the red-hot frying pans, and all sorts of devils—horned ones, long-tailed ones, short-tailed ones, fiends, demons, spotted little devils—and even the pitchforks with which the devils prod the sinners in the cauldrons; they see all this in great detail.

"I've listened to them more than once. And then I ask them: 'How do you know all this? Who has seen this with their own eyes? Has anyone ever returned from that other world?'

"But no one up to now has succeeded in proving it to me— they just heap a lot of abuse on me," Stepan said, flicking his whip to start the horses.

At first, they picked up their pace leisurely, without heeding the whip that was waving erratically over them. They knew that Stepan was not paying any attention to them when he waved the whip around so ineffectually.

"And so, to save the souls of their departed ones, our old women bring offerings of flat cakes, apples, and honey; some even bring fish or a roasted chicken. They say that when you bring a dish to church, then at the very moment that the priest mumbles over it— God puts the same kind of dish before the soul of the departed, and it begins to eat and gain in strength. A soul! Eating! With what is it to eat, when its teeth, and its innards, and its whole body have rotted? And why does it need to eat? Whom is it strengthening when nothing can help the corpse?"

Stepan suddenly turned to the horses: "Let's go, my little ones, let's go! Giddy-yap! Oh, you evil one! Hey!

"But is there really a soul? What do you think, my lady? What do wise people think? After all, educated people know a lot; they have lenses that make it possible to see things no matter how tiny they are.

"The medical assistant was telling me once about cholera; they caught it in a droplet and saw it. I swear to God, the young medical assistant even let me take a look at it. He said: 'It's very tiny, like a tadpole, and it has a tail.' But no matter how hard I pressed my eye to it I couldn't see it—I didn't know how to do it. But some of the other fellows saw it.

"So, what I'm saying is that they managed to catch the cholera and to come up with medicine for it, so couldn't they invent a glass or some other kind of tool to seize a soul by its little tail, or to catch a glimpse of it for just a moment? But it's no use, I guess.

"Let's go, my children! Let's go my little ones!" he shouted at the horses.

"There's nothing in the world that I want more than to know if a person really has a soul and how it survives without a body," he continued.

"Neither I nor other people know this, Stepan!"

"That's just it! Wise, clever people study all sorts of things, but they don't know what's most important. They've invented all kinds of contraptions to feed and amuse the body, but as for the soul— well, it's too bad, but nobody feeds it. It's hungry, it shouts and wails, and it searches for meaning in life, but it's immediately hushed, or it's told things that are fit to be said only to little children. But these wise people voluntarily accept this nonsense and even forbid others to ask about it."

Stepan, agitated and tired, fell silent, and the silence dragged on for quite a while.

Only an oriole whistled, and a nightingale sang out. Green scenes flowed before my eyes—small groves and stands of trees alternated with sown fields; a gentle breeze and a spring song sung by a multitude of voices flooded my ears.

Despite myself, everything was lulling me to sleep, and I was startled and almost fell out of the open carriage when Stepan suddenly called out to me.

"In my opinion, my lady, a cow grows and grows, and the same with a tree. Or take this grain," he pointed at it with his whip handle, "it grows, forms ears, flaunts itself, turns yellow—and then it's mature. It's mown down and threshed; its kernels are ground and eaten; its straw is either eaten by the cattle or it's burned—and that's it! Everything changes back into manure or ashes. Or take a cow or even a horse: it grows, lives, rejoices, works—then suddenly—it drops dead! It dies and changes back into manure.

"But where is that something that grew in it, that rejoiced, feared, suffered? It's no longer there! They say that people have a soul, and animals have vapour.

"Well, fine.

"A person lives: he grows, rejoices, toils, loves, hates, deceives, fights, sins, prays—then death comes, and suddenly everything comes to an end. And there is no soul, nor anything by which to recognise it. Like a plant that has nothing in it, like cattle that have only vapours, so too with a person: he dies—and there is no sign of a soul.

"So in what way is a person's soul better than the vapour of cattle, or that 'nothing' in a plant? There's nothing there, and there's nothing here! You lived, loved, fought, suffered—and that's all you're left with!

"You lived, and you were a person; you die, and you lose both your body and your soul—so why is it necessary to hold masses for it? Why fool yourself that God will place it on a stool in paradise and set a little dish before it? And what need have I of that paradise, when the joy in it is so meagre—a little dish and that's it! My soul is hungry now, it's searching for the truth, it's seeking answers to my questions, and they talk to me about 'a little dish'."

Stepan's unremittingly sad discourse ended on such a bitter and fiery note that it snapped and reverberated like a musical string that was stretched too tautly.

We travelled on. And I could not find within me a single idea with which to console his poor suffering soul, or the tiniest bit of strength to save it.

We were nearing the train station. A freight train whistled.

Stepan lightly tapped the horses with his whip, but they had already perked up their ears and were moving their legs more swiftly.

When we were just about at the station, Stepan suddenly reined them in and turned to me in a feverish manner.

"I've made you sad, my lady! But tell me, please, if you would be so kind, tell me the truth as to what you think: can it really be that a person does not have a soul? After all, I can think. I embrace the entire world with my thoughts. Can my thoughts really be only a delusion, and I only a heap of bones and meat? Can it be that the thinking is being done by these miserable bones of mine, by this sickly meat, and that there's nothing better than them? Is it really . . ."

The bell rang in the station, the whistle resounded. The startled horses tore off so swiftly that Stepan had to use all his strength to control them.

And so Stepan did not receive a reply from me to his agonising questions.

And what could I have said to him?

Has She Settled Her Accounts?
(1899)

A sombre silence shrouded the lord's manor. Vitya, the little five-year-old lord, was lying on his deathbed. The entire household was heavy-laden with sorrow. The maidservants walked about on tiptoe and spoke in whispers. Even the doctor, instead of being driven right up to the porch by carriage, was dropped off twice a day on the little bridge from where he had to make his way to the house through the flower beds. Lady Lehowska, the young widow of a famous engineer, had turned waxen and was wasting away. Vitya was her only child, her only link to her beloved and unforgettable deceased husband. And this link was very fine and tenuous.

The birth of the child had been precipitated by the terrible fright she experienced when her husband, who was inspecting a flour mill he was constructing, was crushed to death by a collapsing stone wall. The lady almost died from grief. And Vitya, born prematurely at seven months, lay silently for two more months among warm pillows before emitting his first cry—on the very day he was to have been born. This cry was not like that of a child, but rather like the squeak of a mouse. Even this, however, was enough for the mother, especially as the eyes looking out at her from the tiny wrinkled face increasingly began to resemble the clear blue eyes of Lord Lehowsky, her deceased husband.

The young mother unreservedly poured all her strength, her love, and her entire soul into this sickly little creature. The maidservants found it strange, and even amusing, that the lady, taking delight in watching her child grow, expected others to see in him the beauty she beheld.

"He's just like a little monkey!" the maidservants whispered among themselves. "A changeling of some kind! If he were one of ours, we would pray to the Lord to have him die quickly, because he'll grow up to be a cripple."

But the lady was of a different mind.

The child did not start to talk until quite late and began to walk even later. The doctors ordered that he be taken abroad for treatment at a spa. The lady did not hesitate. She left her entire estate in the hands of an administrator and began travelling far and wide with her dear child.

Unfortunately, no matter where she went, and what different treatments were tried, nothing came of it. The ailing child stayed weak and pale, like a potato sprout in a cellar in the spring. When he finally did begin to walk on his curving, crooked little legs, a small hump began to protrude on his back.

As time went by, the child's hump grew bigger, while his little arms and legs became thinner. But his comely little head, with its clear blue eyes, increased so greatly in intellect that even a ten-year-old would have been burdened by it.

People came from far and near to have a look at the little freak, and they gazed upon him with horror, or aversion, or both. Everyone said he was not meant to live on this earth, that such children never amount to anything. Only the mother did not recognise this. To her, the crippled hunchback was more attractive than the most beautiful people in the world, and she spared nothing in her efforts to rear him.

She travelled continuously for five years, until finally one God-fearing doctor advised her to stop wasting her money and torturing her child. He told her to return to her own country, where both she and her invalid son might find some peace.

As soon as the news of their impending arrival reached the manor, everyone began bustling about. Those who had been taken advantage of by the administrator looked forward to the lady's arrival as people await God's morning dew. The administrator's underlings began to have qualms about the pilfering he had condoned, and which they hoped she would not discover. The administrator himself hurriedly began to rewrite the office ledgers. Knowing full well whose cat had eaten the bacon, he began making preparations to flee.

The Lehowsky estate had more debts than an orchard has branches. But in the neighbouring district, a new estate had arisen. It bore the name of the lady's administrator—Yastshembsky.

When the last telegram from the lady was delivered to the manor, everyone's nerves became taut, like the strings of a violin.

The lady arrived. The entire household turned out to greet her, for there were still many servants who had known her as a young girl. Peasants from the village also came in large numbers, for even though the administrator continued yelling at them, they had a feeling his profiteering days were over, and they no longer feared him.

The lady greeted everyone kindly, but she did not move away, even for an instant, from the side of the foreign nanny who was carrying Vitya. If he so much as whimpered, she would immediately leave everyone and rush to him.

"Oh, my Lord! He'll be a cripple forever!" the old women lamented.

"But what a nice face he has! And what expensive clothes he's wearing!" the young women said admiringly.

The men reviewed the situation as they left the manor. "Well, fellows, it's probably no use trying to get things straightened out. This lady is interested only in her little hunchback."

A few days went by. The little tyke, no longer subjected to any treatments, began to show some improvement. He eagerly roamed about the orchard, and the spring air seemed to bring strength to him and peace to his mother.

Eventually, some of the people did make oblique and cautious approaches to the lady, alluding to all kinds of matters relating to the administrator's stewardship. When she learned that her maternal legacy was being bled and utterly ruined by a stranger with rapacious hands and the conscience of a wolf, she shuddered, and her heart—despite the degree to which it was devoted to Vitya—was filled with pain.

The widow had no choice but to take things into her own hands. She found all the accounting ledgers and farm records, read through them, and recalled what her father had once taught her about assuming control over her own estate. Having requested that all the books and documents from the office be brought to her, she began checking them painstakingly.

She laboured over her work for days on end, noting in the clean white ledgers submitted by the administrator the information the people were secretly providing her. The more she dug, the more deeply she plunged into the abyss of cheating and intrigue that had been indulged in during her absence.

The people who had been wronged began to lift their heads. The administrator sought every possible pretext to make the lady lose her composure. He even attempted to engage her in quarrels to prevent her from making a true accounting and to ensure that she, and not he, would be the embarrassed loser.

In the meantime, little Vitya, left almost entirely in the hands of the foreign nanny, wandered about all day long as if he were a healthy child. He delighted in the bright sun, the flowers, and the charming Ukrainian spring. It is hard to say if it was because the nanny did not know how to protect him, or if his fragile body could not tolerate all the intoxicating pleasures, or if, perhaps, the time allotted to him by fate had finally run out, but before long, Vitya began to fail and grow feeble. Finally, he became bedridden.

The mother's heart ached, but she had to continue working on the accounts, for the administrator, agreeably but craftily, was now turning to her for instructions on to how to run the farm. He left everything up to her and did almost nothing himself.

The mother had a small desk brought in and placed next to the little bed with its muslin canopy. Keeping track of every breath and movement of the child with her heart, and assuming that his eyes were closed in slumber, she continued counting and adding.

But he was not sleeping, and he watched his mother through his eyelashes. Even now, however, his pale lips, which were accustomed to holding back all expressions of pain, did not betray any injured feelings or complaints that his mother was neglecting him . . . that she no longer loved him . . . that she was amusing herself with those detested books and accounts and forgetting all about him.

One night the little fellow became very ill. At dawn the lady sent for the administrator. When he did not comply with her request, she ran to him herself and told him to fetch the doctor as quickly as possible, regardless of where the latter might be.

"You could send the coachman or the hired hand. Why are you troubling me? After all, I'm not a machine."

"My child is dying! Do you understand?" the lady shouted.

"What's it to me? Am I to bend over backwards trying to help him? I'm neither God, nor a doctor . . . "

The distraught, unnerved mother did not stop to consider that the administrator was taking advantage of the situation to pick a fight. She forgot about everything in the world and, like any mother of a sick child, she let loose with a litany of things that were better left unsaid.

"Ah! If that's how things are, I thank you very much! And I am no longer your servant! My honour does not permit it!" He turned sharply on his heel and made his exit, delighted that the solution to his problem was approaching all by itself.

A few hours later, having learned from the doctor that Vitya had only two or three days left to live, he made rapid preparations for his departure.

"Don't let him go, my lady! Listen to what we're saying! Don't let him go until he gives you a complete accounting of everything," her trusted workers advised her.

But she could not think about that now. The small desk was shoved to one side as soon as Vitya requested that his mother devote herself completely to him. The receipts and tiny scraps of notes were scattered, and a maidservant, sent by the administrator, surreptitiously retrieved them from the garbage.

The poor child suffered, and his mother's anguish was intensified by his tearful pleas to save him and his eagerness to try any drugs the doctor could think of. But it was all in vain— the burning desire of the mother, the medicines prescribed by the doctor, the daily prayer services, and the generous alms given to the poor.

Within three days, Vitya was dead.

"All is lost now," the old hired man said. He had still clung to the hope of informing the lady fully about everything and of having her pursue the fleeing swindler.

It was a warm, sunny day when a church procession, complete with waving banners, gathered in the yard of the manor. Children, dressed in their Sunday best, came from every corner of the village and carried the brocade-covered coffin, laden with lilies of the valley, into the orchard. There, a grave had been dug under a melancholy juniper tree. And so the little lord was buried, and a fine funeral dinner was served in his memory.

In the meantime, without being noticed by anyone, the administrator departed. He emptied the cashbox, leaving only the keys to the office and a note explaining on what the money had supposedly been spent.

This situation was brought to the attention of the lady. But she sat like a stone by the empty little bed and would not move.

What could be done? Where was one to begin?

One day went by, and then another. The lady did not utter a sound. She just fluttered from room to room like a wounded seagull . . .

All the while, the servants were waiting for orders. They went to work, but performed their duties in a perfunctory manner, because they did not know how things would turn out, or if they would ever be paid the money they had earned. Finally, the old hired man, who had taken the management of the estate into his own hands for the time being, told the maidservants in no uncertain terms either to come up with a plan themselves or to advise him what to do in order to distract the lady and make her come to her senses.

They all agreed to turn for assistance to old Granny Vekla, a midwife who had lived through much in her lifetime. If she could not come up with a solution, then goodness knows if anything could be done.

And so, despite the fact that the lady had given strict orders not to admit anyone and not to keep in touch with any of the neighbours, wise old Granny Vekla made her appearance in the manor house. The statuesque, self-confident old woman stepped into the lady's room and, paying no heed to her protestations, drew her close like a little child, blessed her, and began to talk to her.

She did not mention Vitya, comfort the lady, or pity her. Instead, she stated sharply and preemptorily that a lady who was responsible for the lives of so many people and for such a large household did not have the right to forsake everything and lock herself up with her grief—especially when all the workers who had been wronged and robbed were waiting for her to act, and when the time had come to find and punish those who had committed these wrongs.

Little by little, the lady regained her senses. At first, she only listened and stared; then she started asking questions; and finally, without realising it, she began to speak of her own accord. The wise old woman spent two days working her powers on her. During this time, the servants of the manor just winked at one another, as if to say that this old one knew what she was doing.

Then, one night, waking from a dream about Vitya, the lady suddenly began to wail, shedding such bitter and painful tears that the old woman and the maidservants all rushed to her and fussed over her until dawn. Where had all those tears come from? How was it possible that her soul had not flowed out with them? But the old woman knew it was all for the best. The poor lady shouted in vain that she no longer cared about anything, that she no longer needed anything, that she did not care if Yastshembsky stole the entire estate—he could not possibly rob her of more than what fate had robbed her of when Vitya was taken from her. The old granny listened to it all and let her talk until she was completely exhausted.

The maidservants, who were listening behind the door, spread the sad news throughout the manor that the lady seemed to have lost her mind. For really, who could cope with all that had happened to her? Her child was dead (that was God's will, of course), and she had been robbed, royally robbed, of money that ran into the thousands.

Well, no matter how things actually happened, the lady slowly began to look after her household again. She asked a few of the neighbours to help her complete the accounts, and then she went to court to recover from Yastshembsky at least part of the sum that she had already earmarked to found a hospital and a school in Vitya's memory.

After some time, things began to settle into their normal routine. The lady, however, still walked around in mourning, and sorrow never left her face. It was as if she were afraid that even the tiniest smile might wash off her grief. She only smiled with her eyes at Granny Vekla whenever she caught sight of her in the distance, saying: "It was she who made me a whole person again."

The lady regretted that the old woman would not accept payment for her assistance. But that was what the old woman's character was like—if she did not want something, you could even threaten to kill her, and it would not make any difference. And so the lady was left feeling indebted to her.

In the meantime, however, during her ramblings in the woods, the lady often drew near the village, where she had seldom gone before. Quite unintentionally, she found out how people lived there, and she began to ponder the difference between her life as a lady and the lives of the common people.

One fine morning, as she was strolling leisurely down a path, she approached a house at the very edge of the village. There, she heard someone lamenting, but so loudly—that God forbid! She recognised the house—it belonged to Hapa. When she had passed by this house yesterday, she had seen first a funeral, and then a funeral dinner at which the agile young woman was moving about briskly—indeed, almost merrily—as she served the guests. There had not been a single tear or a sign of despondency. She was so amazed at the time, that she felt jealous of this young woman who was so physically and spiritually strong.

But just listen to what was happening now! It certainly sounded as if Hapa's maternal heart could no longer stand the pain!

After all, a child is not just a part of one's flesh—it is a part of one's soul!

And so Lady Lehowska walked softly to the gate, passed through it, picked her way carefully through the potato patch, and was drawing close to the house, when she realised that the wailing was not coming from there. She walked around the house and saw a strange scene by the shed.

A red cow, bloated like a mountain, was lying under the lean-to, and beside it lay Hapa—all dishevelled and without her head-dress—writhing and pummelling the ground. Two or three neighbours were also crying out in distress, invoking God, and clasping their hands in despair. Seven bareheaded children—differing in the colour of their hair, but resembling one another in the ragged condition of their clothes—were sobbing and wailing in an assortment of voices. Even a tiny pot-bellied toddler was screaming—God only knows why—either out of fear, or just to be one of the crowd.

"Oh, my dear little cow, my precious Happiness! What kind of happiness are you if you have brought me such misfortune? I never would have expected this. I certainly never feared it. Why, only yesterday, I took such joy in you as you trotted home so friskily. Oh, my dearest Happiness! Oh, whose evil eye has cast a spell on you? Whose hellish soul coveted my only treasure? What have you done to us, my precious little cow? Why have you orphaned my children? What in God's world am I going to do? What am I going to give my little ones to drink?

"Oh woe is me! O my dearest God! For what sins are you punishing me so cruelly? If you must punish someone, O Lord, then punish me, a sinner, a slut, but not these poor innocent children! Oh, my dearest children!"

Upon hearing this, the children began to wail even more loudly. The young women's shoulders heaved sympathetically.

"How bitterly she's lamenting!"

"And her lamenting is most fitting, poor thing!"

"It would be strange not to lament. The cow was what kept them alive!"

"You see, she didn't wail that way over the loss of her child."

"What a thing to say! That was a useless, whining child, but this is a cow! Just think!"

"Comfort her!" Lady Lehowska snapped, pushing them towards Hapa.

"Hapa, let's go into the house," a young woman hesitantly touched her.

"Oh, I won't go, Khivra, I won't go! Oh, what would I do there? Oh, my dear little children, oh, my unfortunate ones." And she once again pounded her head against the ground. Then she leaped to her feet, as if she had gone mad, and began to poke the cow in its sides.

"Hey, hey, my Milky! Hey there, my Happiness! Don't tease me, don't try to fool me. I've picked some weeds for you. I've poured you some good, filling slops. Get up! Eat something! Don't just lie there, you old lazybones! Oh, what are you doing?"

She grabbed the cow by the horns and gazed intently into its cloudy eyes. Flies were already crawling in them.

"Oh, no! Dear mother of mine! Oh, no! My precious little dove! You aren't teasing! You aren't joking! You've died and turned stiff! It would have been better if I had lain down and taken your place, and you had taken mine! You would have been able to feed my little ones! You would have looked after things for me," Hapa was babbling incoherently.

Lady Lehowska found it both touching and disturbing that someone would grieve so intensely over a cow. And it was all the more distressing to her because only yesterday Hapa had not shed a single tear for her dead child. Even today, she had not said one word about it. She approached Hapa and took her by the arm.

"Stop it, Hapa! I don't know if I should laugh or cry! You're babbling God knows what! How could a cow look after things and take your place? One can always get another cow; what matters is that you and the children are healthy."

"Oh, no, my dear lady! Oh, no! How am I not to grieve? When the cow entered my yard, it was as if I had been reborn. Finally, I had something to nourish the soul, to quiet the children, to observe a holy day. And there was still something left over to take to the market—a pot of butter, or a lump of cheese. And then one could buy some salt, some coal oil, and other things in the store. But now, with only my good-for-nothing Khvedir, how in the world will I be able to get such things?"

"Shame on you! You're such a big, strong young woman, and you're giving up so easily. I saw you yesterday when you were serving the funeral dinner for Petryk. You were simply wonderful! But look at you today!" The lady tried to lift Hapa's spirits.

"Oh, my dear lady! It's not just anything at all! It's a cow!"

"That's exactly what I'm saying! So why are you so distraught?"

"My lady, that was a child," Hapa continued her line of thought. "Over there are the seven that I have, and they're all alive. And who knows, I may drop another ten. How in the world am I to feed them all if God doesn't take some of them? Let Him take them when they're small, like little Petryk yesterday—it all helps.

"But this is a cow! I had to earn money to get her. I didn't eat, or drink—I often went hungry—but I finally got my long-awaited treasure and found some peace. And now, out of the blue, such a misfortune has struck me!" Hapa tore herself free of Lady Lehowska and tumbled headfirst to the ground.

"Shame on you, you foolish woman!" The lady was angry. "Now listen! If you want to, come to my place, and I'll give you money for another cow. Just don't act so shamefully in front of the children because of this carcass."

And she walked swiftly out of the yard.

"My lady!" Hapa screamed in an unnatural voice. The young women, in a state of bewilderment that bordered on terror, cleared a path for Lady Lehowska. But she had already left the yard and was fleeing down the forest path.

In the evening, the old women who sat in the street next to their fences excitedly wagged their tongues about the latest news: how someone had cast a spell on Hapa's cow at dinnertime—they even hinted as to who might have done it—how it had died, how Hapa had lamented over it so properly that the lady had heard her in the forest, and how she was now giving—as God was their witness—she was now giving Hapa another cow!

"Hapa's really lucky! Is it because the lady knows her and likes her?"

"Not at all, dear sisters! Those lords and ladies are a little strange. For months at a time, they don't give you what you've earned, and then they throw away a huge sum of money for nothing at all."

"Well, it's fine for her to do it. She doesn't begrudge the money, because she hasn't earned it."

"That's right! You know, dear sisters, when that Yastshembsky stole her money and took off with it, they ran to tell her about it as fast as they could, but she just said: 'I don't care! I don't even want to hear about it!'"

"But you know, that was because she had just buried the little lord Vitya. You see, that hurt her, because she paid dearly to have that child. However, the money that she hasn't paid out to the people doesn't bother her at all!"

"All these lords have hard hearts. When she was burying Vitya, she didn't shed a single tear. And she didn't say anything to the people. She's haughty, very haughty. She closed herself up in her rooms and didn't come out, even when the people wanted to thank her for the funeral dinner."

"Don't talk like that!" A girl who served at the manor pushed her way through the crowd. "When little lord Vitya died, the lady really grieved—God spare any Christian soul grief like that. She grieved and grieved, but silently, without a tear. And then she'd faint—just drop with a thud to the floor! Then she'd come to. And then the same thing would happen, over and over again!"

"No, my dear woman, say what you will, but they suffer too. Only they don't know how to go about it like we do. They don't talk about it, and they don't scream about it. They're ashamed to, or God knows what! It was only after Granny Vekla did something that her tears finally came."

"Oh, that Granny Vekla is a smart one! She knows how to approach and help not only common folk, but lords and ladies as well."

"So, you see, if you've had to work hard for something, then your heart aches for it. Just as our lady had to work hard in the case of Vitya. Our Hapa, however, finds it as easy to give birth to a child as to toss back a shot of whiskey. Besides, there are already so many of them in her house! That's why she doesn't treasure them very much!"

"As the saying goes: we value only what we work for!"

It grew completely dark. The gate in Hapa's yard squeaked. It was Khvedir, who was putting the skinned Happiness on a wagon and taking her away to bury her. The dogs were howling at the fresh hide that was stretched out on pegs, the oxen were snorting and pawing the ground with their hooves, and the horses were shivering and looking askance at the wagon that they could scarcely see.

After putting the children to bed, Hapa washed the bowls and spoons, and said her bedtime prayers. To her usual prayers she added a new one. It was simple, but sincere:

"Oh, God, send good health and salvation to the soul of Lady Lehowska! Make her as happy as she has made me. And forgive me, O Lord, that I spoke against her, that I called her a silly, foolish person!"

Night descended on the village. Hapa fell asleep beside her good-for-nothing husband.

The lights went out in all the houses; only a single lamp shone in the lord's manor. The lady—having dismissed her hired man, her housekeeper, and her housemaids—was sitting over an open notebook in which she was entering, as in a ledger, her intentions. She noted which ones had been fulfilled, which ones had not, and the events that had transpired. She recalled what had happened that morning and fell into deep thought.

How easy it was to cure Hapa's grief! Why could not everything be like that? She also recalled what a great service Granny Vekla had done her. Would she ever be able to settle accounts with her? This old woman had not only given her a new life and made her a whole person again; she had made it possible for her to begin settling accounts with those to whom so much was owed by her, by her mother, and by all the former lords who had incurred this great debt and left it to her.

Well, then, had she at least begun to settle her accounts? Would one lifetime be enough?

At Night
(1896-1909)

The summer day was burning itself out. The setting sun, etched on the horizon and flaming in pure gold from under the tall, dark fir trees, sank lower and lower . . . until there remained only a quarter . . . a thin sliver . . . a spark—and it was gone!

A bright rosy veil spread over the entire western limits of the sky, and the blackened trees of the old manorial orchard stood out in bold relief.

A summer day is ever so long! From dawn to dusk, there is always so much happening, and this orchard—which has listened to so much—absorbs every sound from the fields and all the noises from the village; it absorbs them, augments them tenfold, and sends them forth as an echo. Just now the singing of young men is rolling in from the field—it is the mowers who are approaching. Suddenly, as if to overtake this singing, a girls' song bursts forth. The two songs flow by independently, call out to one another, and encroach upon each other. Now they are drawing nearer and nearer—until finally the old orchard accepts them into its bosom. Men's bass and tenor voices resonate, reverberate, and merge with the girls' golden filigreed sopranos. The serious song and the light-hearted one—beginning and ending at different times—blend strangely into an unexpected harmony that fills the dark, sheltered grove to the brim.

Now the crowd of workers has passed by. Most likely these same voices are already clamouring harshly and shrilly in the village, but the orchard is still replete with the sound of the singing that has flown by and, in its most distant corners, the reverberations of the songs continue to echo.

The glowing pink splendour has ebbed and faded. The echo has fallen silent. From here and there in the village, an occasional outcry, the barking of dogs, and the scolding of women can still be heard, but they are not capable of awakening afresh the subdued, dark, and dewy orchard. The bustle of the day has come to a close, giving way to the sounds of night. A sparrow-hawk takes sudden flight, a bat whistles, an owl rustles by on its soft wings, a deep-voiced beetle buzzes, and a forest mouse scratches in a hollow tree.

The flashes in the sky have died away, and the shadows have also vanished; blackened tree trunks are painted indistinctly on a dark background, and dewy glades are barely glistening; in the bushes, fireflies have begun flickering. It is quiet. Blissful. Everything is conducive to rest. And everything that is weary and exhausted from toil sinks gladly into this holy repose—forests and fields are sleeping, and the orchard also slumbers; the village and the manor yard are drifting off to sleep.

It is only the young lords' impudent laughter, shouts, and high jinks that spoil the harmony of this sacred rest. But why should they not be running around? Why should they not be playing pranks? They have not exhausted themselves with work during the day, and it is much less tiring and more pleasant to chase around in the coolness of the night than in the oppressive heat of the afternoon.

Healthy, carefree, and happy—they carry on, call out loudly to one another, and sing. And the old orchard, whether it likes it or not, is forced to carry the echoes of their merriment and thereby awaken feelings of envy and resentment in the weary village. More than once, an elderly man or woman—praying loudly to the starry sky before retiring—has spit in disgust upon hearing that echo. And more than once, a village dog has barked and growled angrily.

The stars are beginning to glow ever more brightly in the dark night sky, the dew is falling more thickly, and silence envelopes the neighbourhood more closely. Even in the lord's yard, the shadowy movements and conversations that weave themselves in and out of the light are confined to the veranda where the lords are dining.

The sounds and the streaks of light barely reach the distant corner where the apiary is located. The bees drone like far away bells, and Okhrim, the elderly beekeeper, is wheezing and moaning in his sleep.

Along the path, someone is treading carefully on bare feet. Every once in a while, there is the sound of a dry twig cracking under his step, or the snorting of a dog as it accompanies its master on his nightly rounds.

"Granddad, oh gra-a-a-anddad!"

Silence.

"Granddad Okhrim! Are you sleeping?"

Still nothing.

The night watchman probably jerked his hand in a gesture of disappointment, for the resonant wooden bell-rattle, swinging out of its balanced position, made an irregular knocking sound.

"Ah, it's you Stepan!" the old man called out from his tiny hut.

"Of course, it's me!"

"Making your rounds?"

"That's right! But I see you're already hard at it!" And one could hear a smile in Stepan's voice.

"That I am, my good man—praise God! After all, doesn't one sweat and slave enough during the day? Take today—I caught four swarms and held on to three of them, but one got away on me. Not even a dog would come and help me, not even if I were to rupture myself trying to do it alone!

"There was one time when I thought I was a goner when some bees (a crazed third-year swarm) attacked me up there in the pear tree! I yelled and yelled, and I shouted and shouted—but there wasn't so much as a peep from anyone! Not a single soul responded!"

"What are you saying, old man?" the night watchman burst out laughing. "The orchard was full of people, and there was such a racket that it's a wonder they didn't frighten off the entire colony of bees, and here you are complaining that there was no one around!"

"Do you call them people?" and the old man spit in disgust. "They're damned lords! And those young lords are the worst of the lot."

"But why didn't you call them? Why, there are at least two of them there who are not so little any more—they must be almost ready to sprout whiskers."

"Oh, don't even talk to me about those lazy good-for-nothings! They just race and bound through the orchard, the forest, and the fields all day long as if they were demented—until they're all in a sweat! If only they were doing something—but they're always just fooling around.

"Wouldn't you, my lad, help a peasant swing the scythe? But these blockheads act like children, even if they are just about to sprout whiskers—may the might of God strike them down! Believe you me, not only do you slave away all day long, you have to constantly keep an eye out for them, because they'll run up to you, and one will take away your rake, another—your spade, and still another—your hoe. And then they'll run off with them somewhere! Not long ago they made off with my net and ripped holes in it, and now when I go to gather the swarms, the bees come after me and really give me a bad time."

"You shouldn't let them have the net."

"Don't let them have it? Do you think I want to? Why, the old lady would tear my eyes out herself on their behalf. They run off with things, those young devils, and they lose things, but you can't say a word—if you don't want to get into trouble—and so you just stay quiet and keep looking for what they've carried off!"

"Oh, granddad! It's like people say—they're young, and they're green, and they've grown up in the lap of luxury, so what do they understand? After all, are they to blame? Their mothers and fathers haven't taught them anything, but the children themselves are not really evil; why, take even that Orkadiy . . ."

"I'm not talking about Orkadiy; he's truly a good-hearted fellow, but he isn't one of their breed. His widowed mother has to earn her keep in foreign parts, and things aren't too sweet for her son either. He didn't come here to have a rest—every day he has to teach our lazy blokes something."

"But haven't they finished studying all their books yet?"

"No, not all of them! They say that Stopa—that big bull of a boy—didn't pass his exams again this year. And as for Lyunya, she also spent more time gadding about at home than studying in Kyiv. And so this poor fellow has to lend them some of his sense. But is it only our young lords who are like that? They're all the same—every last one of them, may they all be damned! Orkadiy has told me a great deal about it."

"He has? The one who's always so silent?"

"Oh, it only seems that way! There are times when he comes here and begins talking abut all sorts of things and asking me about everything under the sun—about every last thing that happens in the village. And he himself has seen a lot of the world, and you can see that he's swallowed a lot of his own tears while eating bread given to him by strangers. And you know, Stepan, the young lad says it all so sensibly that even an older person wouldn't be ashamed to say it like that, I swear to God!"

"He probably exaggerates a bit, right?"

"Well, there's probably some of that, as well. You take our young men after they come back home from their stint in the army—don't they know how to flap their mouths and string us a line or two! And because you're just a hick, you have to shut up and listen—for you've never gone anywhere farther than to neighbouring Irpin, and you've never seen anything beyond your own village of Khodorkiv."

Both the old man and the night watchman fell silent.

It was quiet and gloomy. And it became still gloomier when a robust screech-owl hooted in some remote spot, and the strident echo reverberated slowly and became entangled in the dense thicket like a vague sorrow.

"What does the owl predict with its hooting, granddad?"

"Well, they say it foretells the death of someone."

"Yes, that's it . . . Right now it's still in the thicket, but then it will fly in closer, alight on the lord's manor, and blast right into the chimney—I saw it myself! Whose turn is it to die—perhaps our old lady's? She's always ill."

"May the devil take her as quickly as possible, and her children along with her! Perhaps there would be a little more room to move about around here; it might be a little easier to breathe!"

"Come on, granddad, why talk like that? It's a sin!"

"But doesn't someone like that make you sin? Oh-h-h, that damned old woman. It doesn't matter that she's delicate and of the nobility! You should have seen how she laced into poor Todoska today, my good fellow—oh my goodness! And then the girl blurted out: 'If you're going to carry on like this, it would be better if you'd settle accounts with me right now!' Well, the old lady lost all control then and began screaming! She turned white, and lightning flashed from her eyes! Poor Todoska crouched down in fear.

"The old lady just had to do something—she didn't slap the girl in the face, but she shook her so hard that the poor thing went head over heels through the door, toppled down the stairs, and ended up under the porch. The old bag of bones still has a heavy hand—it doesn't matter that she's always pretending to be ill and going off to see the doctor!"

"But she does go! And it can't be just for the fun of it—who wants to take medicine if there's no need to? A doctor isn't good company for someone who is well."

"Huh! Medicines! The doctor! Do you really believe that she goes there to cure an illness? Don't give me nonsense like that!"

"Uh-oh! So that's how it is!"

"Of course! She's an old bitch, but she's still on the prowl . . . ugh!"

The two elderly men fell silent once again.

Old Okhrim had had a good nap, and he wanted to chat, while Stepan, who would have liked to nod off, could not—he had to stand on guard.

"Oh-h-h-h-h! I ache all over, everything hurts—bad weather must be coming, or something. But I'll have to spend all day tidying things up and putting things away—just as if they were expecting guests every day.

"And it's that young Miss Lyunya who gives me the most trouble. One look at her and you can see that the girl is almost ready to get married, yet she plays all day long with the baby rabbits. Or she'll gather up a whole armful of baby partridges or quails and walk around with them. Or she'll prance about on horseback, thinking up all sorts of nonsense. Or she'll pick up the rake or the hoe, trying to show that she's a great worker. But I can see right through her—it's all to flaunt herself in front of Orkadiy, because he's still new around here.

"Or she'll run up to me and say: 'Give us some honey, old man! And do it quickly, right now—it's mother's orders.' So you see, you have to cut out a honeycomb in broad daylight—that's the kind of thing they come up with. And you have to. So I get dressed to do it, but she's off again—only the tail end of her flashes by behind the fence.

"And the pranks that she pulls in the house—God help us! Two chambermaids have more than enough work just to tidy up after such a big girl, you know. And she's never used a needle since the day she was born! 'I don't like women's work,' she says, 'it's so boring! Now, take a rifle, horses—that's my joy in life, but as for all those pigs, chickens, cows—ugh, I can't stand them!' Well, may misfortune strike you, young lady! You don't like cows? You don't take pleasure in housework? Why, just ask any one of our girls—they would fall down on their knees before such a cow if they had one!

"But she, you see, takes pleasure in horses! Well, it's true that when she comes back from riding one, the foam is flying off the poor horse—that's how much she likes it. But as for feeding it, watering it, raking out the manure, and spreading fresh straw for it—well, that's Lavrin's job. She shows up in the barn only the odd time to braid ribbons into its mane or to trim its tail with scissors. 'I love my horse Bulata,' she says. 'I look after him myself.' But, in truth, you're the one who has to work and work until your back cracks, and all this work doesn't count for anything."

"Well, you can't do anything about it!" Stepan spoke up. "God must have sent us such a fate. We didn't create the world, and we won't end it!"

"'Fate,' 'fate'! One could change one's fate if one could get rid of this riffraff. 'We didn't create the world!' Well, if we had, things might have been different."

"But listen, old chap, aren't there good people among them as well? Take that doctor from Kononivka, or the teacher from Sokolivka, or the lady in Yaresky . . ."

"Just listen to you! Are those really lords? Why they're almost the same kind of lords that we sinful folk are, only they're educated."

"They're educated, all right. They're not ignorant like we are, that's it . . ."

"What do you mean—'that's it'! Go ahead and look among the really wealthy lords, even those who are educated. Will you find even one with a conscience?"

"What about Lady Omelyaniv?"

"Ah-h-h-h. . ." the old man was momentarily confused, because he did not know how to respond to this. "Well, she has to be seen as a misfit in their class—they themselves all say that she's got a screw missing. It's just as I was saying—she takes her stupid money and shoves it both where it should go and where it shouldn't. And perhaps, my good fellow, she satisfies her noble pride by saying 'I'm going to come up with something different than all my neighbours—let them all be amazed!'

"Just look, she's built a school—but who needs it?—and a hospital, and some kind of magic lanterns. And she reads something on the holy days, and gathers up the young ones and carts them to school, and now, they say, she's starting up some kind of a nursery for the little ones.

"But do you really think, my good fellow, that she's doing this out of the goodness of her heart? Not so, my dear fellow—that would be a lie! It's only to look good and to gain respect among the common people in order to make her neighbours jealous— believe me!"

But Stepan did not give in—perhaps it was his soft, gentle nature or the effect that the wonderful night was having on him, but he could not accept the cynical views that the old man was laying out before him.

"Well, old chap, no matter what her reason, one still has to thank her for doing all of this for the benefit of the peasants. Why, if she wanted to, she could take all her money, tear off across the border, and squander it in any way she wanted to—and who could stop her?"

"Oh, don't give me that nonsense! They're all painted with the same brush, and it's high time they were all rooted out, to the very last person! That way they wouldn't befoul the land and defile the holy earth."

Stepan fell silent. The old man was wheezing with anger.

Stepan sighed loudly.

"Well, the Big Dipper is over the fir tree—it's time for me to move on with my music," he said, picking up his wooden clapper. "Good night, granddad Okhrim."

"Go in good health!"

Bare feet pattered carefully along the path and rustled in the grass, and every once in a while, the little dog sniffed, growled, and barked. The wooden clapper briskly rapped out its wooden song, and its echo rolled into the slumbering orchard and filled it completely.

In the meantime, the lord's children had quieted down. The boys spread out beds for themselves under the old pine tree, lay down, and rested blissfully after their long, active day. It did not matter that they had not been forced to do any hard work; their young arms had swung rifles with youthful enthusiasm, and their skinny legs had raced around in the swamps and groves; then they had ridden horseback, and later, they played on the swings or did gymnastics. And now it was pleasant to lie face up under the starry sky, to stretch, and to prattle about whatever came to mind, or, breathing silently, listen to the orchard dreaming its dreams, and the old pines and firs thinking their eternal thoughts.

"Stopa, are you sleeping?"

"Yes, I am! What is it?"

"What a dunderhead! Aren't you ashamed to sleep on such a wonderful night? Just look at how deep and starry the sky is. Doesn't it seem to you that the stars are forming a strange design, like an inscription in an Eastern language?"

"That's bo-o-o-ring! It was the stupid Greeks who dreamt up all those Bears, Cassiopeia, Orions, Pleiades and the like. But the resemblance there is like that of a boot to an alleluia!"

"You don't say! Is this a new witticism? One of your own? Most likely you borrowed it from Lord Zigmunt. But all the same, you're a pig, Stopa; there isn't a drop of poetry in you."

"That's nothing new either! Miss Lyunya does much better than that—the wonderful night, and the mysterious conversing of the branches, and the flowers' souls, and the thoughts of the forest—it's all so boring! It's really become disgusting, Lord help us! A night is nothing more than a night—snore and sleep to your heart's content, unless you have an urge to visit the girls in the village; in the morning—put your rifle on your shoulder, and off you go to the swamps! And as for the days—prepare yourself to get through them as comfortably and as profitably as possible. The birds are there to be shot, the flowers are there to be picked, the whiskey is there to be drunk, and the girls—to be loved. And life, my good fellow, is meant to be lived. That's how it is! But delicate youths like you sit around, idle and bored, and indulge in philosophical nitpicking, the devil take you!"

He angrily rolled himself up in his quilt and began to snore demonstratively, so they would leave him alone.

Ilko, the friend whom he had offended, was at a loss for words, and so he remained silent at first, but then he spit out: "Beast! Pig!"

"Why are you swearing?" Orkadiy inquired, as he rounded a corner in the lane and approached him.

"How can one not swear? That beast is in such a paradisiacal spot, but he cares only about his stomach—and this at the age of seventeen! What will he be like when he turns thirty?"

"Ha-ha-ha!" a childish voice rang out. "Our Stopa will be like Lord Buchynsky—it takes two people to shove him through a doorway. No, better yet—he'll be like Petro Petrovych Pyetukh in Hohol's [Gogol's] *Dead Souls*."

"Well, Ilko, what would you do if you were in his place?"

"Me? Why, I'd do great things!"

"Like what?"

"Like I said, great things . . ."

"Yes?" Orkadiy did not let up.

"Well, for example . . . I would collect vast amounts of ethnographic materials. You know," he whispered in a conspiratorial tone, "I already have two sizeable notebooks like that!"

"Well, and what are you going to do with them?"

"What do you mean, what? I'll make a study of the thoughts of the people, of their soul . . ."

"You'll make a study of them? You're fooling around, that's all!"

"Of course—I'm just fooling around!" Ilko snapped back angrily. "But did it ever occur to you, O philosopher, that you too might be able to help the people—the people whose language, poetry, and history you are ignorant of?"

"Oh, my dear little fellow, it's not poetry that's needed here! One needs to empty the wells of poverty, distress, and misery to the very bottom, and only then will one find a way to make things better here."

"But how will you do this if you don't mingle with the people, if you shun them?"

"And do you really think that they'll simply open their souls up wide to another person, just as they open up a wicker basket? As you can see—they had no one to turn to, so they turned to you, someone who flits about like a butterfly, looking for all sorts of amusements."

"Oh, you're the one who's so focused and wise! Are you sure you haven't become a Marxist, or some other 'ist'? It's the fashion now, you know."

"It doesn't matter if I'm a Marxist or not, but I don't have a nobleman's skin, and so my dreams and my wishes are not those of the nobility. And if you really must know—I don't shun the people; I gain their trust, but not the way you do."

The youths feel silent.

Khved, the little boy who had laughed at Stopa a short while ago, was now snoring deliciously. Stopa was also sleeping—or pretending to be asleep.

"Ilko, you know, the beekeeper here is a truly fascinating person!"

"Uh-huh! He's quite the character! Is he perhaps of *kozak [Cossack]* stock?"

Stopa must have been bitten by a mosquito or something, for he bolted up and, annoyed that his sleep had been interrupted, broke into the conversation.

"The devil take it—what kind of a *kozak* is he? What a stupid idea! You're probably making a *kozak* out of him because of his stern and harsh disposition."

"More likely because of the fact that he really gets after both you and Lyunya!"

"Ah, that's nothing . . ."

"Oh, so you take it to be nothing!" Ilko, deeply offended, interrupted hotly. "But I've seen another side of him—he's a wise old man, and he's conscientious; he goes about his work honestly, and he's generous and trustworthy . . ."

"You're saying that Okhrim is trustworthy?" Stopa cried out. "Boy, oh boy! Why, he'll take you by the nose, lead you around, and instil such a fear of God in you that you'll end up crawling to God while you're still alive! That damned old man is a sly one, may the devils flog him! But then—they're all like that. Brrr! I hate them. It's only my mother who—heaven only knows why—gets involved with them. She sullies her hands with their sick ones and feels sorry for those slobbering women and their snotty-nosed kids—but why does she bother with them? Does she want to save her soul? I just don't understand it at all! She herself is utterly nauseated by all of it—I know very well that she's revolted by it, that she abhors it, but she still goes there, saying all the while: 'I'm a philanthropist'! Oh, I can't wait to get my hands on my inheritance—I'll show them a philanthropy or two!"

Orkadiy indignantly rose to his feet, flung someone's clothing over his shoulders, and abruptly departed from the group.

He wandered through the dark lanes for a long time, fixing his gaze upon the serene, vaulted sky and shuddering in disgust whenever the lascivious laughter of Stopa and Ilko reached him—it was obvious that they were rolling with laughter at Stopa's anecdotes.

The young man thought he might go—as he often did—to have a chat with the beekeeper, but the old man's vengeful remarks—that he had overheard—had deeply disturbed him.

"God, what hatred! What rage!" the young man thought, and he quickly headed off in another direction.

The dew did not cool his feverish head; his thoughts crowded in on him, and his head was spinning with questions—what could he do? How could this gap between people be bridged? When would people achieve a state of harmony, of brotherly coexistence? How was one to open the eyes of these ignorant and unfortunate—but infinitely charming—people whom he had come to know only recently, and whom he now genuinely loved. What should he do?

Orkadiy did not know the answer, and he blamed himself bitterly for his helplessness, deploring his urban upbringing that had left him unprepared, weak, and incapable of knowing what to do in different situations. Should he join the followers of Tolstoy or of Neplyuyev?

Something was tearing fiercely at his heart!

He could confine himself to being a village teacher—but the sphere of activity was too narrow, and one had so little power. Should he study to become a lawyer or a doctor, and then go to work in the villages? Or, should he, perhaps, simply become a priest? A priest was capable of doing both good and evil! But there was one disagreeable fact about that choice—one definitely had to get married—brrrr! This delight—about which the youthful dreamer had heard so much from his friends, and which he had read about in books—was still completely alien and disagreeable to him.

Dreams, ideas, reproaches, and plans spun in his feverish head and drove sleep away from him. It was dawning when Orkadiy finally fell asleep by a haystack; he slept through the sunrise, and even through the morning tea.

When granddad Okhrim was sweeping the paths, he saw Orkadiy lying there and wondered why he was sleeping so late, why he was not with the others; but he took pity on him and did not wake him.

And both Lady Zaykivska—the mother of Stopa and Khved—and Lady Ivanivska—the mother of Ilko, Lyunya, and Simochka—peered closely into the youths' faces. This time they gazed with pleasure at Stopa's face, but with suspicion and confusion at Orkadiy's. And for good reason—his face was pale, his murky eyes were darkly shadowed, and his movements were either painfully weak or nervous and agitated.

The ladies began to talk in a roundabout way about the various misfortunes precipitated by liquor and night parties. The others who were present glanced at one another in astonishment, and Stopa and Ilko, choking with stifled laughter, kicked each other under the table. Ilko purposely bothered the girls, so that their squealing would break off the conversation of the two mothers. Only Orkadiy did not notice anything—the thoughts that had sprouted during the night were still roaming through his head.

The mothers, this time without any collusion, vowed to themselves to keep a closer eye on Orkadiy, so that he would not bring about the ruination of their children and, rising from the table, they went for a walk, conferring heatedly about their concerns.

Granddad Okhrim, working on the croquet lawn, listened in amazement to the conversation of the two ladies. Neither he nor they knew what a person can sometimes learn in the quiet of a summer's night . . .

The Shadow of Uncreated Creations
(1899?)

A dark, velvety-black night was gazing with immense eyes at the inky sea, which today was neither roaring nor thundering, but only sighing softly as it composed itself for sleep.

Stars flowed by, trembling on the sea's dark, smooth waves. From time to time, a petulant billow tossed itself up in a crest, or a wave dashed headfirst against an underwater rock, and then the water was ignited with a phosphorescent fire. The wet sand did not rustle, and the speckled pebbles did not chatter as they did during the daily surge of the surf.

Silence settled higher up as well, in the bristly branches of the caragana bushes, and under the spreading boughs of the acacia shrubs, the grey olive trees, and the dense mimosa plants, for the crickets and the cicadas had finished singing their summer songs.

Silence also descended above the mountain that, like a terracotta wall, guarded this stretch of the seashore, so beloved by cottage owners, and protected it from both the sharp wind and the incessant noise of the city. Here, neither the whistles of the streetcars, nor the detestable echoes of the resort's orchestra, could be heard.

Silence reigned everywhere, and here and there the lights of cottages peeked out from among the dark clumps of trees.

Not far from the sea, at the end of a clay path that snaked its way up the mountain, a green light glimmered like a glow-worm before St. John's Eve. With every bend in the path, the light appeared to gain ground on the velvety darkness, expanding and growing in size; shadows flitted across it.

The closer one came to it, the more one could hear bursts of laughter and the buzz of several female and male voices, and when these abated, one's ear caught a soft voice, like the gentle murmur of water, that was reading a story to the listeners, who interrupted it, at times, with their noisy chatter and laughter.

On a small veranda, which obviously also served as a dining room and a parlour, a white table spread with a clean cloth and the bottom half of a samovar gleamed under the green light, but beyond them, everything else sank into a greenish mist. At first, it was not even possible to discern if there were any living persons on the veranda, for their faces, which had assumed an unusual hue from the green rays, made them look like spectres from another world.

It was quiet on the veranda, so quiet that when the voice that was reading fell silent, one could hear the fluttering of the countless moths on the glass lamp as they were drawn to their ecstatic deaths by the alluring incandescence of the hot green waves of light emanating from it. This agitated, thrumming sound combined with the final song of the abandoned samovar and the quiet splashing of the dreamy sea down below to create a strange melody.

The people, of whom there was a good number, over a dozen or so, were sitting without stirring, captivated by the reading of a wonderful new play. All of them—both the young and the middle-aged, the women, the girls, and the young men—had gathered under the glow of this welcoming green lamp and the warmth of the hostess's hospitality.

The reader was no longer a young person; she was rather plump, and not particularly attractive, and it was only her smile which greatly enhanced her appearance and made her more alluring than celebrated beauties. In her lifetime she had known much grief, as a young girl, a married woman, a widow, both within the walls of the school in which she had worked for over twenty years now, and beyond them. None of her experiences, however, had thus far deprived her of the unrestrainable cheerfulness and the unfailing sensitivity that had characterised her in her youth.

Many of her closer associates and girlfriends had scattered all over the world. Some, having found favour with fate, had surpassed her; others had stalled on their journey through life and were left stranded in the past. She, however, had somehow managed to maintain her status as a charming wayside station, both for those who, infused with the ardour of youth, were rushing forward and upwards, and for those who, exhausted and intimidated, were descending from the heights, looking back sorrowfully in their isolation.

During the academic term, there was always someone dropping in of an evening to find some "warmth" in her home, and during the holidays there were more than enough of such visitors! And she participated in the parties, excursions, and social events of the young people, not at all deterred by the fact that her own son, a first-year student, was among them.

This is why the modest little cottage by the sea so often shone with a green light until the wee hours of the morning, and why it drew attention to itself during the daytime with its noise, laughter, singing, and music.

"The sea and young people—these are the two elements without which I cannot live," Mariya Dmytrivna used to say, and what she said was true, for they were the best cure for all her physical and emotional ailments.

The reading on the veranda was flowing like a stream, the moths were thrumming against the lamp, the sea was murmuring incessantly to the silent cliffs. The play increased in intensity, attained new dramatic heights, and completely absorbed the listeners who, up to now, had sat without stirring.

Suddenly, one tall, skinny young man rose to his feet and, nervously cracking his knuckles, began to pace the veranda. Then, a young girl bent her head down low over the table, and the curls on her little blond head, moving out of the green haze, gleamed in the white light, hiding an overly red face and rapidly blinking damp eyes. One lady nervously began to wave a fan made of palm leaves, even though there was absolutely no need to do so, for a gentle coolness was wafting in from the sea. And one young gentleman kept trying to roll a cigarette without any success—his fingers were trembling uncontrollably.

The voice of the reader was becoming tense and resonant, and as it became more and more agitated, its dramatic overtones depicted the personages—whom no one had seen or heard, and who perhaps had never even existed in the world—so vividly, that both they and their grief-filled lives came alive.

"No, that's enough! This is some kind of exploitation! The writing of such plays is . . . cannibalism!"

With these words, a pale youth with curly hair dashed from the veranda and raced down the path so swiftly that the gravel screeched.

"Sh! Sh!" hissed the remaining listeners, who were breathing in unison, as they followed the unfolding of the plot. The final terrible explosion of the drama struck down the suffering protagonist, his enemies were left standing dumbstruck, not daring to rejoice in their victory, his friends retreated in terror, and everything fell silent.

The group of listeners also fell silent, and so did the reader— her voice broke from the tension.

In the immense silence, only the sea murmured, and the restless moths fluttered. And, just like the moths, thoughts and questions were trembling in the listeners' minds: "Who was to blame? Why did it happen? So where was the justice in this?"

The night, the sea, and the silence responded to these questions, but their eternal conversation was beyond comprehension.

"Curtain!" the reader cried out in a resolute and intentionally loud voice, rustling the manuscript as she gathered it up.

"Oh!" sighed all the living beings on the veranda, as if they had freed themselves of a heavy burden. They stirred simultaneously and struck up conversations, breaking and dispersing the oppressive spell.

The young lady who had been bent down over the table, for some time now had been leaning over the railing of the veranda, searching for something in the dense tangle of grapevines. The young gentleman, having finally completed rolling his cigarette, was blinking comically as he attempted to light it from the lamp, and his face assumed a most ludicrous expression.

But the hostess, a candidly sentimental person, did not even attempt to hide her emotions; artlessly, like a child, she dropped her chest to the table and, with her head in her hands, sobbed and wiped away her copious tears.

This simple, naive expression of one's emotions made the difficult moment easier for everyone and evoked an unexpected, lengthy laugh. It was not intended as a laugh at her, it just happened—it was warm, and funny, and pleasant, and everyone understood this without anything being said.

"So that's how it is! So you, Mariya Dmytrivna, I see you're really, how would one say it . . ." boomed a sturdy, black-bearded fellow who, until now, had been sitting, silent as a stump, in a chair that was off to one side.

"Surely you must know that the eyes of our respected lady are always salty with tears; if there's even the slightest mist, they turn damp, and God forbid that there should be rain—they become a veritable salt marsh!" the one who had been rolling the cigarette muttered.

"Well, my good lady! It's a blessing that at least your son isn't here today; you would have embarrassed the young fellow to death!" the bearded fellow laughed kindly.

But Mariya Dmytrivna had also begun laughing, even though her chest was heaving with her ragged breathing, and tears were still running down her face, like a summer shower when the sun is shining,

"Now then! We'd better take off that green night-cap, because it's making everyone look truly ghastly; we all look like drowned corpses that have washed ashore!" A short little chap in gold spectacles ran up to the lampshade and removed it.

Instantly, the entire veranda was transformed in the bright, white light; the moths, fluttering madly, swarmed to the ceiling, and the people began to talk and argue, muting the drowsy splashes of the sea with their clamour. But far down below, the dark-haired lad who had fled from the reading walked silently over the wet sand, and on the veranda, concealed by the shadow of the samovar, a woman's figure sat in silence.

She appeared neither to hear the lively conversation, nor to see the cheerful light; her large, dark eyes gazed into the distance, her ears were filled with private, inner sounds, and her face showed, on all of its features, that she was experiencing something profound, powerful, vivid, and otherwordly.

She was not beautiful like the two young ladies, one of whom was bashfully hiding her tears among the grapevines; and her face, unlike that of the sunny Mariya Dmytrivna, did not radiate spiritual beauty and freshness. No, it was an overcast, stern face with features that were almost classic: long lashes that swept over large dark eyes, in which there usually were no sunny rays or sparks, and which only rarely flamed with the kind of fire that was in them now; and heavy eyebrows, which grew together in a thickset line, and only seldom relaxed. As a rule, her eyes did not speak, and her tightly pinched lips remained silent; only her restless nostrils, like those of a spirited horse, quivered and flared, and her eyebrows, at times, twitched in anger like a flash of lightning.

Always confident, severe, and outwardly calm—this person was alien and incomprehensible to those among whom she happened to be living. Her teaching associates were not close to her, for they thought she was proud; the administrators did not like her for they could find not fault with her, nor would they dare to joke with her; and the people who lived in the villages, where she irreproachably discharged her teaching duties without ever making friends with anyone, feared her.

She was not an outgoing person. It was only Mariya Dmytrivna who had known her for a long time. They had studied together in high school, become good friends, shared their youthful dreams, opened their hearts to one another and, from that time, remained bosom friends.

Mariya Dmytrivna was always surrounded by friends, but Antonina Pavlivna was not like that, and perhaps because the spiritual bond she had with Mariya Dmytrivna was the only one she had ever formed, she valued this long-standing friendship as she would treasure a precious jewel.

On the veranda, the lively conversation of the restless young people swirled about like a moth; they were sifting through the play, taking issue with some of its faults, seizing upon the author's obvious and hidden motives, and then, as is usually the case with young people, they tried to place the young author in a literary group or school. But it was not easy to do so; he was new and unique, and he kept eluding them like a slender fish that slips from one's hands, and this led some of the less prudent youths to refer loudly to the decadents.

"What? The decadents? 'Corpses illuminated by gas'?"

And the fight was on! It was as if the conversation had jumped the rails, and there were roars of laughter and disputes as to what constitutes decadence. Was it a new, developed kernel of originality, or simply a fraudulent fabrication of a bored and completely worn-out soul?

The young ladies, glad to have the opportunity to contribute their bit to the conversation, tried to outdo one another in recalling and reciting excerpts from decadent verses. Yulya, a blond young lady, swiftly rattled off:

"The shadow of uncreated creations
Sways in a dream,
Like fans of latanias
On an enamel wall . . ."

"'I want only that which is not, which is not.' Ha-ha-ha!" Sonya, a young lady with dark hair, was overcome with laughter.

They all recalled whatever they could, without realising that they were not plumbing the depths of those much ridiculed decadents, but simply skimming the foam that was often thrown to the surface by critics and reviewers.

"'Oh, cover your pale legs!'" the gentleman who was smoking the cigarette intoned with comic pathos as he pretended to be a decadent.

The gathering was prostrated with laughter. Caught up in their superficial criticism, they jumped from one theme to another; then they leaped into the field of music, and of painting, deriding the intangible rhythms, the unusual melodies, the inharmonious chords, the blue dogs, green horses, yellow skies and the like; they were totally destroying the mood that was still just emerging from the new works.

Only the dark figure of Antonina Pavlivna remained motionless. Her face was no longer casually thoughtful, but more like a thunder cloud from which lightning was about to strike, and thunder about to crash.

"Oh, oh, oh! My dearest Antonina Pavlivna! Don't you find all this even the slightest bit amusing?" the young lady Sonya, having laughed herself silly, and overwhelmed by an expansive, happy feeling, flung herself at Antonina Pavlivna, seized her hands, and peered into her eyes.

Antonina Pavlina immediately freed her hands and, quite unexpectedly, gave the poor young girl such a look that Sonya lost all her enthusiasm for laughing.

"And you, young lady, do you always laugh? You only laugh! However, the examination of things in greater depth, the search for the true kernel under those husks—you do not find such efforts worthwhile. Perhaps there is more truth in those clumsy, crippled utterances than you might expect? Perhaps that utterance is the cry of a suffering soul filled with a pain unlike any of our commonplace pains, which still has not found suitable words to express it, but which does not wish to put on a false facade with the speech of the marketplace? How would you know that?"

"Oh, oh! Antonina Pavlivna has spoken; it's a miracle!" observed the fellow with the black beard.

Mariya Dmytrivna silently motioned to him with her hands.

"This is very interesting," he droned on in a somewhat irritated tone, "it's interesting, where in those works have you found even one clear, truthful expression or healthy thought? Is it in 'the month is rising naked in the azure light of the moon'? Are all those Balmonts, Hippiuses, and the rest of their brethren really worthy of a favourable word? And are all those painters—symbolists, impressionists, and *tutti quanti [all of them]'*—really worthy of a favourable look? Are all their efforts worth a crust of mouldy bread—the bread that our hungry people lack . . ."

"There is no God but Allah, and Mohammed is His prophet! There is no God but the People, and Yakovenko is Their prophet!" the short Fedorak spoke up maliciously, always glad of an opportunity to interrupt him.

Antonina Pavlivna's nostrils quivered rapidly, and her eyebrows twitched.

"Yes, indeed!" the blond student added. "One would think that Mykhaylo Mykhaylovych is complaining like Judas that Mary Magdalene has spent her money on myrrh instead of having it changed into small coins. For the beggars."

"No!" Yakovenko fired off in a harsh bass voice. "As I see it, all that decadence is only 'the shadow of uncreated creations'!" he thundered emphatically.

The entire gathering applauded such a splendid finale and unanimously burst out laughing.

Antonina Pavlivna was silent for a moment, but she was not one of those who applauds every kind of victory.

"But do you understand, my good people, all the tragedy that is couched even in that much derided utterance: 'the shadow of uncreated creations'?" Her voice, hesitant at first, now rang out confidently, as if she were calling the gathering to a joust. When she rose from where she had been sitting, both her imposing height and her flashing, angry eyes seemed to be declaring war; however, she immediately gained control of herself and, tossing out a haughty: "You wouldn't understand!" she crossed the veranda and disappeared into the darkness.

And only the gravel on the path crackled, and tiny pebbles rolled downwards following the fading footsteps of Antonina Pavlivna.

The gathering sat stunned for a few minutes.

"So much for that!"

"Isn't that something!" Two of them had recovered their senses.

"What happened to her? Mariya Dmytrivna, can you figure it out?"

"Just look at that! Our, so to say, inspector, the 'model bureaucrat' was stung to the quick! That's something unexpected—I'll say!"

They all began to interrogate the hostess about her, and she tried to cope with their questions as best she could.

"Oh, leave her alone! After all, you don't know her! It may be as you say, that she's a 'bureaucrat,' but you don't know that she's a wonderful person (Mariya Dmytrivna thought everyone was wonderful). She just doesn't like to be provoked, and I won't tell you anything, anything at all."

"That's strange! Then what are these little tantrums, if that's the case?" the short little Fedorak would not let up.

"Well, something comes over her at times . . . just don't provoke her, until she herself begins to talk. But where's that crazy Kost?" Mariya Dmytrivna suddenly became alarmed.

"He must be on the seashore, if he's anywhere! He's probably sitting and conversing with the sea!"

"'And the fool stands by the sea, and awaits a reply'," someone spoke up, quoting from Heine.

"I'm telling you, the naughty boy will come down with a cold, and there will be more trouble!" Mariya Dmytrivna complained and, grabbing a warm shawl and disregarding her plumpness, she ran swiftly across the veranda and headed down the path to the sea to find Kost, who had only recently recovered from a bout of pneumonia.

"Entertain yourselves, my dears, entertain yourselves!" she shouted from down below. "Go ahead and sing or something! Just be sure you don't get bored!" her pleasant admonition came to them from afar.

She was running in the dark without thinking about where she was going—her feet, accustomed to the surroundings, knew the way themselves—when, around a bend in the path, she heard heavy, weary breathing, and an uneven gait.

"Kost! Is that you?" she called out.

"It's me!" the latter said abruptly, trying to catch his breath.

"My dearest Kost! Aren't you ashamed of yourself? You've just got out of the hospital!"

"Yes, I know, I know! I'm fine, I'm fine!"

Mariya Dmytrivna managed to catch up with the grim young man, took him by the arm, threw the shawl on his back, and led him into a side path, all the while stroking his arm and his thick curly hair.

"All right, I'm fine . . . leave me alone!" he spoke up, still annoyed, but less so now, as he tried to free himself from her caresses.

"My foolish Kost! How high-strung you still are, how weak! Serhiy isn't here, and it's not for me to say, but just look at you—how angry you are! Oh, my foolish little one!"

As she joked and reproached him, Mariya Dmytrivna gave him a warm hug.

Kost was the friend of her son, Serhiy, and her motherly tenderness, as always, was the best medicine for him—better than any bromides.

Not far from the cottage, however, he grabbed Mariya Dmytrivna by the arm and spoke out passionately.

"But tell me, for the love of God: why do you select such violent, bloody dramas? Isn't it enough that there are so many invisible, silent dramas all around us, at our feet—behind us, ahead of us, on all sides of us—oh, what's the use of talking! And you, who are so good, so very good, for some reason choose to excite your nerves with that bloody fiction! I don't understand it!"

"Just a minute, Kost! Didn't I tell you that today we would be reading this very play, and that it was not suitable for you, but rather for our coarse, sleepy, sluggish nerves? Why did you come?"

"That means yours are—coarse, sleepy?" Kost smiled.

"Maybe they are! But I had a good cry—I bellowed, I swear to God, like a cow—and now I feel contented and cheerful, and if my mind finds analogous incidents in our contemporary life, then that's all the better! This can only evoke . . ."

"Oh, what's the point!" the young man dismissed the conversation with a gesture of his hand. "But you have another nice habit—to bring more and more new people into our closely-knit, group . . ."

"But how could it be otherwise, Kost? Should they be chased away, or what? And what kind of undesirables did you see there, my young man? Why this disgruntlement?"

"What kind? Well let's take that old, dried-up blockhead!"

"You mean Antonina Pavlivna? But she's my very best friend from my high school days."

"May she be damned! She sits like an idol, sparks flash from her eyes, the devil himself hides in her eyebrows, and there's not a peep out of her! But because of your small diversions," he bowed mockingly before her, "one has to subject oneself to all sorts of pain! And what is she, after all? An old maid, 'a model bureaucrat', phooey!"

"Hush now, Kost!" Mariya Dmytrivna closed his mouth with her hand. "You're a naughty boy! You don't know her, or the great injustice you're perpetrating. Antonina Pavlivna is not at all like the image people have painted of her and affixed to her as a label. She isn't a dried-up bureaucrat, nor an old spinster, nor a blockhead—but on the contrary, she is a highly sensitive soul, perhaps more sensitive than all of us put together.

"What difference does it make that she doesn't talk endlessly as I do? Or doesn't distract you with witticisms like Vonsovych? Or doesn't get into trendy currents of thought and work? What she does have—her thoughts, her faults, her errors, the bad and the good—all that is her own, not borrowed from anyone. And it shouldn't be you of all people who censures her, for no one would get along as well with her as you, even though each of you stands firmly on your own analogous yet disparate starting point."

"I?"

"You and no one else! For she's as crazy as you are . . . yes, yes—this bureaucrat! Think about the story of the frog princess—that's exactly the case here. But enough of this! We'd do better to go and call forth from her that which is stirring within her at this moment."

"I don't want to! I even fled from the sea because she came there uninvited!"

"Now, Kost, that's nonsense!" Mariya Dmytrivna energetically seized his arm, got a good grip on it, and headed off so quickly down the path leading to the sea that he didn't even have time to realise what was happening.

Higher up, on the veranda, the guests were getting ready to sing. A clear, girlish soprano cut the black velvety silence like a gold thread and then fell silent, but its pure echoes seemed to continue floating, vibrating, and dissolving. A baritone, no longer young, but well-developed, picked up the same phrase, but with confidence, with the consciousness of a mature soul that one could hardly expect from the previous voice. Another soprano voice rang out and poured forth with a joyful chirping sound; a high, heavy bass voice began to drone; still another voice, a tender, unsteady, but piercingly sensitive mezzo-soprano, joined the group, but something did not go well—the singing stopped, and everything was drowned out by the sound of uproarious laughter, as if quicksilver had rolled out in droplets through the air.

But the bass and the baritone were preparing to start something else, and a soprano joined in hesitantly, as if asking permission.

It was just then that Mariya Dmytrivna and Kost ran up to the sea.

There, at the very edge of the surf, the tall figure of Antonina Pavlivna could be clearly discerned.

Mariya Dmytrivna rushed up to her: "Tosya, my darling! Don't make things worse for yourself! Give rein to your thoughts, free your soul!"

"I feel stifled! Sad!" Antonina Pavlivna replied.

"Stifled? My dearest! You say you're stifled? But are you the only one? We're all stifled, we're all troubled, but you . . . You have the keys to the kingdom of heaven, but you're throwing them into the abyss! Comfort us, give us at least a glimpse of that heaven!"

She cajoled Antonina Pavlivna, and Kost listened in amazement to this conversation; obviously there was a bottomless spring in Mariya Dmytrivna's heart that generated special words and caresses specific to everyone's need. These, perhaps, were the charms with which she attracted everyone to herself. What surprised Kost even more was the fact that the tone of her voice evinced a sincerity he had never heard before. And all for "it"— for that "wooden idol," as he stubbornly continued to call her.

Antonina Pavlivna remained silent at first; then, thawing slowly, began to return her friend's caresses. All at once she straightened her tall figure, put her hands behind her head, stretched, and began pacing the shore. Quickly returning to Mariya Dmytrivna, she had just opened her mouth to begin singing when she noticed Kost, innocently casting stone after stone into the sea and gazing intently at the phosphorescent slivers that they kindled on the black waves.

"Who is this?" Antonina Pavlivna inquired, shuddering.

"Oh, that's Kost! It's just our crazy Kost. Don't pay any attention to him. Sing, Tosya, sing! I beg you!"

"Ah!" a warm, rich contralto floated through the air, and, without pausing, it sang:

> "So does one's youth pass without a trace,
> And soon it will all be over . . ."

Sorrow, nourished generously through the years, wound like a cold snake through that despondent singing.

> ". . . And when you look all around—
> it's all so empty, so pale—"

The second strophe flowed haughtily and more fervently, while the fourth strophe burst forth with passionate irony:

> ". . . Evidently, death is my laurel wreath!"

"Oh, what idiotic words!"

"Then sing without the words . . ." Mariya Dmytrivna spoke in a whisper as she sat on the sand, hugging her knees, and pressing her face against them.

Kost hurriedly threw stones as if he were under contract to do so. And the sensuous contralto once again floated out over the gentle murmur of the drowsy sea, agitating the listeners, growing in strength and finding new tones, different ways of expressing the revulsion born of a boring, mundane existence.

Pebbles and clumps of earth tumbled down the paths, and bramble bushes and trees cracked under someone's feet.

But the singer did not notice anything; her voice kept flowing onwards, like a river that had been pent up for a long time and now, having broken the dam, was searching avidly for a new channel.

The sea also heard the grief of Vanya from "Life in the Time of the Tsars," the aria of Ratmyr, and the passionate singing of the Gypsy from "Il Trovatore." The proud songs of Queen Amneris alternated with the pearly cooing of Italian songs. And when she sang the role of the mother of the Maccabees, it seemed that this terrible, tragic figure would appear at any moment from behind the dark cliff at whose feet the phosphorescent waves were lapping.

Gravel stopped falling down the paths, branches no longer cracked, and only quiet breathing and, at times, a whisper, could be heard not too far away, behind the acacia shrubs that were dangling their beards over the bank from a clay precipice.

At times, Kost cast whole fistfuls of pebbles into the sea, while at other times his arm appeared to be petrified. But Mariya Dmytrivna did not even raise her head.

To one side, from the neighbour's cottage, a patter of feet could be heard, and from the other side, someone was jumping over the bushes and stones, without being at all careful. The caragana bushes swayed and rustled. A few whispered reproaches could be heard. Someone sneezed; someone cried out in pain.

Mariya Dmytrivna raised her head and waved her hand.

"It's fine! No need to worry! Anyone can come and listen!"

The listeners, no longer under any constraints, stepped out boldly, but carefully, from their uncomfortable cover. Forming a wide semicircle, they surrounded the singer who was pacing back and forth over the wet sand, pausing, and leaning over the water, all without noticing that her shoes and the hem of her dress were completely soaked.

"Tosya, aren't you tired?" Mariya Dmytrivna spoke up tenderly.

"Tired? It doesn't matter! Don't interrupt, Manya; instead, tell me: what do you want me to sing for you?"

A baritone coughed gently and suggested somewhat hesitantly: "Perhaps one of our folk songs?"

"Ah, so you're here as well?" Antonina Pavlivna turned around. "Well, let it be a folk song!"

"No, sing something of Shevchenko's that Lysenko has set to music. Something from Shevchenko's *Kobzar* would be better!" the girls implored.

"Fine. Lysenko it shall be!"

The girls hugged each other in delight.

And once again, the sounds flowed forth; they carried a Ukrainian soul on their wings out over the sea, and the eternal sea approved and clapped softly.

In these songs, a girl wept: "I'm rich, and I'm beautiful!"; an unfortunate soldier's wife sorrowed: "I fell in love, and got married,"; a luckless, lovelorn maiden grieved: "In the garden by the river,"; an unwed mother wept and sang her final legacy: "Oh, lullaby, lullaby, my child."

"Dramas! Once again, we have dramas!" Kost groaned as he flung a good-sized rock into the water with both hands.

But it was the painful groan, not the splash, that reached the singer's sensitive ears and, solicitously respectful of his delicate nerves, she moved on to other themes. In "Above the gulf of the Dnipro river" an epic picture was painted. With the participation of sopranos and a baritone, a quartet was struck to sing "A cloud is floating beyond the sun." And the singers did not notice that the night was floating away, that the stars in the sky were shifting.

"Antonina Pavlivna!"

"What is it, Kost?"

"Do you know 'The *kozak* was walking down a road'? Not the formal arrangement, but just as it is sung in our parts, in Kurhan?

"Of course!"

"And what about 'By the ravine, by the ravine, the wheat spreads in a field,' also in the folk manner, in three voices?"

"I know that one as well."

"Then, let's have it!"

"Kost! For the love of God! It's too soon for you to sing!" Mariya Dmytrivna pleaded.

"It's nothing!" Kost refused to be dissuaded.

And Antonina Pavlivna's contralto and Kost's soft, but achingly beautiful tenor joined in a strange duet which probably contravened all musical conventions, for the role of the *kozak* was sung by the contralto, and that of the girl by the tenor; and the trio that followed was even more unconventional, for the main part was sung by the contralto, while the tenor only added clear, tender descant notes against the background of a smooth bass voice.

"Is this really a folk song?" the listeners asked them.

"It's a genuine folk song!"

"Well, yes; we know it's a folk melody, but whose arrangement is it?"

"It's a folk arrangement! Just a peasant song!" Kost said heatedly.

Mariya Dmytrivna rose to her feet and asked somewhat diffidently: "Tosya, you know, what about our song?"

"'The well is deep, the keys are golden'? No, Manya, don't ask this of me! I feel a great strength today, and I could sing it just as it should be sung, but I feel it would be too hard on him!" she pointed at Kost.

The latter arrogantly shrugged his shoulders: "Don't bother about me!"

"Ah yes, my young man! But who talked about the 'savage' dramas'? Have you forgotten that?"

Bowing graciously, she chided him with respectful sincerity. Kost flushed a flaming red.

"You're right!" he responded quietly.

The sky had brightened. A swallow had swooped by once or twice, and a martlet shrieked as it flew out of an earthen hole.

"Well, it looks as if the singing is over! There won't be any more!" someone said at the rear of the group, and the listeners, servants from the neighbouring cottages, slowly began to disperse.

Antonina Pavlivna silently watched them leave.

Yakovenko, deeply moved, approached her.

"Antonina Pavlivna! I won't begin to pay you compliments, because no matter how many of them I might pile on you, they would still be inadequate. But tell me: who taught you to do those things with every motif? Who taught you how to create? Ladies and gentlemen," he turned to address everyone, "I have heard many famous singers, and I would like to think the rest of you also have not wasted your time during operas.

"I repeat, we have all become accustomed to immortal images created in music, but here I have heard something new, something novel—completely fresh shadings, and a new, original soul in every word! Not to mention the folk songs. I have never heard them sung in this manner! We heard that, at one time, you were preparing for the stage, but to have such a great talent and to bury it, that is a mortal sin!"

"Mr. Yakovenko!" Antonina Pavlivna interrupted him sharply. "Anyone could say that, but not you!"

"Aha, 'the knight of our daily bread' got hoisted on his own petard!" Fedorak observed.

"You say that it is as if I'm creating, you hear a new 'creation' in my singing, but this is just . . . 'the shadow of uncreated creations'! Is it worth . . ."

"Tee-hee-hee! 'The shadow of uncreated creations'," Sonya, who had grown tired of being silent, quickly repeated.

But she was struck dumb when Antonina Pavlivna turned around to face her directly: "Yes, my dear young lady! 'The shadow of uncreated creations'!

"And do you think that this 'shadow' is something light? Like a fog that disperses in the rays of the sun, like a shadow that vanishes when twilight falls? Do you think that it is something fictitious, an illusion? You err in making light of it. It is a heavy burden to have these 'shadows of uncreated creations' behind one's back; oh, how very heavy!"

"Oh!" Kost exhaled sharply.

"There, there now," Mariya Dmytrivna sighed mournfully, as she attempted to restrain her friend.

"Talk! Go on, talk!" Kost and the blond student pleaded simultaneously.

"What can I tell you? Where am I to begin? You heard my voice . . . my manner surprised you . . . But you did not hear a voice, you heard only half of one—the other half has been shattered into splinters, slivers.

"O you young people! Do not squander the power in your soul! Do not choke it, no matter what it is like, in the name of even the holiest ideals, for even the holiest ideal will be defiled by the sacrifice of the suicide and will bring you, instead of a wreath, only pangs—not of morality, and not of the judgement of people— but of your conscience. Are you listening? Of your very own conscience that sits in the bottom of your soul.

"We have obligations to our country, to the law, and to morality, and in fulfilling these obligations we are being virtuous, but we forget the greatest obligation—to our own nature. 'Of what benefit is it to a man if he gaineth the world, but loseth his own soul?'

"I take this to mean the following: what good does it do you if you understand the whole world, but do not know your own soul? And what good does it do you, if in polishing your soul to a diamond-like perfection, you strip it of its original beauty? But what if it isn't a genuine diamond, but a pearl which you will only ruin through polishing it? And what if it's even softer than a pearl, and your polishing grinds it into sand?

"What will you find for yourself in exchange for your forfeited uniqueness? With what will you replace the emptiness of your robbed soul? With respect from the community? With gratitude from those whom you have made more fortunate? With the consciousness of a fulfilled obligation? Or, perhaps, with the pity of those who were witnesses of your self-sacrifice?

"No, and a hundred times, no! We only fool ourselves with all those virtues in order to suffocate the worm that incessantly gnaws at us.

"Why do we see so few truly fortunate people? I see careerists at the pinnacle of the mountain—well, are they happy? No, because they're already trembling with anxiety about how to stay there, so that other careerists, younger ones, won't topple them.

"I see rich people, who never have enough, or for whom everything has lost its meaning. I see so-called 'happy marriages' in which people, gritting their teeth, only imagine happiness, 'for it would be ingratitude to demand something more from human existence.'

"I also see those 'rulers of the hearts' surrounded by luxury, adulation. But don't they choke their hearts 'for the sake of Turkish delights, for the sake of ill-starred greediness'?

"And as for intelligent workers—where is their blessedness, where is their peace?

"The kind of blessedness that children know, or the exhausted body when it rests and regains its strength?

"Why is this?

"I think it is so, because we do not live with our entire soul, but with only half of it, with a small part of it.

"We respect our body; we don't let a day go by without looking after it. But we do an injustice to our soul every minute, shoving it under the feet of our intelligence, subjugating it to its reckoning.

"It is not surprising that the wronged soul groans quietly, and that, like a slave, it weaves cunning snares; but just let the mind loosen its reins a trifle—and it will be hard for it to go on living!"

The sea was completely silent, lulled to sleep by the kindness of the night; the trees were silent in the drowsy air, and the people were silent, deeply moved by the passionate speech.

Kost was as taut as a violin string, the blond student was twirling a little branch, and the faces of Yulya and Sonya were filled with amazement bordering on awe. The men were frowning, scowling. The pale lady who sang mezzo-soprano was listening intently, just as a decrepit old horse, reduced to pulling a water-cart, listens to the sound of a military bugle.

Mariya Dmytrivna was sitting with her head in her hands, rocking like a Jewess in mourning.

"Forgive me, Antonina Pavlivna!" the teacher Holosov, who up to now had been silent, spoke up. "What reason is there for such a tragedy? And from whom? From you, whom everyone is accustomed to consider a model of strength and good judgement!

"Just recall your colleagues in the pleasant little group in which you grew up as a young person—are there many of them left who have remained true to their vows? You and Mariya Dmytrivna, and two or three others—and that's it!

"Who has stuck it out? Who has not betrayed himself or herself? Who has not broken down?

"Just recall Aleksandrova, Kramarenkova . . . Perhaps Vitalsky? Or the unfortunate Verbovy? Or Rudenko and Sushchnasky, who now have become magnates, and who have forgotten that they were once human?

"I was not in your group, Antonina Pavlivna, because I was completing the Teachers' Institute then, but I knew those people. I liked them, and my soul flew to them. But to my grief, when I arrived there, I found only confusion: some had been jailed, some had been sent to Siberia, some had been dispersed in other ways. And which of them returned as a whole person? Which of those who remained has delineated his or her field of endeavour and is still working on it?"

"But what offence did Aleksandrova commit? Surely it wasn't that she gave herself up to the gendarmes and did not beg for mercy from them?"

"What was so good about that? She broke herself and broke the entire cause . . ."

"But she threw herself entirely into the cause with her whole soul, not with half of it. Do you understand me?" Antonina Pavlivna was becoming angry.

"I don't understand! I don't want to understand! It's a good thing she died in captivity! What would have become of her if she had returned—just a bundle of rags!"

"Well, what about Vitalsky?"

"Vitalsky is a happy Russian now, and that's that!"

"And Kramarenkova?"

"Oh, don't touch Kramarenkova, don't touch her!" Mariya Dmytrivna intruded into the conversation. "She's such an unfortunate woman, such a wonderful mother . . ."

"'Woman'! 'Mother'!" Antonina Pavlivna broke in disdainfully. "But what is she as a person? Where is all her talent?"

"So you see," Holosov took over the conversation, "how few of yours remain—out of the women, only the two of you. The rest have either grown lazy in affluence, or dissipated themselves in the warmth of their families, or, crippled by poverty, degenerated into robots.

"You alone have remained faithful and firm, like a soldier under a banner; you have not abandoned the duties of a true populist, and you have not trampled the Ukrainian soul."

"You have not buried your talent in the ground," Vonsovych summed up.

"But the main thing is: you did not fold your arms, and you never stopped working," Yakovenko could not resist adding. "And how many children were there who flowed into your care completely ignorant, and flowed out enlightened?"

"A lot of enlightenment that was. And it will really last a long time!" Antonina Pavlivna retorted sarcastically with a bitter edge to her voice.

"But all the same, our dear Antonina Pavlivna, but all the same, it is not you who should be complaining and bringing 'despair to the front lines' as the Muscovites say."

The young people were staring at Holosov, and they did not notice that dawn was already breaking, and that the silvery morning star was sparkling on the horizon.

"Ladies and gentlemen! I invite all of you to exalt our respected friend, our famous pedagogue, and, most importantly, a person who has honourably upheld her sacred duty, and who is so unvanquished by life that she is able to set all of us, and all of you young people, aflame with her wonderful singing, with her passionate words. Long live Antonina Pavlivna! Together with her faithful friend, Mariya Dmytrivna!"

"Hurrah! Hurrah! Bravo!" the gathering, that had become weary of listening, shouted and clapped.

The students were in ecstasy. The young ladies were happy they could move, and they bustled about, laughing and clapping. Mariya Dmytrivna radiated happiness. Antonina Pavlivna, with an offended mien, as if she wanted to shut her ears, listened to this unexpected conclusion to the speech and impatiently waited for the ovation to subside.

"Oh, we will never understand one another. I sense that we will never understand one another! Of what benefit is it to you that I have been teaching adequately, and for such a long time? Of what benefit is it to you that I, so to say, hit the mark, while some of the others, who gave to others their whole soul, have perished?

"Did you know me earlier? Did you listen to me as you listened tonight? Did you experience before, what I know you have experienced today? Neither my work, nor my long life awoke in you those chords aroused today by the play and by my singing. And why was that? Because both the young author and I, as I sang, gave the people—even if just for a short time—our whole soul, and not half of it. Are you listening? During that time, this soul grew wings which carried it and others to the heavens. Is a teacher able to do this? Has the young author been able to do this in his job as a worldly doctor? Is it the 'sacred matter of duty' that has done this?"

"But why is she still dissatisfied?" Fedorak whispered.

The acute hearing of the singer caught this whisper.

"I am dissatisfied, my good people, because all that with which I endowed you today was nothing more than 'the shadow of uncreated creations.' And no one is to blame except me, that they have become only 'a shadow' and 'uncreated creations'. I myself slaughtered my soul as a sacrifice to the sacred task. But in doing so, what did I do to myself? What did I do to the people? I deprived myself of the blessedness of creativity, I deprived the people of comfort and, with my sacrifice, I defiled the holy cause in which I no longer believe, and which I now serve only out of habit.

"O young people, it is to you that I'm appealing! Before stepping on the path of life, before you arm yourself with all kinds of knowledge, bend down to the very bottom of your soul, draw out that tiny, frightened 'I', examine its unique strengths carefully, and develop only them. Do not be afraid that there will also be faults and evil there; be frightened only of trampling another person's soul when you happen to come across it in your journey.

"Do not set yourself the goal either of material wealth or of people's respect. Do not try to make yourselves better by following someone else's prescription. Do not walk down well-trodden paths; walk down your own paths, even if they are strewn with stones, thorns, and mud.

"It may be difficult, distressing—so be it! But work will make you strong. And if you die in the effort—it is better to die on your own path, to be broken like Aleksandrova, to disappear under the burden of your beloved work like Kramarenkova, than to carry throughout your life an armful of untapped strength, and then, in your old age to experience the coldness and the anguish of 'the shadows of uncreated creations' that surround you." Her voice rang out, then suddenly broke, like a snapped string.

No one moved.

The morning star was rocking on the morning sea. A rosy streak was glowing in the east.

"The sun!" the young lady Yulya shouted.

The slender needles of the sun's rays splashed straight up from the sea and scattered like glowing coals over its calm surface. In that instant, the sea seemed to close its eyes and, without waking up, to smile like a pampered child in its mother's care. The gentle breeze breathed on the shore and on its wonderful panorama of rosy cottages, gold mountains, and dark green clumps of trees which ran like an arc over the semicircle of the green bay.

The gathering stood, entranced . . .

"It's time to go home," Yakovenko observed.

"And how!" Vonsovych added.

"Where has the night gone?" the others wondered.

Opposite them, at the very edge of the water, the figure of Antonina Pavlivna stood motionless, and for some reason the pale lady was crying softly, but inconsolably, notwithstanding all the solicitude of Mariya Dmytrivna.

"There's a 'shadow' for you . . ." Vonsovych began to say mockingly.

"Shadows disappear in the sun; fog is dispersed by the fresh wind," Yakovenko added.

"Here's that 'shadow' which has 'brought despair' to you . . ." Antonina Pavlivna turned towards them.

"That's not true! It hasn't disappeared!" Kost and the blond student shouted passionately.

In the neighbouring cottages, the servants were beginning to go about their chores. A distant streetcar whistled somewhere beyond the mountain.

It was time to go their separate ways. The townspeople bid their farewells as they hurried to the train; the cottagers dispersed to go to bed.

Mariya Dmytrivna was attempting to convince Antonina Pavlivna to lie down as well, but the latter refused decisively and started up the incline, where the figures of Yakovenko, Vonsovych, and Holosov could be seen in the distance.

She wanted to be completely alone, and she purposely slowed her pace, but then the blond student and Kost showed up from behind a thick mimosa plant.

"Antonina Pavlivna, we'll accompany you part of the way. May we?"

Antonina Pavlivna stopped walking and reflected for a moment: "You may."

The youths had also purposely slowed their pace to avoid being in the same coach with the three who were up ahead.

But, for some reason, the conversation did not go well. The youths had many questions they wanted to ask, but Antonina Pavlivna wanted to regain control over herself in preparation for her meaningless, mundane existence, and furthermore, the train was whistling and rumbling.

Before they arrived at the station at which the youths were to get off, Antonina Pavlivna turned to them: "Well, my young friends? Has all this gone right past you, and has 'the shadow of uncreated creations' vanished from before your eyes like a shadow—as it has for those gentlemen?" She pointed at Yakovenko, Vonsovych and Fedorak, who were roaring with laughter and flattering some corpulent beauty.

"Oh, no! We'll remember! For the rest of our lives! Forever!" the two spoke up simultaneously.

Antonina Pavlivna smiled half-contentedly, half-worriedly, and waved her hand in a gesture of dismissal. The train stopped.

The youths jumped out and sincerely bade farewell to Antonina Pavlivna: "Farewell! God bless you! Thank you! Thank you, O Spark of God . . .

"Believe us, we won't forget!"

The youths were still shouting something, but the train screeched, shuddered, and moved forward, humming over the rails and clanging on the joints.

Antonina Pavlivna bowed to them, and they waved their caps and continued yelling something, some kind of thanks and promises . . . These promises were sincere, and easy to give, for they were both still young . . .

The Avenger
(1912?)

Even from a distance, the home of the old woman Vekla
Hnybida, in the village of Sukhoverbivka, was easily recognizable.
It was completely surrounded, in the old-fashioned way, by a straw
wall so thickly overgrown with caragana bushes that not even a
cat could crawl through it. Nowadays, even the poorest among us
are ashamed of such hedges—there are fences everywhere, either
built of pickets, or woven out of various kinds of willows.

But the old woman was not in the least concerned about her
hedge and had given no thought to changing it for a more up-to-
date fence. For one thing, she was poor—her husband Kharko, for
many long years the village herdsman, had died tending his herd
on the steppe. Moreover, the shrubs had entangled themselves so
thoroughly in the straw wall and were bracing it so firmly, that
she did not have to worry about it.

The only problem with the wall was related to the chickens. If
one of the hens broke away from the flock and began to lay her
eggs in the thick caragana bushes, she suffered scratches to her
hands, her clothing, and her face, as she searched for the wayward
fowl and brought it into line again.

The young people liked to cavort in the cool shade of the
caragana bushes. Mischievous boys hid their belongings among
the roots and under the prickly branches, and young couples
happily cuddled there, knowing that the nearby neighbours—their
avowed enemies—could not see them.

The old woman did not prevent either of these groups from
engaging in their activities, because these matters did not concern
her; she really had no time to worry about them. She had all the
housework to look after and, because her husband had died, and
her son was still in school, she also had to do all the work in the
yard.

Although living in poverty, the Hnybidas had managed, somehow or other, to eke out a living. Their only son Petro grew up, completed the two-grade school with good marks, and was hired on as a junior clerk in the district office.

The old woman dreamed about the time when her son would become a respected householder in the village; she would see to it that he married well, and they would live comfortably and peacefully.

But things did not turn out the way she planned.

Her husband caught a cold in the fall, spent three days or so in bed, and died. His only consolation, as he lay dying, was the knowledge that he had managed, one way or another, to see to it that his son had a decent position in life—that he would not have to be a village herdsman like his father.

He took great pains to instruct his son to take good care of his mother, who often denied herself a scrap of food to ensure that her son, in spite of their impoverished state, would have everything he needed. He adjured his son never to become a bloodsucker that preyed on the community—as is usually the case with village clerks.

The son listened attentively to his dying father and vowed that he would fulfil all his wishes.

The winter dragged on interminably.

Petro grew weary of sitting at home every evening, and even though he loved his mother, he began going out in his free time. The merrymaking in the street did not appeal to him, because drunken vagaries were contrary to his quiet nature; therefore, he began borrowing books from libraries in other villages—he had already read all the ones in his own village—and in this way, he became acquainted with other young people who were interested in reading and recommended books he should read.

Goodness! It was if he had been reborn!

Everything that he read amazed him so greatly that he felt as if the sky were falling on his head, or the ground were slipping away from under his feet. The young fellow would not have been able to cope with this radical transformation in his way of thinking if it had not been for his new friends.

The times were also changing.

Just as in the early spring—when the soil and the water are still caught in the grip of an icy covering—tiny rivulets begin burrowing their way under the snow and secretly preparing for the sunny resurrection close at hand, so the groundwork for the revolution was proceeding, stealthily and clandestinely, but without interruption. Anonymous sympathisers—like butterflies, like birds returning home from southern migrations—flew in from everywhere, bringing with their fiery words a new vision of the world to the darkest corners of the land.

At first, the village viewed these students with suspicion, having more than once heard unfavourable comments about them from the city folk; however, after seeing for themselves these wholesome young orators overflowing with love and courage, they began to listen more carefully to the speeches which, at times, they could hardly understand. And when the officials, the police, and other such devils began to hunt them down, the villagers took an even greater liking to these harbingers of spring.

The agitators appeared and disappeared, but sometimes they were caught and beaten in full view of the people. At other times, rumours abounded that they had been thrown in jail or murdered.

They were so young, so happy, so defenceless, and so unworldly, and the people felt sorry for them and for their cause which could perish—because of their naiveté—without ever illuminating remote regions of their country. And so, to replace them, the villagers began sending their own people, who were known to everybody, and who were more aware of the local situation, but who would not be noticed by the enemy. Actually, it was not the village that sent them forth; they themselves, fired up by the new ideas—like insects awoken by the sun—crawled out of their dark crannies and carried the subversive teachings to the neighbouring villages.

Petro was among the first to go.

His elderly mother did not understand what was happening to her only son, and at times she upbraided him for becoming lazy. But he always hugged his mother and managed to calm her fears, reminding her of his solemn vow to his dying father.

More than once, after hearing his conversations with his new friends or listening to the orators at the clandestine meetings that were held in her house in the shelter of the caragana hedge, she asked her son what it was all about and where it was headed. And her son, if he did not have to hurry off somewhere, explained to his mother as much about the teachings of the coming new order as her old mind could grasp.

Old Vekla was frightened; she shook her head, argued, and did not believe him. But then, as she mulled things over in her sluggish mind, she would become somewhat more receptive to her son's ideas.

There was only one thing that her son asked of her. He begged her to refrain from visiting the village gossips and to say nothing about the meetings in their home, so as not to endanger those who came to them and placed themselves under their protection.

Before long, Vekla, who was not talkative by nature, became totally conspiratorial—she learned how to remain silent without even blinking, no matter what she was asked, or how she was approached.

She learned how to tell a lie with a convincing expression on her face in order to defend the people under suspicion, and when they actually were in her home, she went about her work in the yard in a completely calm and indifferent manner, so that it would not even cross anyone's mind that there was something amiss.

She even did more than that. Taking advantage of her advanced years, the old woman often pretended not to see or hear well and, little by little, her fellow villagers became accustomed to regarding her as someone who was getting on in years and was no longer all that well.

And life went on; incendiary incidents became the order of the day, and the people were agitated.

Old order lackeys of every stripe were rummaging everywhere and hunting down the agitators. But, in spite of all their efforts, they had no success in the village of Sukhoverbivka. Whenever they descended upon it, all traces of their quarry vanished, as if swallowed up by water. They would search and ask, but confronted with half-wits who would make them look like fools, they would have to leave with nothing better than that.

The chief district clerk and the officials were not greyhounds from elsewhere, but rather villagers themselves who, as long as they were not being attacked too strongly, did not betray their own people. But it was impossible to hide from them any longer.

At first they hinted to Petro, and finally they came right out and told him that he should quit his job as a junior clerk, so as not to bring their district office under police suspicion. Petro understood what they were saying, agreed to leave, and even thanked the senior officials for the warning.

He fixed things up around the house, bought food supplies and fuel for his mother, hid his books and other possibly incriminating articles, packed his bags, and set out—so he said—to look for work.

"Oh, my dear Petro! My heart aches, and I sense that something bad will happen!" his mother grieved. "Where are you going? Tell me the truth! I'm not your enemy, I don't want to betray you—I just want to know how I am to go on living without you, and how I am to behave so that I, by chance, don't make things worse for you."

His mother's sensitivity touched Petro.

"Now, now, mother, don't worry! I truly am going somewhere to look for work, but then again—who knows how things will work out! It may be that I will have to experience something else, but it can't be helped. The times right now are like this—if you don't sow good grain now, what will you reap later? You saw, mother, that those 'orators' were also young and poor like I am. In all likelihood, their mothers and fathers were anxious about them, and perhaps more than one has been thrown in jail—that's what these times are like! But I've given the matter some thought, and you can be of great service to me and my friends. As a herdswoman, it would be easy for you to do this." And he began to tell her in great detail what it was that she should do.

Petro left home and vanished.

For three months or so, two peddlers at a time would spend the night at Vekla's cottage. And they always disappeared silently, leaving behind a pile of literature in the form of proclamations and fliers known as "butterflies."

The old woman, just as silently, hid the colourful flock, and later dispersed them in the yards as she went around gathering up the cattle.

When winter came, and she no longer tended the community herds, the old woman sat mostly at her spinning wheel; however, sometimes, at night, she would get up and go somewhere. And in the morning, when the people went to water their cattle, they found pamphlets in their yards. After everything had been delivered, the old woman once again sat down to her spinning.

When something scratched softly at her window, she would cautiously open the door, and her secret visitor would leave her more literature to be distributed. And once—alas!—he brought her disturbing news that her Petro had been sent to prison.

The old woman uttered a cry of alarm, but she did not weep.

When the bearer of this news left, she hid the pamphlets he had brought in a hole in the earthen floor and sealed the hole with a mixture of mud and clay. In the morning, she went to see an old spinster who took in knitting, to put in a rush order for warm stockings and mitts; then she herself began getting ready other articles of clothing.

The old woman travelled to the city to take the clothes to Petro. In the meantime, Petro's trial had been held, and the prisoners were being readied for their trip to Siberia. The old woman barely managed to arrange a visit with her son; she vowed that she would avenge him in any way that she could. Petro tried in vain to convince her that it was her continuing help that was needed, not personal vengeance.

The old woman did not change her mind about one thing. Petro went to Siberia, but in the village of Sukhoverbivka the silent propaganda continued to gain momentum.

The police racked their brains—there was illegal literature in all the homes, but no one could say where it was coming from.

Old Vekla tended the herds and kept her silence.

The Maiden-Seagull
(1892)

In the Black Sea there is a forbidding, silent island; from a wildly overgrown, verdant plain, the reddish peak of a single ochre cliff pierces the sky. No white cottages huddle on this cliff, and no leafy branches cover it; only a solitary green path—where a streamlet erodes the coppery soil in the spring, leaving velvety grass in its wake—wends its way down one side. Beyond it everything is sterile and still . . .

Well, perhaps not everything. Over there, at the edge of the sea, where grey breakers rage relentlessly on the promontory, a flame hovers at night, while by day, seagulls, lamenting forlornly, circle over the water.

What cliff is this? What flame? And why are seagulls so enamoured of this grim cliff?

It is said that once, long ago, a man from parts unknown came to this deserted island. An evil fate pursued him in his wanderings through the world, and he could not find a safe harbour anywhere. Carrying a little child and his meagre belongings out of his boat, he crawled into a cave and began living there. How he lived, and what he ate when he first set foot on shore—no one knew. But it was not long before people came to know his generous soul.

Every night he lit a huge bonfire so that ships and fishing vessels skimming over the emerald waves could see its flames from afar and navigate safely past the rugged cliff and the treacherous, unmarked shoals. And if a vessel did crash, he would courageously venture forth alone in his small boat to rescue the unfortunate victims left floundering in the sea.

The grateful people gladly tried to give him large gifts—money and treasures that they carried in their boats; but the stranger refused everything, taking only such provisions as he needed to sustain himself and the child, and some wood and tar to keep his fire going.

Before long, everyone knew about this strange old man they called "the sea stork," and they also found out about his child who, like a mermaid, was rocked and caressed by the waves, and left unharmed, even comforted, both by the silent stones and the roaring storms.

And the old man's daughter grew into a wondrous beauty; her colouring was fair, like the foam on the sea; her curly hair tumbled riotously to her knees like aquatic nettle, her blue eyes shone like the sea in the early morning, and her teeth, framed by her coral lips, gleamed like pearls.

She feared nothing—neither storms, nor thunder, nor menacing waves—for the sea was her domain. When there was someone to be rescued, the girl flung herself boldly into the sea alongside her father. And the raging sea would not lay claim to anyone she touched.

One time, having swum to her heart's content, the girl fell into a tranquil sleep on the warm sand. The sea was also drowsing peacefully, and from among the rocks lining the shore, she could hear whispers as she slept.

Three creatures had gathered—an osprey, a dolphin, and a fish with golden fins.

The fish said: "Because she rescued me, I'll bring her pearls, coral, and bright gems from the depths. There I was, lying far out on a sand bar, where the angry waves had tossed me. The sun was beating down on me, scorching my gills, and a rapacious white-feathered kingfisher circled over me, bringing with him my certain death. This kind child took me in her hands, smiled at me tenderly, and slipped me gently back into the sea—and I revived."

"I'll teach her to swim, dive, and dance gaily in the waves," the dolphin said. "And I'll tell her wonderful tales to repay her kindness towards me—for when I was in need, she fed me, generously sharing her food with me. There were many times I would have died if it had not been for her."

"As for me," the pensive osprey spoke up, "I'll tell her something that no one knows. When I was far beyond the sea, I heard that ships and galleys bearing strange people called *kozaks* *[Cossacks]* are bound for our shores. They are audacious men with forelocks, who fear nothing; they don't offer gifts to the ancient sea, as other merchant sailors do; they just scourge the waves and slice them with their oars. And so the angry sea has called down its wrath upon them, and evil fate has doomed them to perish in a watery grave. And, all their treasure is to be given to the rocks and sandbars, and to us—the servants of the sea.

"No one knows this great secret, and I will tell it only to her—the kind-hearted one—because I, too, was saved by her. One time, a villain pierced my wing with an arrow, and I was expiring on the emerald waves. This dear girl caught me, uttered charms that staunched my blood, annointed my wounds with curative herbs, gave me food, and cared for me until my wing healed. That is why I'll tell her this great secret . . ."

"Hush!" the awakening waves rustled. "Be quiet; it's no concern of yours. No one should venture to discover the will of the mighty sea; no one should be so bold as to argue with such a formidable foe!"

The waves, grumbling wrathfully, flung themselves against the rocks and the cliff.

Terrified, the dolphin and the fish dove into the depths, and the osprey lifted itself up and flew way.

But the waves had awakened too late.

The girl had overheard, and she leapt to her feet, calling: "Come back, O osprey! Come back and tell me everything you heard. I don't need pearls, or coral beads, or enchanting tales, or spirited dances—just tell me everything in detail, so that I know where to watch for these men with the long forelocks and how to rescue these unfortunate souls in their distress."

The sea was infuriated, and it roared: "Be still and don't ask, you foolish child! Obey the sea and don't contend with it—for the sea punishes very severely!"

But the girl thought: "It doesn't matter to me! Roar all you want to, O emerald waves; grow dark with anger, go mad with rage! I will not sacrifice these courageous men; I'll pluck my unfortunate brothers from the jaws of the sea! But I won't say a word about it to my father, for I can see that bad weather is brewing, and he is old and feeble, and unable to pit himself against the elements."

The day burned itself out, and the sun dove into the sea. A great silence ensued.

In the twilight, all that could be heard was the old man's muttering as he prepared to rekindle the nocturnal bonfire. His daughter bid him good-night and went into the cave to lie down. But as soon as the old man began fussing with the fire, she stealthily jumped into their little boat, readied everything, steeled herself, and sat down to await the storm.

The sea was still calm, but there was a muffled roar in the distance. A thundercloud, the sea's accomplice, was approaching. Blinking its dreadful eyes, it blew at the tiny stars, and the stars vanished in fear. Now the wind, its messenger, swept the shore; it whistled, and blew, and tried to put out the fire. But the old man, guessing its purpose, poured more tar on the logs, and it blazed even more strongly. The wind retreated in embarrassment, and everything became still.

Then the storm cloud roared once again as it approached, and a phalanx of marauding winds whirled, howled, and jabbed the sleepy waves in their sides. The waves rushed wildly at the cliff, which pelted them with stones. Ravenously swallowing these treats, the waves crashed against the cliff once more.

The cloud drew still nearer; thunder rumbled, lightning flashed fiercely, and the storm drove and pounded the unfortunate galleys mercilessly, snapping the masts, ripping the sails and bathing them in the salty waves.

The dauntless oarsmen fought with the sea; the men with the forelocks did not give in!

But now the sea caught up with them, rocked them violently, and dashed them against the cliff—and the cliff, catching sight of its delectable prey, howled like a rapacious beast. In the blink of an eye, all the galleys were smashed!

The girl was fearless; she skimmed over the water, unerringly steering her craft, daringly plucking the drowning men from the sea, and swiftly bearing them to safety. Many were already on the shore, but many more were perishing in the sea.

The girl did not yield to fatigue, nor did she deign to listen to the menacing words of the maddened sea.

"Go! Go away! Don't even think of contesting my power. These spoils are mine—I won't give them up without exacting a ghastly price! Go! Turn back, you foolish girl! You will be punished by a dreadful fate! Retreat!"

The girl did not listen—she paid no attention! A mighty wave surged and crashed, forcefully seized the frail craft and, casting it far beyond the sand bar, smashed it as if it were an egg shell. The girl wept, not from fear, and not for her boat, but because of her immeasureable grief, for she knew she would not be able to save the unfortunate men.

"No! I must try again!" Tearing off her clothing in a flash, she flung herself into the sea.

The enraged sea did not spare her—it voraciously swallowed its favourite daughter. But a righteous fate looked down upon her. And, instead of finding death, the grieving girl burst flutteringly from the sea in the form of a grey seagull and, keening bitterly, flew out over it . . .

The old man had no idea what his daughter had done until he was told by the *kozaks* she had rescued. Overcome with grief, he cast himself into the flames of the fire he was tending. And so, both the old man and his daughter perished—but not entirely.

Every night, a fire wanders over the cliff, and grey seagulls, multiplying in great numbers on its face, circle over the sea, calling out forlornly when they catch wind of a threatening storm, warning sailors and travellers on the sea and, bearing witness to days gone by, keep eternal the memory of the glorious maiden-seagull.

The Lovers' Quarrel
(1893)

The cheerful sun rose in the sky, glanced around, and smiled benignly at its beloved, youthful progeny still drowsing in love's embrace.

Who are these offspring of the sun—these fortunate lovers?

The fair one is the enchanting earth.

Jagged mountains crown her in an azure wreath; verdant meadows and luxuriant orchards elegantly gird her; and her reddish robes drape in heavy folds, adorned at the hem with strings of speckled stones.

The lover is the boisterous sea.

His silken turquoise coat-tails undulate gently, sparkling in the sun's rays as if strung with precious gems, and foam embroiders the length of his turquoise mantle with bands of pearls and overlays its hem with copious lace.

The sun smiled for a second time; the earth awakened first and, blushing, as if embarrassed, began to don dark ribbons of shade over her transparent veils of fog. But the sea slept on and, without awakening, continued splashing and cuddling his beloved, kissing her softly.

The sun smiled for a third time and said: "Love each other, my fortunate ones!"

The earth sighed, smiled blissfully, and glowed in all her beauty.

In a dark abyss among the mountains, an evil wind lay hidden like a snake; he concealed himself there for the night, resting after completing his daily work—flying endlessly above the earth, ever alert and attentive, and forever circulating lies.

Noticing that the saintly sun had smiled warmly at someone, he grew jealous and felt compelled to interfere. Crawling out quietly, creeping stealthily through the ravines, and lurking under bushes, he kept a watchful eye to see whom the sun was greeting.

And he discovered who it was. His heart roared with hatred; he lifted his lowered forehead from the grass, rustled among the branches, petulantly tugged the oaks' bushy thatch, and soared upwards on mighty wings.

He flew about, persistently cajoling and persuading the earth to betray the blue sea.

But to what end? The earth did not listen; blushing happily, she continued to gaze serenely at the sea like a faithful wife. The evil wind was even more enraged—he howled, whistled, and hissed like a snake.

Abandoning the earth, the wind swooped down to the sea, jabbed him in the sides, and whispered falsehoods, implying that his beloved had betrayed him, and that, instead of opening her arms to him at night, she had embraced the dark sky, brightly embroidered with stars.

The sea did not heed him and gently murmured: "You're lying, you're lying."

The devious liar did not fall silent; he continued weaving ever more cunning and outrageous lies. Finally he succeeded.

The sea, convinced by the enemy, rose from his sleep, leapt up abruptly, glared angrily at his beloved, and asked: "Is this true, or isn't it?"

His beloved did not respond; glowing rosily in the sun, she tenderly extended her embrace to him.

Her smile offended her loved one; he rushed towards her and began reproaching her, saying that she probably did not love him if she did not heed either his lament or his tears.

The earth remained silent.

"Tell me, is it true? Is it true?" the enraged lover now asked severely.

The earth said nothing, but her smile vanished, a shadow flitted over her face, and her dazzling garments faded.

"Ah! Then it's true! So this is how you return the love of your devoted companion. You no longer dare to look him in the face!"

The earth wrapped herself more tightly in a dark veil and did not reply.

The sea grew furious; he roared, fell into a rage, spit pearly foam, burst into angry tears, and wildly tossed about the golden sand and the precious stones—gifts his loved one had given him.

The wind rejoiced like a preying eagle that, circling above a flock of terrified grey geese, takes pleasure in their fear.

The incensed sea roared madly for a long time.

Wrapped in a dark twilight, his wrongfully accused beloved gazed silently at her implacable companion.

The indignant sun hid its face in a blue cloud, everyone felt sad and uneasy, and only the wind exulted—he roared, hooted with laughter, and screamed until he was satiated, and then, exhausted, he trailed off to rest in the abyss.

The sea was still infuriated; however, now there was no one to provoke him, and his reproaches gradually abated.

Wearying of his anger, and completely confused, he asked disconsolately: "Is it true? Is it true?"

But his beloved remained silent.

The sun, retiring for the night, glanced out from a cloud with an angry red face—the jealous sea would not calm down, and the earth would neither forgive him nor greet him with a light-winged breeze.

The golden sun went to sleep; lively little clouds—placed on guard by the sun—scattered in all directions, and the bright silvery new moon shone radiantly in the serene, deep blue sky. It bent down low from on high, peered at the sulking lovers, and then generously scattered its gracious silver rays over the earth and the sea.

The earth cast off her coverlet and, glowing radiantly once again, smiled at her beloved.

Startled at her wondrous beauty, the sea caught fire in the moonlight and, with a breast brimming with love, flung himself at her feet, kissing her, and begging her forgiveness.

The moon, winking slyly at them from above, gave a final nod and retreated behind a mountain.

The shy earth opened her arms more widely, and her fragrant, warm, breath wafted over the sea; her beloved quivered and sighed; and they swooned in a passionate kiss . . .

The Poplars
(1893)

Tall, and slender like arrows, four green poplars reach up to the luminous sky, converse with the wind, exchange greetings with the sun, and whisper among themselves without the wind's assistance. And on dark, calm nights, the mellifluous sea calls out affectionately to them.

In their midst, a dark well, built of stones, washes their roots, glitters enigmatically, and remains mysteriously silent . . .

Morning and evening, Tartar girls hasten to the stately poplars; their white veils wave in the breeze, their finely plaited braids tumble down their backs, their voices ring out warmly, and their eyes, glowing and sparkling, speak without a word being uttered.

Why are these girls so enamoured of the poplars? Why, after passing both a swiftly flowing river and all the other wells, do these dear chatterers hurry every morning and evening to the well amidst the poplars? Why do they take a long time to draw the water, showing no interest in returning home? Ask them—they will only look at you in surprise and, without saying anything, turn to gaze warmly once again at the poplars.

Why, at midday, do the children play so amiably here—and not over there, under the warm sun, or over there, in the shade of the mountain? Ask them—the foolish little ones will not tell you.

Why does this old man, gnarled with age, sit silently under the poplars for days on end, only occasionally muttering something and shaking his head? Ask him—and the wise old man will smile and sweep his hand around at all of God's creation, and then his faded eyes will quietly and tenderly fall once again on the poplars.

There is no answer—not from people. But the poplars rustle and sway; their leaves flutter as if they were plaintively pleading for someone to comprehend their mute language, listen to their story, and relate it to the world.

Now the sun is setting; the expansive, undulating sea accepts it into its embrace from the red sky, and the sun's final glance rests benevolently on those sharply tapered poplars. And the wind, bidding them farewell, once again rushes over their tips; the branches shake in confusion and rustle angrily, but the wind, frolicking merrily, has already darted away. The evening star fades, the azure sky darkens, and everything grows drowsy.

Only the poplars murmur plaintively, and the sea calls out to them—and both it and the poplars regret that the steep bank does not allow them to come together and engage in earnest conversation.

But now the moon, bright and serene, floats out from behind the mountain—and everything smiles, everything brightens; the dark Alma river gleams like a snake among the willows in the meadow, and the grey wormwood on the hill glistens like silver. In the transparent air, the poplars stand like nuns attired in black robes, whispering softly. Everything is alert, ready to listen to the strange tales that the wistful poplars will tell them.

The poplars nod their heads for the first time—and a tranquil drowsiness embraces the entire world; and the sea, settling in to sleep, laps gently against the shore.

The poplars sway for the second time—and everything that existed either today or yesterday vanishes and is forgotten; the moon covers its beaming face with a small white cloud.

They stir for the third time—and a scene from times long past rises before one's eyes. Dark graves stir, headstones emerge and fashion themselves into a city, and the grasses and tall weeds stretch to the sky and surround the entire steppe with orchards. The Alma river murmurs, spreads over the meadows, reaches up to the cliffs, and glitters—like a silver fish flashing its scales.

A breeze blows gently, and the entire city comes to life. People rush to and fro, camels bray, flocks of thick-fleeced sheep call out, girls sing as they fetch water, youths on horseback caracole, and the sun—not the moon—is shining in the sky. All of God's world is singing, celebrating the joyful summer, and sending the swiftly flowing Alma to greet the turbulent sea and tell it about its quiet happiness.

The breeze blows for the second time.

From beyond the mountains, a cloud rises and moves in slowly. No, it is not a cloud that is moving in, and it is not thunder that is rumbling; it is the enemy approaching with its army—and the dusky, umber mountains are groaning with grief.

Panic reigns everywhere; flocks of sheep scatter, and cattle bellow in confusion; but the people are worse than animals—some chase fiercely after their own kind, while others, weeping and cursing, flee from them. In the market itself, a bloody slaughter is raging, and people are cut down like stalks of rye sheared by a sharp sickle. The market square turns crimson with blood, and a dreadful uproar reverberates through the mountains.

Everything falls silent, all is quiet, everyone is sleeping—some have fallen asleep forever, while others will sleep for only a short time until the enemy, now drunk with blood, sobers up enough to go on a rampage once again.

There is only one large building where no one is sleeping; here, army officers are carousing, and there is the clamour of voices and raucous laughter; music thunders, wine flows, and the tears of the comely male and female captives are also flowing.

And over there, behind a wall, servants are clearing and preparing a room; the entire floor is spread with expensive carpets, and on top of them are placed soft furs, velvet robes, and silk pillows embroidered with gold. The victors will sleep sweetly and deliciously there after their hard work!

In a small dark hut, four beautiful young girls are imprisoned. They are not weeping—all their tears have been shed; they are not talking—they have lost their voices from grief; they sit like mute, white stones and shudder silently when someone passes by the door.

And the youngest one asks: "Why don't they kill us? Have they taken pity on us, or have they forgotten about us? Or are they ashamed that they've already caused so much grief?"

"Oh, dear sister, you're still young and foolish, even though you're equal to me in height!" her older sister responds. "Those cursed ones feel no shame; they have no pity for girls; and they haven't forgotten about us, unfortunate that we are. They won't kill all of us right away; people die only once in their lives, but we who have no fate are doomed to die twice. Dying people always plead and beg to be granted at least an hour longer to live, but we'll be weeping and pleading with them to put us to death sooner—and they won't listen. The women, girls, old men, and youths who died today all know in what state they will arrive in the next world, but we—we're neither women nor girls . . .

"Sisters, companions, let's escape—flee from captivity! I see a crack in the attic. Let's escape to the open sea!"

The girls' eyes light up and sparkle; they leap to their feet and, quietly and nimbly, like mountain goats, crawl in a flash out of the attic to the roof. The moon spots them and hides behind a dark cloud, and the orchard conceals them with its branches, as they run through it. The sea that they are approaching breathes freshly and invitingly at them as it laps against a small boat, rocking it caressingly on its waves.

"Sisters, oh sisters, they're gaining on us!"

"Don't worry, little sister, there's a well close by."

"What good is that?" the youngest sister asks.

The girls run up to it.

"Let us embrace, my sisters! Farewell, my dear little swans!" the oldest one says. "Oh, brother-well, conceal us and protect us from shame, my dear one!"

The pursuers are gaining ground; they run up, search all over—but there is no one. The orchard whispers mysteriously, but the dark well is silent; it will not reveal anything. And the sea waits and waits; then, growing angry, it raises its waves and smashes the little boat against the rocks, without ever having greeted its beloved guests . . .

The turbulent hour passes, and the centuries tread with a heavy step over the spot where the ancient city once stood; the walls crumble, the orchards wither, and the Alma that brimmed with water, scarcely gurgles over the stones. All the former inhabitants and their enemies have died, and darkened graves stretch across the steppe. The deep well still remains silent, while in its depths a hidden spring gurgles.

And now the second hour begins. The forgotten city comes alive once more; indigent little suburbs spring up, and Tartar girls, fetching water, trample the overgrown path to the well once again.

The deep well can no longer remain silent; it wants to relate the old tale to its dear new guests. And at the very moment that the mute well has this thought, four slender poplars take root and encircle it; they rustle and whisper, greeting the sun in the sky, the distant sea, and their lovely young visitors. They tell them a strange tale, and the deep well listens mutely, while the sea first weeps and then storms—enraged that the bank will not let it draw nearer to the lovely, pensive poplars.

The Cliff
(1893)

A long, long time ago, royal palaces crowned a tall Crimean mountain, and dense, verdant orchards ran down a ravine to a river that writhed like an infuriated snake between its steep, wild banks. Fields of wheat billowed in the steppes, countless herds grazed in the meadows, and a cheerful people inhabited thriving villages, not silent cemeteries. A boisterous sea greeted the happy shore with emerald waves, and the sun smiled warmly at the blissful land.

And the mistress of all of this—the mountains, the steppe, and the people—was the Crimean Queen.

This queen was beautiful beyond words: tall and slender like a cypress tree, rosy like the dawn, and as lovely; but her eyes, her alluring dark eyes, blazed from under her velvety eyebrows like menacing lightning from under a black cloud.

Yes, this queen was rich, and comely, and formidable; but she did not take pride in her realm or her beauty—this widowed queen took delight and pride only in the sons that their father, the young king, had left her. The widow forgot her grief when she looked into the eyes of the infants, and their chattering awakened hope in her heart; the queen was waiting for the star of good fortune and glory to once again shine upon her.

One fine morning, the queen went for a stroll in the orchard with her sons. The sun generously showered its gold upon them, the fragrant flowers nodded their heads, and the birds in the branches chirped happily. But, for some reason, neither the sun nor the queen's flowers cheered the princes—their delicate faces were pale, their shining eyes lacklustre.

"O my dear sons, my dearest children!" the queen exclaimed. "Tell me—what can I do to make you happy? Do you want expensive stallions to be brought to you? Do you want the finest weapons to be given to you? Or do you want young boys your age to be assembled here to play with you and amuse you?"

"O Mother-Queen! We don't need horses—we're weary of them! We don't want weapons—our eyes are tired of looking at those shiny delights. There's no need to call together our age mates—they're tired."

"What? They're tired? How dare they be tired?" shouted the grim queen. "Fine—I'll have these boys hanged, and then I'll command that other lads, better ones, be gathered together."

"No, dearest mummy, no. There's no need to do that—it won't cheer us up. Instead, give orders that a boat be built for us—we'll sail and bathe in the blue sea."

The queen ordered that a galley be built. She hung it with velvet and spread it with rich carpets; a silk sail fluttered on the mast, and both the bow and the stern sparkled with gold.

The galley wound its way gently down the river, but it was not the wind that pushed it—elegantly garbed servants guided it with red chains fastened to a cable. And it was not the wind, the tempestuous wind, that was bending heavy ears of grain in the fields—it was the fierce and blazing mien of the queen that was making her subjects bow down before her.

For a long time, songs resounded among the amazed mountains, and the steep banks were speckled with colourful clothing by the time the galley finally reached the sea. And down by the sea stood a red tent—so that the searing Crimean sun would not burn the bodies of the princes, so that the sea wind would not ruffle their princely hair, and so that none of their vassals could gaze upon their indescribable beauty.

The young princes went out on the sea; crystal-green waves, embracing their supple, slender waists, splashed their silky hair, and droplets of water spiralled like pearls over their delicate bodies.

But their eyes did not brighten. The pensive queen sat silently—trying to think of a way to make her beloved children happy.

She swept her eyes over the sea—and music instantly poured forth, drowning the roar of the waves; but her children did not listen to the music.

She swept her eyes over the sea a second time—and exquisite girls began to dance. The princes lowered their heads even more.

At a word from the queen, the musicians stopped playing, and unseen singers raised their voices in an enchanting song that floated rhythmically over the waves. But it was in vain that the song resounded—it passed right by the princes' ears.

Then, suddenly, the princes took notice of something—a small white sail that glimmered in the distance, on the waves.

A shabby little boat drew nearer, and in the boat stood a young girl, singing in a clear voice. Her marvellous song spread and echoed over the water, a cheerful smile hovered on her full, rosy lips, and her eyes shone and showered sparks. Her decrepit little boat was full of holes, but this did not bother her; she was happy, and she sang, breaking off occasionally to say a word or two, or to bestow affection on her servants—the fish and the birds of the sea. Fish swam in droves after her, birds flocked in her wake, sea weed wove itself into wreaths around the boat, and the boat itself was filled with little animals.

No one had ever seen this girl before, no one could understand her song: everyone looked on in silent amazement.

She did not pay any attention to the proud queen, nor did she bow to her; she just sailed on, straight ahead.

"Who is it? Who is it?" they all asked one another.

No one spoke to her; no one stopped her. The girl began to beckon someone with her finger.

No one could guess what was happening—but a wretched slave who had listened tremulously to that bewitching voice a long time ago, forgot that his arms and legs were bound in heavy fetters, and that the galley master was standing behind him with a whip.

"It's fate! It's fate!" he cried wildly and jumped into the sea.

The chains of servitude wanted to hold him even now and bury him in the depths; but the girl just waved her hand—and her entire retinue rushed towards the drowning man. The fish and the birds dove into the water and pulled out a young man; the girl took him into her boat, clasped him to her bosom, and planted a kiss on his lifeless lips—and he immediately revived, and his chains fell off of their own accord.

The white sail flashed by, and everything vanished in the azure expanse.

The fabulous vision disappeared, the people stood silently, and the princes' eyes blazed with a new question.

"Who was it? Who was this enchantress?" they asked.

"Who is this rude person? Who is this rebel?" the queen inquired grimly.

Everyone was silent; no one knew.

And the galley returned upstream, carrying in it the infuriated queen and the awe-stricken princes.

Days and weeks passed, and the years flowed by. The young princes grew up, and even their mother could no longer keep them in the palace.

Like the wind on the steppes, they flew on their horses from one end of the kingdom to the other, searching for freedom and asking about fate. They rode through all of Crimea, and they walked through all the orchards, all the mosques, and over all the mountains.

They asked impoverished people.

"There is no freedom," the poor people replied.

Then they asked people who possessed wealth.

"There is no fate," the rich people replied.

The princes grew worried and kept gazing out at the sea. Seeing this, their mother ordered that all the boats and galleys be burned, that fishermen be threatened, so that they would not dare put out to sea, and that not a word be uttered anywhere about the young girl who had come from somewhere beyond the sea.

One day, a storm washed up an old boat on the shore. The princes' eagle eyes spotted it from their tower, and that very night they disappeared, along with the boat.

The haughty queen was infuriated, enraged that her children were scorning her, their noble lineage, and a life of luxury. She ascended the steep precipice and cursed them, so that, no matter where they were, they would not find happiness in a foreign land and would have to return, be it dead or alive.

Time flowed by like a wave on the sea, but the implacable queen would not lift the curse from her sons—she awaited them, waited for them to come, to submit to her will or be punished.

"O our Sun, our Queen! Look down upon us and bend your ear mercifully to the voice of your faithful servants."

The queen's eyes flashed.

A messenger on the threshold was telling her that a sailboat could be seen on the sea; it neither drew nearer, nor went away, but always floated along the shore, as if seeking permission to land. So, what was to be done with it?

"Bring me my sedan chair!"

And the sedan chair appeared, forged with gold and encrusted with pearls. Six servants carried the queen to the shore; behind her trailed a long retinue of servants and slaves.

The queen was on the cliff. She glanced out, realised why the little boat was wandering aimlessly, and commanded that a welcoming signal be flashed to it.

The little boat sped like a swift seagull to the shore, and when it was drew near, the queen could see her children bowing down low before her.

"Why were you disobedient? What kind of gift have you brought me from beyond the sea?"

"We found freedom, mother, freedom, and great strength and courage, on the sea, and we've brought you our young heads to bow before you."

"Ha-ha-ha!" the queen roared with malicious laughter. "Freedom and rags, and, in addition, your foolish heads. It's clear that you no longer care about the will of kings and elegant clothing. You're not worthy of them! Get out of my sight!"

"Mother, O mother!" the sons pleaded.

"Get out of my sight! And don't show up until you bring me a royal gift from the sea."

A high wave crested furiously under the oars, the sail fluttered on the mast like a bird, and in a short time the little boat disappeared from view in the grey mist.

Once again the days and the nights passed by—but the queen's rage did not flow away with them as a leaf floats away in water. Still as beautiful as ever, and still as grim as ever, she sat on her throne and waited silently for her rebellious sons.

Two years went by, and once again the slaves informed her that a white sail, like a seagull, could be seen on the sea, and that it was heading for the shore.

The queen and her royal retinue made their way to the sea. Red tents were erected, and a joyous reception with food and drink awaited the dear guests. The queen stood on the very tip of the cliff, and her maternal eye could already discern her sons' handsome faces, their silky moustaches, and their shining eyes.

"Mother, O mother!" they called out jubilantly to her.

"My children! How handsome you are, how young! But where are your elegant garments? Where are your faithful servants? Don your princely attire, groom yourselves properly, and bring your gifts from beyond the sea to your poor mother, who has waited for you for so many days and nights. Go, show yourselves to your people who have been waiting for such a long time for their young princes. Your kingdom awaits you, and good fortune, and glory."

"Mother, we don't need a kingdom—we're rich without it; elegant garments won't make us look better, because we're clothed in happiness that shines like gold, and we don't need any good fortune other than the one that we now have. We only ask most sincerely—forgive us our rebelliousness, understand us with your motherly heart, and embrace us . . ."

"What kind of good fortune have you found?" the queen asked in surprise.

"Mother, good fortune is love! The love of that girl . . ."

"I remember, I remember. So that's your good fortune—the marvel that you've brought back from beyond the sea? The love of a lover of slaves? And for it, my worthless sons, you've traded your kingdom, and your mother, and your native land? Get out! I won't forgive you!"

"Mother!" they pleaded tearfully. "Forgive us! Understand us!"

"Fine, I forgive you," the queen flashed her eyes. "I forgive you! Just bring me your beloved, that good-for-nothing who steals sons away from their mothers, as a present to me; let me see her, let me take vengeance on her."

The young princes did not obey their mother—but the high waves swiftly carried them away.

The queen smiled after them. "Now they're mine for sure," she thought. "Just look how quickly they departed!"

The queen returned home. She waited one year, then two years, then three, and then four; she became sallow, faded, and grey-haired from old age and anger.

Then, finally, a messenger bounded in great haste to her from the sea. The queen went to the shore and made beckoning signs—but the tattered sailboat did not draw nearer. The queen was furious that the servants were taking so long to build a raft. At last it was ready; they rowed out to the boat and towed it back to shore.

It docked; two pale and weary travellers with curly hair were lying motionless in it.

The queen leaned over them: "Quickly, give me that evil thief right now. Oh, where is she?"

The princes remained silent; they did not rush to the shore, nor did they ask for their mother's kindness; they only looked sorrowfully into her menacing eyes.

"Oh! Where is she? Where?"

"She isn't here," the older son sighed quietly. "Love is like a flower—today it blooms, and tomorrow it's wilted. And that is how our good fortune withered for us."

"My children, my poor children! Why are you so exhausted? So pale? Who has tortured you? Tell me, and I'll wreak vengeance on them."

"No, mother, no one is to blame—we exhausted ourselves wandering over the earth in freedom, without fate; we've grown pale and thin because we gave all our food and water to people that we met along the way—people who were searching for fate and freedom, just as we were."

"They were relatives of some kind, right? Closely related, I presume? Who were they, my children?"

"Who were they? Giaours—Christian slaves—mother; they were fleeing from an oppressive captivity."

"Enough, enough, you cursed ones! O thrice cursed! You're no children of mine; you have no royal blood in your veins, no sense of honour. I have nothing to say to you, no kindness to offer you. You have no mother, so die, damn you, die!"

As she cursed them, the queen rose to her full stature and, lifting high her arms, cursed them once again for their love of freedom and their good hearts.

No sooner had she uttered these words than she was turned into stone, transformed into a high cliff. Her elegant attire was turned into red clay, and her grey hair into thistles.

Dumbstruck, the children fell at her feet with pleas—they yearned to melt her obdurate heart with their tears—but the grim cliff flung rocks down on them . . .

The sons burst into bitter tears.

From that time on, the haughty cliff stands by the sea; the rains wash it, and tempestuous winds scourge it, tearing plants out of its red soil. And at its feet, the blue sea splashes and groans—it's the children who are still pleading with their mother to free them from her curse.

When the older son speaks—the violent sea foams, blusters, roars, crashes on the cliff, and grabs at it powerfully and threateningly, demanding a word of forgiveness; and when the younger son speaks—the sea coaxes and splashes, gleaming like crystal-blue silk.

But the cliff does not listen—it remains sternly silent and, from time to time, casts down a rock.

And so, all of them are waiting—the sons await the time when their mother's heart will soften and turn generously towards them; and the mother waits for the moment when her children will submit and lay at her feet the fate and the freedom lost in the sea.

The Phantom
(1900)

Centuries go by, one after the other, slipping away like waves on the sea; and, like the waves that carry sand into the depths only to wash it up on the shore again, time also drifts by, first obliterating without a trace what once existed, and then unveiling its abyss and revealing, to everyone's surprise, the distant past.

All in ruins, covered with earth, and overgrown with weeds, lay ancient Chersonesus, silently mute about days long gone by. Another time ensues. In the forgotten ruins, new people gather, people who excavate and lay open the silent mound, searching inquiringly for the truth about bygone days. White ruins glisten bashfully under the cheerful sun; empty cisterns gape darkly and grimly; smashed gods, no longer standing proudly in ancient temples that have long since crumbled, hide their mutilated bodies in thick weeds, in the ground. It seems that the transfixed city is sighing, almost groaning, under the pickaxes, the sharp spades.

Terrified by the racket, a gloomy apparition floats out of dark caves and ravines and hovers over the lifeless city. Not daring to show its face in the bright sunlight, it can be seen and heard only at night, when it drifts like a little cloud in the sky above the city, or wanders like a bluish flame over the stones, sighing and rustling its invisible wings; and, weeping and moaning without end in the melodious waves, it whispers and culls pebbles on the promontory that juts out sharply into the sea.

The moon lights the sky, and out of the white foam, out of the fog, arise strange figures that weave in a dance in front of the cliff; and then the cliff comes to life—the grey weeds on its forehead stir, and, all atremble, a stone breaks away from the cliff and hangs over the sea.

But look, that stone is no longer simply a stone—it is a hoary old man in dark attire; his bald head gleams in the moonlight, and his thick grey beard falls to his knees; in one hand he holds a hammer, a chisel, and a compass, and with the other, he is inveigling his most beautiful guests to come to him from out of the sea. And they all come up in turn—a lively girl, an elegant woman, a slender youth, a proud giant with the face of a tsar, a small child; they approach the old man, piteously pleading and entreating him about something.

The old man peers intently at them—every one of these figures is horribly mutilated; on one—an arm is missing, on another— the legs, the head, or half the body. Seeing this, he groans hoarsely and shoves them back into the sea; the figures wail and, striking the sea, shatter into fragments. He gathers the pieces together, counts them, scatters them again, and sighs heavily. And, as soon as the morning star rises in the east, the hoary one hurries to the cliff, looks around sadly and, catching sight of his devastated city, groans and drops like a stone into the water, while his soul floats quietly, like a phantom, over the ancient, crumbling ruins.

At one time, very long ago, when these ruins were known as the famous Chersonesus, when swarms of Greek galleys rocked gently on its shore, and the bank was an anthill of activity filled with the bustle and hum of people, the declivity was graced by temples, orchards, and houses. At that time, the old man did not wander gloomily by the sea, and it was not the waves of the sea that greeted him, but waves of people, both his compatriots and foreigners, all of whom glorified him. For Menander was a distinguished sculptor.

When he was still an infant, the benevolent gods endowed Menander with a great talent—in his hands, inert stones became animated, marble appeared to breathe, copper stirred, and ivory, all kinds of wood, and clay came to life in marvellous figures. His fame spread far and wide. Visitors travelled from distant lands and even from ancient Greece to bring offerings to the benevolent gods in the temples of Chersonesus and to gaze at Menander's exquisite creations.

"What a fortunate young man Menander is," everyone chorused. But he was only half fortunate; his widely acclaimed fame did not cheer him, because artistic concerns and civic problems weighed heavily on his soul, dimming fame's glittering rays.

Chersonesus was growing and flourishing, and its inhabitants had come into their own. They had gained recognition, but they still were not satisfied—in every breast there beat an envious Hellenic heart and a compelling desire to gain still more acclaim, to appropriate all the glory of ancient Hellas. Every youth dreamed of a triumphal laurel wreath.

Menander also dreamed of such a wreath, but it tortured him and pained his sleepless brow like a wreath of thorns. He worked untiringly, but his work load increased daily and, along with it, so did his troubles; he was always dissatisfied with his efforts.

"It's not right! It's still not right!" he grumbled angrily.

Young Menander was oblivious to everything; neither the pleasures of rowdy youths, nor the attention of attractive girls, whose eyes followed him like flowers track the sun, enticed him. He lived and breathed with only one purpose in mind—to learn to mould and carve with his chisel better than anyone else had ever done and, in so doing, to make Chersonesus renowned throughout the world.

Menander travelled through all of Helas; he familiarised himself with even the smallest stone in the Acropolis, and then rushed off to ancient Egypt; his determination to succeed also took him to the mysterious countries of the East and to proud Rome. Fatigued, emaciated, and grim, Menander returned home. His chimerical idea continued to tantalise him, but would not allow itself to be caught—because his time had not yet come.

The weary Menander set out among the people to seek comfort. And comfort was quick in coming—a most beautiful girl, Pheano, chased the gnawing, worrisome idea out of his heart. The lovers were happily married; the first year flew by, and then the second.

But in the third year, the forgotten idea reappeared, gripped his heart, and sucked at him like a snake, confusing him and sapping his strength.

Oh, woe to Menander, O woe to him! More than once he revealed his thoughts to his beloved wife, seeking her sincere counsel. The spirited, frivolous beauty had no inclination to pay attention to his strange dreams or to his fanatical plans; she just laughed at Menander's determination.

With every passing day and hour, the situation worsened. Menander began escaping into his atelier. When he locked himself up there, he could not be dragged out for weeks on end. The impassioned Pheano wept, complained to her relatives and trusted neighbours, and then began to pester the authorities to levy a fine on Menander because he did not want to live with his wife.

The entire family gathered; neighbours tried to reason with him; both relatives and strangers got involved—but it was all in vain!

The stubborn Menander gave everyone the same response: "I have to create that for which the great gods have given me my life, my talent, and my Hellenic heart. Surely we did not swear to devote our lives and our work to gain glory for our Chersonesus, only to break our solemn oath for a woman's whims?"

Having said this, Menander fell silent. Unable to come up with a reply, all his advisors—both his relatives and his neighbours—disappeared from his yard. Renouncing his wife and small children, Menander locked himself up in his atelier and continued nursing his obsession.

Pheano did not have the strength to tolerate the situation for long; finding life without love unbearable, the passionate beauty died a sudden death. Brought to his senses by his grief, Menander attired his dead wife and, pressing himself close to her corpse, pleaded and wept, wishing to take delight in his wife's beauty for the last time, for all eternity.

But suddenly he trembled, grew pale, and his eyes sparkled like the stars; his old chimera had reappeared, but now he solved the intellectual riddle.

"I've found the answer, I've found it!" Menander shouted deliriously. "Here it is, the secret of living beauty—her brilliant eyes are shut tight, her delightful colours have faded, and her beauty has turned into cold, white marble. But wait! I'll paint the cold marble, I'll give it glittering eyes, and I'll endow those eyes with expressiveness—and the marble and the copper will come alive, and through that wondrous statue you, my unfortunate martyr, will be resurrected, and I will gain renown and bring glory to my beloved country forever! Forever!"

The years flowed on. Menander took delight in his beloved children—his son Phales and daughter Zoya. And in his dark atelier which he did not permit anyone to enter, reigned a large statue of Demeter, the goddess of fertility and the protectress of marriage. It was an exact replica of his late wife Pheano; behind her, Eros, the god of love, glanced out from a corner. In the atelier there were great numbers of stones of varying hues—pink, white, and yellow marble—bundles of ivory, chests filled with precious stones, and piles of silver and gold.

But it was not this treasure that Menander hid from the people, it was his own grand plans.

A few more years went by. Menander's children grew up, and he himself began to grow old; his black curls were sprinkled with frost, and his once handsome face was furrowed by his thoughts. But he did not see any of this, because he was caught up in his own worries—what kind of head should he place on Aphrodite, the goddess of love and beauty? Out of what should he mould Helios, the god of the sun? Where could he find a model for Ares, the god of war?

His head filled with problems, the indefatigable Menander went for a walk one day in his splendid orchard. This orchard, cultivated by Zoya and Phales—in defiance of the wind and drought—around the edge of a promontory overlooking the sea, was thickly sown with flowers, and surrounded by a stone wall. It was only on the very lip of the precipice that there was no wall—and the turbulent Black Sea tirelessly roared and sang there. This was where Menander liked to sit and ask the sea for advice.

Now, as Menander approached the familiar summit, thoughts crowded his head, and there was no one to comfort him or offer him any advice. He recalled his departed Pheano: "Why couldn't we live in harmony and in love? Why was it that even though she loved me with all her heart, she could not sense what was dearest to me?"

He recalled the love that was his in the past; he recalled the passionate kisses and the soft, tender conversations. And truly, at that very moment, he could hear passionate kisses, and loving talk, and sweet sighs—in a dark thicket under an elegant pink shrub sat a pair of fortunate lovers, oblivious to the entire world.

"Zoya, my dear!" the surprised father exclaimed.

The startled girl shuddered, leapt swiftly to her feet, and stood before her father; her face was flaming, and her body was swaying like a poplar in the wind. But she lifted her eyes, that up to now she had always kept bashfully lowered, and looked straight at her father—and her dark eyes were shining like stars.

"Aphrodite in the flesh!" Menander exclaimed fervently, and a thought squeezed his heart like a vise—who was it that dared to take such an inexpressibly beautiful girl from her father? Glancing up, he saw a slender foreigner with curly hair standing beside Zoya. His azure eyes shone like the sky, and on his white forehead lay both calm courage and a sensitive intelligence.

"Tell me, who are you? Who are you, O wondrous one? Are you the incomparable Helios himself? Or a human child that resembles the god?"

"My name is Partocles and I hail from distant Zante. Do not be angry, O kind father—it must be the will of the gods that, just at the moment when my galley was entering the harbour, your lovely daughter came to the shore, appearing there like a dream incarnate. And our eyes met, and our hearts called out to one another—yes, it must have been the will of the gods, and now, as you can see, we, the fortunate lovers, are standing before you. Be merciful to us, our benevolent father."

Joy and happiness now reigned in Menander's courtyard. Zoya and Partocles were united in blissful matrimony, and Menander was completing two marvellous statues in his atelier. A pink marble body glistened, agate eyes showered sparks, and dark hair cascaded down a pale back from under a gold wreath—this was Aphrodite. Next to her stood Helios. The youthful white marble body was full of beauty; the proud face was framed with exquisite hair fashioned of pure gold; the eyes were blue sapphires.

The third statue was of Ares; dark, and made of bronze, it was not yet completed—it still lacked a head. The body was slender and muscular, with taut sinewy veins weaving like ropes throughout it; the severe statue was replete with courage and wrath.

"Where can I find a face with the expression that I see so vaguely in my thoughts? What a shame! That image no longer exists in our country! It may well be that I'll have to travel to distant Sparta to find it."

Thus spoke Menander, so full of his own problems that he did not know what was happening in his country. And what was happening now, had happened many times before.

Chersonesus had caught the eye of its jealous neighbours; more than once, uninvited visitors had arrived from the steppes beyond the Black Sea. Today they swarmed on the city like locusts and laid siege to it from all sides; the pounding of horses' hooves, the creaking of wagons, and bloodcurdling, wild cries terrorized the city, filling it with wailing and groaning.

The gate to the city was locked, the guard on the walls was tripled, and both the old and the young hastily prepared for battle. None of this concerned Menander—he remained, as always, in his atelier.

Was this a reason for stopping his work? Was there a shortage of soldiers in Chersonesus? Were the walls not high? Was it possible that the barbarians had become smarter and stronger than the Greeks? Let them sound the alarm—he would not leave his work. But his servants were running to him, bringing sad and terrible news.

And now the youthful Phales ran into the atelier and flung himself headlong at his father's feet: "It's a great misfortune, father! Our city is perishing! The enemy's numbers are growing. Let me join the guards on the walls!"

The alarmed father looked at his son, and his eyes glowed with a grand passion: "My son, my hope, my joy! May the righteous gods strengthen your right hand in this rightful cause. Go then, hurry; offer your strength to your native land."

Phales rushed off like a whirlwind, but Menander stood motionless, and a few uninvited tears involuntarily fell from his glowing eyes.

Glancing around, he seized his chisel and exclaimed: "The moment has come when I can finish my wondrous statue! This is when Ares will be made incarnate!"

Like a stormy petrel pursuing violent waves on the sea, terror, confusion, and despair were chasing the panic-stricken inhabitants through the city.

"O my wondrous statues! My dearest children, my most glorious gods of Olympus! Where am I to hide you?"

The unfortunate Menander was troubled. He called together his servants and ordered them to carry his treasure down to the sea and hide it in a dark cave known only to him.

Before the servants finished their task, a wave of people, carrying the body of his beloved son Phales on their shoulders, surged through the gate to his home. Wailing, he rushed towards his son, but another wave, this time of invaders, was already attacking and breaking down the high city-gate.

He glanced up and was seized with terror. The attackers looked neither like people nor animals—they were wild, savage, dirty, half-naked, and clothed in animal skins; the snouts of wolves and bears were stuck on their heads; tails of animals dangled behind them; in their hands they carried huge bows and heavy oak mallets.

Partocles was defending Menander's courtyard, slashing the enemy to pieces, while Zoya, white as chalk, passed him weapons. But the brave young man could not withstand the attack—he fell like an oak tree struck by lightning—and the rapacious mob broke into the yard. Not wanting to be captured alive, Zoya ran like a fleet-footed deer through the orchard towards the sea; the pursuers were almost overtaking her when, like a butterfly, she soared over the cliff and plunged into the open water . . .

The horde surrounded Menander, marvelling at the strange statues. And then a couple of them let fly their feathered arrows. The arrows, rebounding from the marble, broke and fell at the feet of the gods, while the gods stood motionless, calmly flaunting their beauty.

And Menander, like a lioness with cubs that is approached unexpectedly, rushed to defend his gods. Old, unarmed, and grey-headed, he glared ferociously at the wild attackers. An unspeakable terror gripped them and, dropping their mallets and arrows, and bunching together like sheep, they fled through the city-gate like frightened geese. Menander, left alone like an orphan, gave thanks to the gods for protecting his atelier and his works.

The years passed by. Chersonesus forgot all about the evil hour; it grew still richer; and once again, as in the past, internal discord seethed and tore apart the civic life of the city.

This was when the wise rulers decided that, instead of fighting and quarrelling—to the derision and delight of the barbarians—it would be better if they placed themselves under the almighty arm of Glorious Rome. And Rome, more power to it, did not refuse. It sent its army, established a government, clipped the wings of anarchy little by little, and gradually took over everything that had made Chersonesus powerful and rich up to that time.

The Romans took it all with their strong hands, saying: "It's ours according to the law."

And Chersonesus began to die, not on the field of battle, not in honourable combat, and not in enemy captivity, but in the strong embrace of the Romans, slowly expiring from their care and kindness.

Menander knew nothing about all this—he appeared to have gone completely mad. After he stopped grieving over his dead children, he shunned people entirely. Working ceaselessly, he prayed to the gods to prolong his time on earth long enough for him to complete all the gods of Olympus, and to place them in the most beautiful temples—for the glory and honour of Chersonesus, and to the wonder of pilgrims who gathered there from all over the world.

The Roman villains also heard about the old man. Ignoring the fact that none of the old man's countrymen would dare to interrupt him when he was working in his atelier, they gathered in a large crowd and noisily barged into his workshop, where they abruptly halted, thunderstruck. Before them was revealed a petrified Olympus in all its untold beauty.

Only the ancient Menander, busily working on the statue of Zeus, the supreme god of the heavens, was sighing and muttering to himself: "You're old and poor, Menander! You've squandered your wealth, and now you have nothing with which to adorn glorious Zeus in a manner befitting him."

The Romans exited silently one by one, ran to their lord, and told him about the strange old man. And the very next morning, the patrician sent Menander opulent gifts—ivory, gold and silver—so that he could adorn Zeus appropriately.

It was as if the hoary sculptor were reborn. Spending whole days and nights in his atelier, he worked as if he were young once again, forgetting all about thirst and hunger, and his advanced years. He was consumed entirely by his work. And, from under his masterful hands, a wondrous statue arose—golden lightning bolts forged out of gold, elegant garments made of silver and decorated richly with precious stones, and eyes that blazed with priceless gems. At last Menander finished; he stepped back, looked at his creation, flung his tools away and, prostrating himself before the figure, he laughed and cried . . .

It was at that very moment that the Roman patrician, accompanied by his entourage, entered the courtyard. He took one look at the stature and fell at the feet of old Menander: "O Great One! You have no equal in this world! If the famous Greek sculptor Phidias were to come to life, he too would bow down before you. I, a Roman, the honour and the toast of my army, the friend of Caesar himself—even I am bowing down before you. Accept my congratulations for now, and tomorrow, prepare yourself to receive felicitations from the entire country.

"And as for you, my nimble servants, go and inform the inhabitants of Chersonesus about a great event. Tomorrow morning we will transport the immortal works of Menander from these cramped quarters and place them under the open sky, before the eyes of the people. Break off branches of laurel and myrtle, pick flowers, weave countless wreaths, bring perfumes, herd the sheep and the finest bulls with twisted horns to the temple. Let the priests, the servants of the gods, don their most elegant robes. We shall all pray together, thank the eternal gods, and award old Menander a laurel wreath.

"But no, this immortal beauty must not be permanently displayed here, in provincial Chersonesus—your path leads to Rome, grandsire. There, Caesar, and the army, and a multitude of people will greet you in a worthy manner. The most imposing temples in Rome will be made famous through your works, O grandsire, Caesar himself will call you his master sculptor. All of Rome will reverberate with warm applause, and winged fame will soar over the entire world, calling out your name."

The great patrician orator might have continued talking in this way for a long time, but the exhausted Menander could not endure any more—he lost consciousness, swayed, and would have collapsed if people had not supported him.

"At last I've attained my goal! At last! Glory to you, O immortal ones," Menander breathed.

"Rest now, Menander, and as soon as the sun rises, I'll send an elegant procession to fetch you."

Everyone departed, and the praises came to an end. Only the sea roared in the ravines, and the moon came out from behind the hills; now it rose high in the sky, came to a stop above the clouds, and everything sparkled in its marvellous lustre.

Menander could not sleep; rising to his feet, he went straight to his atelier to gaze once more at his creations. And the moon crept in after him through the door and flooded the marvellous Olympians with its silver rays.

"I'm so fortunate, O god, so fortunate! Why could not Pheano and my beloved children have lived to see this moment? I've attained my goal. My native city will gain glory and, perhaps, because of the sincerity of my offering, the eternal gods will be kind, and well-disposed to my native land . . .

"But wait—what am I saying? Just a minute, Menander! Tomorrow is a great holiday . . . there's an elegant gift for the gods . . . and laurels for me . . . with the permission of, and by the order of, a Roman lord! And thereafter they'll take my dearest ones to Rome, for the glorification of that city! Glory for Rome!

"But what about my Chersonesus? Why have I lived, laboured? To have these foreigners seize from my native Chersonesus what rightfully belongs to it? To have them take everything away and then abandon my Chersonesus? To have its name forgotten, to have it die in the eyes of the world? No, that will never happen! I will not put my city up to ridicule! I will not give even a single kernel of my soul for their glory!"

What could he do? He lacked the power to stand up to Rome! The old man vacillated for some time. The moon was sinking into the sea and growing dim, and the sea was settling down and growing drowsy before the dawn.

"O my dear ones! My very own! Children of my soul! I created you, and I'll conceal you until the proper time arrives—our time has not yet come, or perhaps it has passed forever. It is better to have you perish along with me than to hand you over to the enemy."

Before dawn broke, Menander's servants completed a most difficult task—they carried all the gods out of the atelier and positioned them on the edge of the promontory above the sea.

"I want rosy Eos, the goddess of the dawn, to greet my gods here, on the plain, and not in my dark workshop; and I want the sea to roar a morning greeting to my gods." Thus spoke Menander, as he gave his weary servants leave to go and rest.

Remaining alone on the cliff with his gods, he looked all of them over intently, kneeled before them once more, prayed once again, and toppled them, one after the other, into the deep sea—before plunging into it himself.

The waves came up, splashed against the shore, and then all was silent. No one heard or saw the loyal sea hide from the jealous eyes of Rome both the exquisite creations of Chersonesus and the one who had worked so devotedly for his country.

Centuries passed by, one after the other like waves on the sea; they carried away and drowned in an abyss the Romans, the inhabitants of Chersonesus, and many others, and levelled their dwellings to the earth. But, like a wave, time drowns the past in an abyss, and then brings forth a long-forgotten story. And people listen to the story, and it resonates like a living string in their hearts.

The sea under the cliff weeps: "What's in the past is no more, no more; it will not arise in its former beauty, but its glory will not vanish like the foam on the waves, like the pebbles in my depths . . ."

Hearing the sound of this mournful singing, the hoary Menander steps heavily along the shore, scatters the tiny fragments, counts them, presses them together without finishing his counting—searches once again, groans, and asks the sea: "Tell me, has the long-awaited hour gone forever? Or has it not yet arrived?"

The Starlings
(1901)

How splendid, how marvellous, are southern climes!
A starling's heart, however, is drawn to the north.

All these bulrushes, slender cypresses, and lush orange and lemon trees have become repugnant; the fiery sun, the yellow sand, and the pointed pyramids are now repulsive; even the benevolent Nile and the delightful, boundless blue sea have lost their appeal.

Beyond a more distant sea—the Black Sea—forests and groves shimmer with a bluish haze in the damp coolness, valleys striate the flat green steppes, sown fields—checkered and striped—present a medley of colours, and villages drown in luxuriant orchards.

How loathsome these cacti—these lifeless scarecrows—have become, as have these palms that stay forever green.

Wormwood and mint, periwinkle and rue, a cranberry tree, willows over the water, a cherry orchard by a pond, thatched roofs, and the soft black earth of ploughed fields—all these appear nightly in the starlings' dreams.

Here the sun is growing even hotter. And from their native north, the malevolent wind has ceased blowing.

A bird's heart can hold out no longer.

A flock of starlings, sensing the signs of spring in their beloved Ukraine, gather together and rise up in flight.

Away they fly swiftly, ever so swiftly.

It is not far now; the sea is behind them . . . Beneath them spread the steppes and the silky green sprouts of winter wheat . . . Here and there, white patches of snow still linger, but clear fresh water, murmuring and gurgling, is awakening the drowsy earth.

The journey ends.

Breaking off into smaller groupings, the winged sojourners fly to their native parts.

Starlings alight on branches still barren, and a cheerful greeting to the fresh new spring resounds in the air.

People rejoice, vernal grass smiles at the sun, the white osier, taking heart, bursts into bloom, and the hazel nut tree hastens to catch up; the pussy willow arrays itself in silvery catkins, and the elder-tree fills out its protuberant buds.

Throngs of birds rejoice and sing!

Only long-beaked ravens and grey-headed old men do not rejoice; they presage disaster and blame the early spring.

"Hey-hey-he-he-he-hey!" a starling—singing out like a tiller walking beside a plough, neighing like a colt, and squealing like tiny goslings—laughs heartily, flapping its wings.

Hearing these cheerful songs, children rejoice and play.

But black crows and ravens, strutting with a dignified air, gaze at the red sky in the west and caw forebodingly.

A wind blows in from the north; murmuring streams fall silent, the emerald grass darkens, and red ants tuck themselves out of sight.

A leaden cloud moves in, and snow comes tumbling down.

All night the storm rages; all night, dispersing the singing springtime guests from their nests, thatched roofs, and bird houses, it chases them into tight crannies, attics, barns, and sheds.

Shivering, wet, cold, and hungry, the starlings wait for the redeeming morning.

And morning arrives.

Into the high, clear sky bursts a vividly pink star; the sun, white and cold, floats out after it. Yellowish pillars, like menacing guards, stand on both sides of the wrathful sun.

The frost shakes its beard and moves out over the earth to forge and reinforce icy bridges.

And the unfortunate birds alight on a pathway and, praising beauty loudly and sincerely, beg the sun to look down warmly and benignly at their oppressed native land.

Their pleas are in vain!

The frost grows stronger, and the sun, rising still higher in the sky, shows no compassion.

The earth is petrified; the river is mute . . .

On branches covered with frost, the starlings continue hopping and chirping . . .

The sun conceals itself behind a cloud. Snow falls thickly, soaking the starlings' wings, blinding their eyes, and freezing their bare little legs.

The snow covers the roads and yards, and there is nothing for the starlings to eat. Hungry and cold, they hop and chirp.

And the snow continues falling and falling . . .

A gander glances up and laughs uproariously.

Ducks quack derisively in chorus.

A turkey, wishing to address an oration to the poor little birds, puffs himself up and stalks around like a German, but, unable to come up with a single word, flushes and turns livid with anger.

All around them, tittering sparrows chirp, a magpie screeches a new little fib, and a peacock, settling near them, censures the starlings insultingly for returning too soon to their native land, a land still bound in chains.

Full of hope and faith, full of love for their native land, the starlings, shivering from the cold, announce in their songs the arrival of spring . . .

And the snow continues falling and falling . . .

Lyubov Yanovska
1861-1933

Biographical Sketch

Lyubov Yanovska was born in Eastern Ukraine into a family with a literary tradition. Her maternal grandmother's sister, who wrote under the pseudonym of Hannah Barvinok, was the wife of the renowned Ukrainian author and activist, Panteleimon Kulish. Lyubov's mother, encouraged to write while growing up under the tutelage of the Kulish family, was sent to France to improve her language skills, so she could translate Kulish's works into French.

Lyubov's father, Oleksandr Shcherbachov, was a published author. Although they shared an interest in literature, Lyubov's parents were diametrically opposed in their national views. The father, a Russian who supported the tsarist policy that stifled all non-Russian languages and cultures, punished the children if they spoke Ukrainian; the mother, determined to raise the national consciousness of the Ukrainian people through educational and cultural organizations, wanted the children to know their native tongue.

The marriage could not withstand the tensions, and when the family broke up, Lyubov's mother took the younger two of their four children to Petersburg in the hope of carving out a new life for herself. Unable to do so, she suffered a mental breakdown and died.

For Lyubov and her siblings life became difficult. Her father was forced to leave a well-paying job in the civil service and, unable to find steady employment, was reduced to eking out a living digging graves. Lyubov received an education only because some benefactors recognized her innate musical talent and encouraged her to embark on a career as a concert painist.

In school, Lyubov was taught that Russian was the language of intelligent discourse, and that speaking Ukrainian was tantamount to committing intellectual suicide. Fortunately for Ukrainian literature, Lyubov, during a stint as a tutor, met and married Vasyl Yanovsky, an older, well-informed member of the Ukrainian intelligentsia.

After the marriage in 1881, the couple moved to the country, where Lyubov embarked on an intensive program of self-education in Ukrainian language, literature, history, and culture; she also immersed herself in the life styles, customs, and traditions of the peasants among whom she lived.

In 1897, her first short story was published and, before long, she was writing novels and plays. By 1900, she had established herself on the Ukrainian literary scene.

The success Lyubov Yanovska experienced in her writing career did not carry over into her personal life. Her husband, a difficult man who was much older than she, became ill, and she nursed him for more than twenty years. Despite this drain on her time and energy, she kept writing and, propelled by her highly-developed sense of social responsibility, worked actively to improve the life of the peasants.

Admiring the resilience and stoicism of the peasants, but distressed by the limitations they faced in trying to better their lot in life, Yanovska set up literacy classes for adults and children, encouraged the dissemination of books among the peasantry, and organized drama, choral, and instrumental music groups. Under her direction, villagers presented a number of her plays and even staged an operetta for which she wrote the lyrics.

On several occasions when her husband was receiving medical treatments in Kyiv, she met some of the leading writers of the day, including a number of women authors. In 1903, she was invited to attend the unveiling of a monument in Kyiv dedicated to Ivan Kotlyarevsky, whose parody of Vergil's *Aeneid*, written in Ukrainian in 1798, earned him the title of the Father of Modern Ukrainian Literature. At this unveiling, she was enthusiastically welcomed into the Ukrainian literary establishment.

After moving to Kyiv in 1905, she actively participated in literary circles, organized women's associations, and joined the world-wide women's movement. Deeply committed to improving women's lives in all levels of society—a goal that she viewed as crucial to effecting social change—Yanovska gave inspiring talks at conferences devoted to women's issues. In recognition of her efforts, she was invited to attend an international women's conference in Stockholm, in 1911, an honour she had to decline due to failing health.

Despite her physical limitations, Yanovska worked tirelessly on committees to assist women and children left destitute by the First World War. As a result of her selfless dedication to these causes, her precarious health suffered a further decline and, after 1916, she was no longer able to write.

In 1923, the Ukrainian literary community organized celebrations in honour of the 25th Anniversary of her writing career, but Yanovska was too ill to attend. Later that year she suffered a paralytic stroke; she died in 1933.

Yanovska's writing reflects her deep understanding of and compassion for the peasantry and the intelligentsia of her day, both of whom were caught in the debilitating mores and structures of their separate worlds. Her works bridge the older ethnographic-realistic school of writing and the newer modernistic-psychological movement.

Oksana the Thief
(1897)

Ukraine awoke from her winter sleep. The snow melted; leaf green winter wheat, straightening out its slender blades crumpled by the snow, stretched happily upwards; pale green grass, forcing its way up through the ground, covered the valleys, ravines, fields, and hills like a brush. The spring sun endeavoured to warm the young offspring that he had abandoned for the winter, and they, in turn, gazed cheerfully and lovingly into their dear father's eyes, bathing and warming themselves in the golden rays of his love. Mother Earth was hastening to show the father her precious little ones and, every hour, every minute, she brought forth either a tiny blade of grass or a marvellous flower.

Birds, realising that the spring sun had returned, and that nests awaited them in densely tangled branches, flew back home from many different climes. Their wonderful salutations echoed far and wide as they greeted the sunrise with their exuberant singing; and every evening they sang late into the night, bringing joy to the weary, and either happiness or grief to enamoured young couples. Frogs croaked in ponds, and bulls lowed in response; beetles droned, and ants and other insects stirred. And Mother Earth drowsed peacefully and joyfully under the azure-blue expanse of the bright, vaulted sky.

Human beings—fatigued and enervated—revived and rejoiced under the benevolent vernal sun. They renewed their dreams and roused from sleep the boundless hopes within their hearts.

Farmers—exhausted by their heavy toil, and stupefied and deadened by numbing poverty—came alive again as they gazed upon the world's nuptials. Forgetting about their own afflictions and bitter fate, they regained their faith in people and their belief in God's succour.

Girls' hearts, inflamed by the ardour of first love, fluttered and throbbed; cheerful spring songs—containing no mention of betrayal, anguish, or the grief of a broken heart, and no hint of the drudgery of everyday life—spread far and wide.

It was only Oksana who was not singing; nor did she leave her yard to join the other girls in their promenading. Like all the young women, she listened to the nightingale and fell under the spell of the enchanting spring; but she was not able—or perhaps, did not know how—to find herself a friend and join the group.

She was already past her twenty-third birthday. All her girlfriends had married long ago, but no one had ever asked for her hand in marriage; it was almost as if there were no partner for her in the whole world.

But then, who would want the pock-marked Oksana—a penniless orphan, the drudge of her aunt? She had been brought, as a little girl, to the home of her Uncle Maksym and her Aunt Sofiya, and from that time she had toiled incessantly, without ever resting or straightening her bent back; despite this, however, she still did not have a wedding chest ready, nor did she have any decent clothing. A worn kerchief, a reddish apron, and a torn jerkin constituted her wardrobe.

From the age of nine, Oksana had learned to make do without enough to eat or drink. Her body—nourished only by potatoes and hard work—was stooped, for it had shot up like a plant that grows without sunlight. No one thought of Oksana when smallpox vaccinations were being given, and so the girl was pock-marked for life.

She did not know any songs, for she had experienced neither happiness as a child, nor acceptance as an adolescent. As she grew older, she did not participate in the games and social evenings of the young people, for the young men laughed at the pock-marked Oksana, and the pretty girls shunned her.

Oksana found joy only in hard work—but she did not have the strength for it. The epithets "good-for-nothing," "loafer," and "lazybones" were always on the lips of her Aunt Sofiya.

Among people who believe that one has the right to live only as long as one is strong enough to work, nobody ever asks if a person has the energy to do things, or if too high a price is being paid for one's crust of bread. And so, no one asked Oksana how she was coping with her backbreaking work, and no one paid any attention to her stooped back, covered with a shirt drenched in bloody sweat. But everyone did ask her: "How much work have you done?"

Oksana, looking at the strong and healthy people around her, tried her utmost to keep pace with them, and expended every ounce of her strength on her uncle's field and garden.

In winter, it was even more difficult for the sickly Oksana to work in a stuffy house filled with fumes from a small lamp; she lost weight and grew weaker. The thread on the distaff came out uneven, the skeins were improperly made, and her aunt's rebukes did not abate.

But Oksana did not complain to anyone about her life or her misery, because she herself could not understand why there were times when a snake seemed to draw near her heart, and why, for no reason at all, unwelcome tears trembled on her eyelashes. No one beat her, no one was chasing her out of the house and, after all, was this not a happy situation for an orphan? She had a crust of bread, a warm house, and a jerkin on her back.

Why should she be sad? Why should she be weary of life? Nevertheless, she was sad, for her heart yearned for genuine kindness and a caring word, neither of which was forthcoming. Only the stars and the bright moon knew the grief in her heart, for it was only to them that Oksana was able to pour out her grievances about her life without feeling any shame.

Every spring, Oksana joyfully awaited—as one awaits a sister or a true friend—the arrival of her beloved swallow that chirped so delightfully in her uncle's yard.

One evening, when she happened to be sitting on the earthen embankment abutting the house, a sonorous nightingale settled down on a green branch in the orchard, not far away from her, and began to lure his beloved with his pure song. For a long time, Oksana sat and listened attentively to that enchanting singing, and her heart began to beat more quickly. Almost against her will and good judgement, her heart filled with a desire for unconditional love, for a warm and boundless tenderness.

"Who am I to be dreaming about love and hoping for a partner? How could I expect fate to allow me, a hapless orphan, to nestle against a loved one's breast, to feel hot kisses on my lips? These distressing thoughts must go away, and my agitated heart must calm down! I am fated to go to my grave without knowing any joy, without experiencing a moment of happiness!" Oksana reflected soberly.

But her heart did not obey her; it throbbed more quickly and melted with an even greater desire.

Beyond the orchard, a shadowy figure emerged. Oksana jumped up in alarm, crossed over into the orchard, and concealed herself in a shadowy nook. As she did so, the figure moved forward into a brighter spot, and Oksana recognised Oleksiy. He was the most handsome youth in the village; black-browed, swarthy, and tall, he had no equal. No girl would have refused to accept him if he had sent matchmakers to ask for her hand in marriage. No girl would have refused him, even though everyone knew that he was unfaithful and inconstant in his love.

This evening he had been waiting for Odarka in her orchard, but either she had not shown up, or something had angered him, and now he was cutting through other people's gardens to visit Melashka at the other end of the village.

Catching sight of Oksana, he stopped, walked up to her casually, and said: "Hello!"

The word "hello" is neither clever nor profound, but to Oksana, it seemed like enchanting music, a gift of some kind, a favour.

"Hello!" she replied, her cheeks flaming.

"Why are you sitting here alone? Are you sad?" Oleksiy inquired.

"Do I have to be sitting with someone? It's stuffy in the house, so I came outdoors for a little while."

"I'll sit down for a while as well." Oleksiy surprised himself with his own words as he settled in.

Oksana became even more abashed. Oleksiy lit a cigarette and said nothing for a few minutes. He already regretted sitting down next to this pockmarked girl; and, to make matters even worse, it was the first time in his life that he did not know how to behave with a girl. No jokes came to mind, and just what was he supposed to say? What could he talk about with Oksana?

The moon came out from behind a cloud and shone on the silent couple. Oleksiy glanced sideways at Oksana and was struck by her inflamed face. The clever libertine realised at once what was exciting the young girl's heart, and a lascivious smile crossed his face.

"Oksana, my dear," he said, "you know what? I feel sorry for you."

"Why?" Oksana inquired softly.

"Why? Because you have no one to love you. But in my opinion, you're a very nice girl. What are all those dark and fair-haired beauties good for? They fade, wither, turn yellow like the leaves in autumn, and not a hint remains of their former, fleeting beauty! But a pure heart—now that's true beauty. Nor will this beauty ever wither, turn yellow, or shrivel.

"And you, Oksana, have a very good and pure heart. You are capable of falling in love and, having fallen in love, you would never be untrue. This is why I like you; this is why I feel sorry for you.

"I've been meaning to get to know you better for some time now, but somehow things have never worked out. This is the first time such an opportunity has come up, and now we can have a nice little chat.

"I'm tired of all those Khymkas and Mariyas! You may not believe me, but it's tiresome to even look at them, for they act like little bitches: they fight for my attention . . . You don't resemble them in the least; that's why you appeal to me.

"It's too bad though, that you're sceptical . . . I can see it right now, I can sense you don't believe me . . . I'm right, aren't I?" Oleksiy wanted to know as he peered intently into Oksana's eyes.

Oksana sat motionless. She was hearing someone speak about love. She was sitting alone with a young man, and she was experiencing a moment of happiness—all for the very first time. Her heart was beating joyously; she felt warm and wonderful. A genuine, youthful love, without any mistrust, without any doubts, enveloped her.

Did she believe him? She would fly to the ends of the world with Oleksiy! It seemed to her she could live forever without the sun, without water, without bread, and without people, as long as Oleksiy warmed her with his love and never left her.

She forgot about her own unattractiveness and the taunts and sneers of this very same Oleksiy. She experienced a tremendous sense of power and felt that she was truly a human being, not the worthless pockmarked Oksana whom no one wanted or needed.

Oleksiy did not stop talking; more skilfully than any nightingale, he crooned to her about true love, about dark nights, about a green orchard. And how could she not believe him? How could she renounce this extraordinary happiness, push Oleksiy away, and stop listening to his sweet words? Where was she to find the strength to quiet her heart?

The girl did not have the inclination, nor the will power, nor the sense, to think about insincerity or treachery. She listened to the nightingale—and to Oleksiy—until the very break of dawn.

II

Mother Earth celebrated a wedding; she married off her sons and gave her daughters away in marriage. And now she was anticipating the joy of grandchildren. She kept giving her children more to eat and drink so that they, in turn, would feed her grandchildren well.

And the precious grandchildren she had been hoping for finally arrived. How wonderful they all turned out to be! The cherry trees—her daughters—appeared to be preening as they turned red with their berries. Big round apples peeked out from under the leaves of the apple tree; the golden spikes of rye filled out and ripened.

The sun shone more warmly and caressed these most beautiful grandchildren. The birds ceased their singing and began to feed and raise their little ones. A feeling of urgency permeated the fields and orchards; there was no time now for songs or loving caresses.

Oksana also became sad and worried. The brief love affair had ended, and now the time of bitter reckoning was upon her.

She had not known happiness for very long, for Oleksiy had visited her for not much more than a month. But how much suffering would she have to bear now? How many reproaches would she have to listen to? How many hot tears would she have to shed?

All the same, Oksana did not feel sorry for herself. Nor did she complain about Oleksiy, even though he abandoned her and left her alone with her grief. After all, he was the only one who had ever caressed her, who had given her happiness, even if it was for just a moment.

The girl feared her neighbours' taunts most of all. For now, they were still silent; however, time was passing by, and the day that was worse than God's judgement day finally came.

The village woke up early. The sun was delayed somewhere, but more than half the villagers were already up and about. Doors and gates were squeaking, calves were calling out to cows, and old women, pale and sleepy, were irritably exchanging remarks by the well.

Oksana's Aunt Sofiya was also up, and before she set out to do her work, she woke the young woman. While Sofiya milked the cows, Oksana prepared the feed for the hogs. The aunt did not care about anything as much as she cared about the hogs. There were two of them, both as big as calves, sitting in the pen.

"Oksana, clean the trough well, put some barley in it, and add some water," the aunt reminded her niece while she busied herself around the oven. "But be sure no one casts an evil spell on them; be especially wary of Motrya, because she casts an evil eye on everything she looks at. Don't open the wicket when anyone is going past the sty; wait a bit until they've gone by."

Oksana had heard these instructions more than once, and she herself was careful to avoid an evil eye, for she took care of her aunt's possessions as if they were her own.

Oh, if she had known what was going to happen that day because of those hogs, it would have been better if she had torn the place apart rather than open that accursed wicket.

She had just poured the feed into the trough when, as if to bring about her ruination, the devil brought Motrya to the sty. Oksana tried to close the pen quickly, but she did not manage to do so on time; Motrya saw both hogs.

"Ah, how shiny and smooth they are! And what muscles they have! And how nicely they're eating!" Motrya praised the hogs, thus casting her spell even more strongly.

Oksana spit three times and whispered something to counter the spell, but she did not dare to chase Motrya away from the pen.

Just then Sofiya glanced out the window. When she spotted Motrya by the pen she turned cold with fear. Before Oksana even knew what had happened, her aunt was already at the sty.

"You miserable wretch! You're my worst enemy!" Sofiya flung herself at Oksana. "What have you done? My hogs are as good as dead! They'll never live now! They're already not eating or drinking as they used to, and they're not looking at me the way they should."

Then she began shouting at the top of her lungs: "You damned tramp! How long am I to keep on clothing and feeding you? Is this how you thank me for covering up for you? Now let everyone know, let the whole world know why, what for—for what reason— you've eaten all the crab apples that were stored in the cellar; why you're girding yourself with three ropes."

The aunt's reproaches, resounding far and wide, echoed to the outer edges of the village. Older women stuck their heads out from behind the stiles, while children rushed up to Oksana, surrounded her, and stared intently at her pale face.

Sofiya rushed to the house, grabbed a pair of pants off a hook, picked up a cap, and then passed the clothing back and forth under the hogs while whispering the traditional, prescribed charms. Little by little, she calmed down completely.

Oksana, however, did not calm down, for now every person in the village knew about her shame, about her ill-fated and tragic misadventure.

"How am I now to live in the village?" the girl thought. "How am I to look my uncle and the neighbours in the face?"

Her aunt, having already forgotten about the tongue-lashing she had meted out that morning, acted as if nothing had happened. She gathered up some of her husband's shirts and sent Oksana to the river to wash them. There were not that many shirts, but it seemed to Oksana that they were heavier than stones.

A single thought, as heavy as iron, oppressed the girl—where was she to go? Who would welcome her—ridiculed and disgraced as she now was? What could she do?

Finally, she was struck by a happy thought. Aunt Horpyna lived some twenty kilometres from this village, and had once asked Oksana to come and live with her.

"I'll go to Aunt Horpyna's," Oksana thought. "I'll help her. I'll work as long as I have enough strength to work, and then . . . And then our merciful Lord will help me live out my days somehow."

She quickly finished washing the shirts, hung them up to dry on the picket fence, collected her few wretched rags, and left her uncle's home.

III

In her lifetime, Oksana had seen all kinds of poverty, and she had endured much at her Uncle Maksym's home. But she had never before seen the kind of abject penury in which Aunt Horpyna lived.

Horpyna had been widowed as a young woman, and she had been too sickly to bring some order to the farm that her husband, a drunkard, had left her.

Now, in her old age, Horpyna was left with only her little hovel, but even that was sagging and peeling. With the little that she painfully earned by reaping for a small share of the yield, she could not even afford to heat the house adequately, let alone save enough to buy straw to fix the thatched roof; and so the hut was left with almost no thatch.

Despite the old woman's poverty, the other villagers respected her, and occasionally helped her out. A few of the women came to her expressly to seek her advice, and they listened to her as they would listen to their own mothers.

Horpyna rarely went out into the street, even though young women from all corners of the village congregated near her house. She did not like to "flash her teeth" in laughter, but neither did she whine or complain about her fate, even though life for her, a lonely, sickly woman, was often hard.

For some time now, she had been looking for a good soul who would stay with her and help her live out her life in greater peace and security, but no such woman had come along. It was with great joy, therefore, that she welcomed Oksana, and even promised to sign over her cottage and yard to her.

The old aunt's kindly appearance and warm words immediately reassured Oksana, and she thanked God for giving her the idea of leaving her quarrelsome Aunt Sofiya and moving in with Aunt Horpyna.

The aunt and the niece quickly finished catching up on all the news, and began deliberating and discussing ways of earning more money.

"I'll hire myself out to work in the tobacco fields, Aunt Horpyna," Oksana said after giving the matter some thought. "The pay there is good, and I'll earn enough to buy a bit of fuel and some blessed bread."

"No, my daughter, don't do that, because field workers are hired for longer periods of time," Horpyna advised, "and when that happens, girls are often led into various kinds of loose behaviour; I don't like girls like that, and I never have.

"Look at me: I was widowed as a young woman, but no one can say a bad word about me, because I refused to hire myself out like that. I live very modestly; I earn my bread with my sickle, and I don't need any more than that.

"I didn't even marry a second time. The devil take all that! I don't like it when a widow—and one with children at that—rushes to the altar.

"And God forbid that I should hear something bad about a girl—it's best then that she not even speak to me, for I would never greet her as long as I lived. That's how it is! I'm advising you, my daughter, to have respect for yourself and to behave in the same manner.

"Perhaps God has smiled upon me by sending you to me; now I'll have someone to care for me in my old age, to close my eyes when I die, to dress me in my funeral shirt. Our merciful Lord has taken pity on a lonely widow, and He's sent you, an orphan, to my home.

"It's up to you if you decide to stay, but as for me—I won't send you away, and I won't part from you as long as I live. We'll reap together to earn some grain, and if you don't want to do this, then I'll reap by myself, and you can go work in the melon patch. The wages there are quite decent; but, most importantly, you won't be hiring yourself out for a longer term."

Oksana found it difficult to listen to her aunt's words, for she could already hear reproaches in them, but she did not have the courage to confess and tell her aunt the truth.

She bowed her head down low and fell silent.

"What have you decided, my daughter?" Horpyna inquired after a little while. "Perhaps my advice doesn't appeal to you? I'm telling you what it would be best to do, but you do as you see fit. It's up to you."

"I'll hire myself out as a day labourer," Oksana, without looking at her aunt, replied almost inaudibly.

IV

Early the next morning, Oksana set out for the melon patch. Her life settled into an unvarying routine. The field work was difficult for all the women, but it was twice as hard for Oksana.

The quack grass, with its long, sinewy roots, had entrenched itself deeply and firmly in the ground, and a great deal of strength was required to get rid of it with a hoe. The lazier girls lopped off only the tops, but Oksana, who did not like to cheat in anything, hoed properly and thoroughly. For her efforts, she was given better wages and asked to come to work every day.

In the evening, Oksana returned home weary and faint with hunger, but at daybreak, paying no heed to her swollen legs and the pain in her abdomen, she once again set out for work.

Aunt Horpyna took a liking to her hardworking niece, and thanked God for sending her such unexpected assistance. Bit by bit, things began to improve in their home; *pyrizhky [turnovers]* and *balabushky [filled buns]* appeared on their table on Sunday, and they scraped together enough to buy themselves boots for the winter. In a word—Horpyna's life improved considerably.

Oksana brought home money all summer and into the fall. She had hopes of earning a fair amount during the harvest, but things did not turn out as she had planned. Just before the beginning of the Lenten period, she became so ill that she nearly died.

Horpyna called in all the women healers and pleaded with them to help her niece. They examined the girl and immediately discovered what evil had befallen her, but not one of them dared to tell Horpyna the truth. They simply advised her to take good care of Oksana and not give her any heavy work to do.

The old woman kept asking over and over again what kind of evil it was, but she could not get a clear answer. Maryna said the girl had fallen ill because of an evil spell; Lepestyna said it was the ague; and Sanka laid the blame for everything on Oksana's liver.

Horpyna began giving Oksana steam and herbal baths, and the young woman did seem to improve a little; but there was no point in even thinking about sending her out to work. In the meantime, the money they had earned was soon gone. Bitter frosts set in, grain became dearer and, to make matters even worse, there was no firewood or food—there was nothing in reserve. Hunger and cold did not bother to sneak up to Horpyna's house—they strode right in.

Then, a week before the Christmas Lenten period, a final misfortune struck them—Oksana gave birth to a son. The girl had hidden the truth from her aunt to the last moment, and even though ugly rumours about her had spread throughout the village, they had not found their way into Horpyna's house. The old woman had never dreamed she would live to experience such shame, and the calamity caught her completely unawares.

At first, Horpyna cursed both Oksana and her newborn son. She also cursed Oksana's father and mother, and vowed to chase the unfortunate girl out of her home. But when she saw the older women undo Oksana's long braid and hide it under the head-dress worn by a married woman, Horpyna's kind heart could not remain hardened; she lamented over the girl like a real mother, and publicly forgave her hapless, adopted daughter.

Oksana—much to the surprise of all the neighbours—did not cry at all; not a single tear ran down her cheek. She lay silently, got up silently to don the head-dress, and listened silently to all her aunt's curses and reproaches.

V

Horpyna quickly forgot about Oksana's sin and loved the little baby as if he were her own grandson. For nights on end, she fussed with him and rocked him, and it seemed that she herself became healthier and happier. Nothing mattered except little Trokhym; everything else seemed superfluous.

The concerns of the two women were focussed entirely upon him—that he stay healthy, that he not catch a cold, and that no one cast an evil spell on him. Horpyna was already secretly counting the years until Trokhym could marry, while Oksana, like the good witch in fairy tales, was bestowing talent, intelligence, health, and good fortune on her son.

The little boy brought joy and happiness into the hovel. He appeared on this earth like an angel with a myrtle branch to reconcile his mother with her sad fate, beautify her ill-starred life, and prove to both the wretched, unfortunate women that if the heart has someone to love, bright and joyous moments can occur amidst all the grief and misery of this world.

The women would have raised Trokhym without any mishaps or problems if there had only been enough food with which to feed him. As it was, they were short of both grain and firewood, and often had to go hungry. The mother, limited to a diet of potatoes and *palyanytsi [flatbread]* made out of rye flour, began to lose her milk, while Trokhym, who was always cold, could not stop hiccuping.

The women were despondent and anxious—they had no idea how they would manage to survive the winter. Despite all their efforts, they could not come up with a plan, and with each passing day the baby lost more weight and grew more waxen in appearance. A coating of frost covered the walls on the inside of the dilapidated house, the bread dough froze in the kneading-trough, and there was nothing left in the trunk that could be sold.

The two women, ignoring their own feelings of shame and the gossip of the villagers, borrowed and begged everywhere, promising to work off the loans. Eventually, they found themselves so deeply in debt that people began to refuse to help them or give them any more loans. Spring was still far away, and how were they to survive for even another week without any food?

The women were distraught with worry. Horpyna blamed herself for not having secured enough grain during the summer, while Oksana, distressed by the thought that her child was crying from hunger, berated herself for having earned so little.

The day finally came when the last measure of flour was kneaded into a dough, and the last bundle of straw was thrown into the stove.

Oksana silently rolled out the bread, placed it in the oven, and sat down at the table with a lowered head. Horpyna, seated on the ledge of the large oven, was rocking the baby and quietly wiping away her tears.

"Mother!" Oksana turned to Aunt Horpyna. "Are you sleeping?"

"No, I'm not. What is it, my daughter?"

"Do you know what I've decided to do to keep Trokhym warm?"

"No, tell me."

"We'll put the kneading trough on top of the oven, put Trokhym inside, and then cover him with a blanket; we'll leave only a small corner open, so that he can breathe."

Horpyna gladly concurred with such a good idea, and in a moment the women had fixed up a cosy hut for the little boy. They had just managed to place him on top of the oven when someone knocked on the frozen window. Horpyna hurried to greet the unexpected guest, while Oksana rushed to clear the table.

"Good day!" the guest stated as he walked into the house and, glancing at the young woman, he added: "Are you Oksana?"

"Yes, I am," Oksana replied and, without knowing why, she shuddered.

The guest was a corpulent young man of medium height, and his long, hooded top coat made him look even more portly. His small grey eyes flitted over the house in a hostile manner, and then his gaze settled once again on Oksana.

The women stared silently and fearfully at the strange guest.

"So, you're the young woman called Oksana?" he inquired once more.

"Yes!" the young woman replied again.

"Where's your child? Show it to me," the guest requested.

"Our child is no business of yours, good sir. The Lord has sent it to us, and may it continue to grow with God's blessing," Horpyna stated.

"Yes it is my business. I've come to hire Oksana as a wet nurse for my child. Show me your baby, and tell me how many months old it is. My son is just nine days old."

"Oksana won't hire herself out! Find someone else!" Horpyna retorted with blazing eyes.

"What nonsense! You foolish women will be swollen with hunger before long. Do you suppose I don't know and can't see what your life is like? You're gathering scraps of bread throughout the village like beggars. The entire village would be happy to be rid of you, because you're in debt to everyone."

"Yes, we are, dear sir. But this also is none of your business. We'll pay back what we've borrowed; no one will have to do the work for us, and no one will have to pay it back for us. However, even though we're poor and worse off than beggars, as you put it, we won't serve you, and we won't abandon our own child as if it were—may God forgive me for even saying this—a puppy of some kind. You're rich, so you can hire ten wet nurses with your money; but we'll feed our own baby by ourselves!" Hopryna stated emotionally.

The guest was very much surprised at this show of stubbornness in the face of such crushing poverty. As it was, he was hiring this pockmarked young woman, if not with a feeling of revulsion, then with great reluctance; and here this woman was putting on airs!

"Do you know who I am, old woman, who it is that is hiring your niece? Are you thinking, perhaps, that I don't have any money and won't be able to feed her? Let me tell you that I am Illya Yosypovych, the very same Illya Yosypovych who sells fish in all the markets. Have you heard of me?"

"It's all the same to us who you are, and what your name is. But if you want to hire her, then of course you'll have to feed her, for no one will work for nothing! But I'm telling you for the second time, that we need neither your money, nor your food!" Horpyna spoke sharply to the townsman.

Illya Yosypovych could see he was not making any headway, so he suddenly began speaking gently and a trifle humbly.

"I swear to God you're not doing the right thing, old woman," he began in a soft voice. "You have no reason to forbid Oksana to come with me. Do you think I can't see what kind of a wet nurse your niece would make right now? But if the mother is fed, then it will be better for the child as well. And I, praise the Lord, have enough of everything. You can eat as much meat, bread, rolls, and milk as you want or desire.

"Then again, in terms of warmth—can a child live in such a cold house? Just look—you can see your breath in here! But if a child is fed properly and laid down to sleep in a warm house—so that it can kick its legs and play as much as it wants to—then it will grow and be healthy.

"It is my intention to pay your niece four *karbovantsi [dollars]* up front. You can buy some straw, some grain, and the rest will be for milk; so, as you can see, you'll be a winner and not a loser in this situation. Four *karbovantsi* a month is good money; and if she nurses him for a year, you'll have forty-eight *karbovantsi* in money alone, not mentioning anything else. Of course, if you don't want to nurse for a whole year, then tell me now, and I'll go find someone else."

"No, dear sir! No matter how we have to do it, Oksana will stay with her own child. Heaven forbid that something should happen to her child while she's not here; she would blame me for it for the rest of her life. No, I'll never agree to such an arrangement. How can one leave such a tiny baby without a mother? God forbid. I'll never let such a thing happen!" Horpyna was so agitated that it almost seemed as if someone were taking Oksana away from her by force.

"I'll clothe her as well; I'll give her a jerkin. After all, you should have some Christian charity and show some pity for my child as well!" Illya Yosypovych pleaded. "Your little boy is four weeks old already, but mine was born only nine days ago. And keep in mind, old woman, that if your niece refuses, I'll find someone else right away. Let her nurse him for at least a month."

"Don't even ask, because I won't let the young woman go. Do you really think she'll give up her own child for four *karbovantsi* a month? It doesn't even come to one *zloty [fifteen pennies]* per day. If at least we had our own cow, but this way . . . It's too hard for an old woman like me to run around the village every day trying to find milk; and I'd have to leave the child home all alone. No, it's no use even thinking about it!"

"But listen," the fishmonger tried to convince the old woman. "I'll arrange for a whole month's milk supply myself, and I'll even see to it that you have straw for the oven!"

"No, I'll never let Oksana go away to be a wet nurse! No, no, dear sir, don't even bother trying to change my mind. Spring isn't far off now; we'll get by somehow. We'll manage, and then God will help us!" Horpyna stood her ground.

Illya Yosypovych turned to Oksana.

"Why aren't you saying anything, young woman?"

Oksana blushed. She did not know what to reply. During the conversation, she had been experiencing a struggle between her mind and her maternal instincts. She desperately wanted a warm house for her son; she even imagined how contentedly he would lie on his white swaddling clothes, how he would laugh, coo happily, wave his arms, and kick his legs; and how, with each passing day, he would grow and put on more weight.

This is what she was thinking and imagining; but at the same time, her heart was fainting at the thought of leaving him, if only for a month.

"This tiny baby is the one person in the whole world who needs you," her heart seemed to be saying. "It is only to him that you are the dearest and the best. Are you going to leave him for some filthy money and go and nurse someone else's child?"

But her mind argued: "Won't a month pass by very quickly? Four weeks will fly by so swiftly that you won't even realise it; and in the meantime the child will have as much cow's milk as it wants . . . and the house will be heated . . ."

"Well, Oksana, what do you think?" the fishmonger inquired. "Tell me once and for all what your decision is; I have to know, because it's time for me to return home."

"Perhaps I should hire myself out for just a month, dear aunt?" Oksana hesitantly turned to Horpyna. "He's giving the money up front, and he'll arrange for the milk, and it would mean that you could buy some flour and straw right away."

Horpyna was silent; she too was having second thoughts. She felt badly that the little fellow would be left without his mother; but how could one not take ready money when there wasn't even a crumb of bread left in the house. Perhaps this Illya Yosypovych had been sent to them by the Lord Himself to save them—along with Trokhym—from a cold and hungry death.

"Do as you know best! You're the mother, and it's your child. But I won't be able to manage Trokhym by myself: let the gentleman add at least another quarter of a *karbovanets* so I can call a girl to help me when I need it."

Illya Yosypovych added another quarter, and in a short while, after feeding her dear son one last time and showering him with hot motherly tears, Oksana was on her way to earn some money.

VI

At times, a month slips by like a day; at other times, a day stretches out as if it will never end. It was long days like these that comprised Oksana's month in the town; things were made even worse because everyone there took a dislike to her because of her appearance. It was the master himself who hated her most of all.

He had thought he would hire someone who would be a wet nurse for his child and a mistress to him; as things worked out, however, he had happened to find one who, despite her pockmarked face, was not tempted either by gifts, or promises of any kind. Illya Yosypovych approached her from all angles without any success. Finally, he went and found himself another young woman who was more amenable to his advances. All he had to do was wait until Oksana had finished earning the money he had already paid her.

Oksana's last working day fell on Christmas Day. Guests descended on the home; the godparents also came, bringing all sort of treats for the little baby and his wet nurse. Oksana delighted in her gold head-dress and brocade apron; she delighted in them, but she also had some regrets. She spent most of the time looking at the beautiful clothing of the master's child, and she could not help thinking about her aunt's house where her little Trokhym was lying in a coarse shirt on a torn blanket.

"If only I could dress him in this tiny cap and white shirt," Oksana thought to herself. "My child is dark-haired, and this shirt would look so good on him! The godparents didn't know what to give me. How happy I would have been if, instead of the head-dress, they had given me the same kind of cap and shirt they gave little Mykola. Will the head-dress make me look any better? But as for a child—how adorable it looks when you dress it up. I'll soon be leaving for home, and I don't have even half a *kopiyka* *[penny]* to buy my son a treat."

Recalling the wretched poverty in her aunt's cold, decrepit cottage, Oksana felt depressed as she gazed at the merchant's wealth.

In the evening, the new wet nurse came, and Oksana was told to leave. She kissed little Mykola warmly, bid farewell to everyone, thanked them for their hospitality, and began packing her things.

As she was doing this, the little cap and shirt that she had been eyeing earlier were hanging in full view on the edge of the cradle. Without being fully aware of what she was doing, Oksana reached out and took what appealed to her and tempted her. She took what did not belong to her and stowed it in her bundle.

The horses were harnessed. Oksana said good-bye once more and departed for home.

It was the first time that Oksana had ever dared to take something that did not belong to her, and she felt as if the kerchief in which the cap and shirt were hidden was burning her hands.

"But after all, do they need such a trifling thing? It isn't as if they can't afford to buy another one," the young woman consoled herself. "If I had stolen it, then may God have mercy on me, but I just took it as a present. I'd gladly pay for it myself, or work it off, if they wanted me to."

Nevertheless, Oksana's heart did not stop trembling, and she kept looking behind her as if expecting someone to come after her.

And she had good reason to feel that way.

No more than a half-hour after Oksana's departure, the master's kinswoman noticed that her gift was missing, and she raised such a ruckus that the entire household was upset.

They looked absolutely everywhere; they searched all the corners in every room, but it was nowhere to be found. There was nothing left to do but to chase after the wet nurse and search her; and that was what they did.

When the servant caught up to Oksana and asked her about the gift, she did not even try to conceal it. She untied the kerchief, gave back the stolen item, and wanted to continue on her way.

"No, thief, I can't do it this way; you have to go back to the master and return it to him yourself!" The servant smiled venomously, and his voice was filled with censure.

"But I'm giving it back to you without any fuss, my good man; I'm not hiding anything; I only thought that it was such a trifle, something they didn't really need. I wanted it for my little Trokhym," Oksana pleaded.

"That's none of my business! I was ordered to catch up to you and make you come back; once you're there, you can talk to the master as best you know how! Turn around, Petro, and let's go back home!" he shouted at the wagon driver.

Petro turned the horses around, and Oksana had to go back to answer for her deed in front of all the guests and servants—to be laughed at and ridiculed by them.

They drove into the yard. Before the young woman knew what was happening, she was pushed into the biggest room, among all the drunken guests. Questions and reproaches were fired at her.

At first, Oksana, unable to utter a single word, stood silently with a bowed head.

"There you are, you thief!" the master shouted. "You've ruined our holidays, and for that I'm going to have you thrown into prison. Jail the dog!"

"You should be ashamed of yourself, you worthless tramp!" the master's sister rebuked her.

"But it isn't as if I stole it," Oksana said hesitantly. "I took it for Trokhym!"

"So, you didn't steal it? What nerve! We found the stolen item on her, and she says she's innocent!" the kinswoman of the fishmonger shouted.

"I just took it. I just took it from the cradle, but I didn't mean to steal it. I swear to God that I didn't steal it! I just wanted a little present."

"She's even swearing that she didn't steal it! Jail is too good for you! You should be sent to Siberia! You should be drowned! Hanged!" the master raged.

"That's enough. Forget it. May she be damned!" said a storekeeper, so drunk he could barely move his tongue.

"What do you mean—forget it? The gift cost a whole ruble! Should we let people get away with things like this, then be reduced to begging for rags ourselves? Or what?" the kinswoman rattled on.

"In my opinion, she ought to be spared," the teacher put in a word for her. "Can't you see by looking at her that she's not a thief? Just think—why did she steal it? She didn't steal a silver spoon, or anything that's costly or precious; she only took it as a present for her child. She didn't steal it, she just took it. You should take pity on her. After all, she was a mother to your child for a whole month."

"But she didn't work for me for nothing, did she? I paid her, clothed her, fed her!" the master argued.

"Well, I understand she didn't work for nothing," the teacher spoke up again. "But is it possible that four or five *karbovantsi* would compensate for all her suffering? She must have spent more than one sleepless night with your little child. And just think how anxious she must have been during this past month, not knowing what was happening to her own infant?"

"You should be ashamed of yourself, my dear sir!" the master's sister interjected. "Are you the one who should be defending a thief? As a teacher, you should be instructing people how to behave, not telling them to go against the law!"

"But I'm not telling them to go against the law. I'm only saying that this woman is not a thief; it's just that she—like many other uneducated people—does not always fully understand when she is doing something wrong."

"Heh-heh-heh!" snickered the master. "You would make a good lawyer, my good sir. You really know how to defend young women; but I've never been one to spare thieves, so in this instance I'm not going to spare her either! If she wants a present for her child, let her earn the money and buy one. It's none of my concern that she doesn't have enough money. I'm not to share my wealth with her, am I?"

"What's there to discuss at such length!" the priest put in his word. "According to both God's law and the tsar's law, it's not right to condone or feel sorry for thieves. Are you a Christian?" he turned to Oksana.

"Yes, I am," Oksana whispered.

"Do you know, or have you heard of the commandment—thou shalt not steal?"

"Yes."

"That's just it! You've heard it, but you still continue stealing! In my opinion, our people are spoiled and lazy; and for that reason they should not be pitied. You stole something—so suffer the legal consequences! That's what I would do, Illya Yosypovych."

"For rags that cost a *karbovanets* you want to put her in prison?" the teacher stated reproachfully. "You want to shove her into a school of iniquity, which she'll enter as a naive child and leave as a hardened criminal? Have some fear of God—don't do it!"

Everyone attacked the teacher, and the most vocal among them was Illya Yosypovych himself. He would not give in, for he did not want to renege on his idea of sending Oksana to prison.

A short while later, a police official and witnesses were called in. There was an interrogation, everything was written down, and Oksana was arrested.

Three months later, a deputy was leading Oksana out of a big red building which housed the legal chambers. Horpyna, with Trokhym in her arms, rushed forward to meet her niece.

The aunt stared intently into Oksana's eyes without saying anything, trying to guess what kind of sentence the judge had given her. But Oksana's face was blank; it showed neither tears nor happiness—nothing.

"How did it go, Oksana? Why aren't you saying anything?" her aunt flung herself at her.

"They've sentenced her to prison!" the deputy answered for Oksana, and then added: "Move along more quickly, young woman, move along, because I have to take the next one away as well."

Horpyna began shaking and turned cold all over. The old woman's last hope for God's mercy and human justice vanished. Forgetting that she was standing in full public view, and that people were looking at her from all sides, she threw herself at the feet of the deputy, lamenting and crying.

"Be kind, be merciful!" Horpyna pleaded in a flood of tears. "She's not to blame, she didn't steal it! Tell the judges to let her say it under oath . . . she'll swear the same thing even on the Holy Gospel . . . or in her confession."

"Get up, old woman, because I can't do anything about it. And as for you, Oksana—or whatever your name is— move along; let's go, because I don't have time!" the deputy said indifferently.

Oksana silently extended her hands, took the child, and started out after the deputy.

"Oksana! My dear little Trokhym! Oh, merciful God! Where are you going, my children?" Horpyna wailed mournfully, barely able to keep up with the deputy and her niece.

Oksana silently looked back at her aunt and slowed her pace so that she could keep up. Step by step they approached that terrible building from where she would emerge disgraced, branded forever as a "thief."

They came up to the high, white walls; the iron gates opened. Oksana kissed Horpyna warmly and, without uttering a single word, crossed the threshold of the prison with her child. The gate closed behind her; the lock clicked once, and then a second time.

Oksana disappeared behind the white walls, taking with her into the prison her good name, forever besmirched and destroyed.

"Farewell! Farewell, my dear Oksana! Farewell, my dear little Trokhym, my darling child!" Horpyna called out softly as she clung to the iron gate beyond which could be heard the quarrelling and the crying of women thieves—Oksana's new companions.

The Death of Makarykha
(1900)

Winter has heaped snow upon us this year with a generous hand; all around, as far as the eye can see, the steppe stretches white and even, with neither a dip nor a hillock—everything is smoothed out under her white muslin veil. Only the "dark mounds"—those giants of the steppe, the sole witnesses of the distant past, of the glorious days of the *kozaky [Cossacks]*—are slightly visible.

On farmsteads, sheds and enclosures are drifted over and buried from view. Cottages, banked with weeds and buckwheat straw, loom gloomily from under their white thatches. Everything is shut tight, hidden away, as if even the hope of awakening to a new life in the spring has either fallen into a sound sleep in the hearts of the farmers, or vanished completely from them. The unceasing work of the summer and autumn has passed.

The grain has been threshed, and the straw is in stacks, but the completion of the backbreaking work has brought with it an end to golden dreams. This year, as for countless years in the past, the depleted fields did not yield a single kernel more than the absolute minimum needed by a farmer's family to stave off starvation, and not a stalk of straw above what was needed to ward off a freezing death in a cottage.

"Children, sit quietly on the *peech [a large clay oven with a sleeping area on top]*; don't open the door unless you have to; don't let out the warm air that, praise God, still lingers in the cottage from the long winter," the mothers urged their children, shutting tight the mouth of the *peech* with a charcoal-encrusted metal cover.

"We should bank the sheds more steeply—the heifer won't be as cold and will eat less," the anxious parents fussed, and they fastened the doors in the enclosures still more snugly.

And now, a dark cloud approached menacingly from a colder clime; snow began to fall, strong winds came up from God knows where, and a blizzard began to rage. The farmers bundled themselves up still more tightly, as if they were enclosed in a shell, and farmsteads that bustled with happy people in the summertime grew dark and funereal.

The first crowing of the cock resounded; the watchman came out, struck his wooden clapper once, and then a second time, went as far as the village gate, turned back, struck his clapper once again, and then, falling silent, drowsed in the shelter of a villager's shed.

On this night, the farmers had gone to sleep early, and almost all the lights were extinguished. There was only one cottage by the mill in which a lamp was still burning. In it, a sick woman, Tetyana Makarykha, lay on a bare plank bed adjoining the *peech*. She had slipped off her pillows and, for a good hour now, had been calling her husband to adjust them, tuck the blanket in around her, and help her turn over to her other side.

Makar was not responding—he was sleeping like a dead man. Finally, the sick woman's efforts caused blood to gush from her throat and flow over her shirt and pillows; she fell silent, but the grief, winding itself like a snake around her heart for the two months she had been ill, did not abate.

"Is death truly coming to me so suddenly and so unexpectedly?" Tetyana grieved. "O Lord, O Holy Friday! Protect me, guard me from death! I'm still young—I haven't been on this earth for even forty years yet. Be merciful to me, O Queen of Heaven! Let me at least live long enough to rear my children."

Her two little children—a boy of five, and a girl of seven—were deep in their first sleep. They had no way of knowing that they were spending their final night with their mother.

Thoughts were racing one after the other through Tetyana's head, and every one of them was more bitter than wormwood and darker than a leaden cloud. She recalled her entire life—like a single day—and a sigh involuntarily escaped from her pain-ridden breast.

"Was it worth working that hard for so many years—denying myself food and sleep—to end up like this? My entire life has been spent humouring others, working first for one neighbour and then another; and now, when I've finally managed to get my own little nook, my own crust of bread, I'm no longer capable of doing anything, and it's time to die."

Tetyana had started working for others when she was ten and, at the age of twenty, got married and moved to another village. Her husband was hardworking but spineless, and her mother-in-law and five sisters-in-law devoured her alive. She put up with it for one year, and for a second one, but when the third year came, she thanked her new family for their hospitality, and went to live among strangers once again.

Before long, her husband joined her, and the two of them put all their efforts into earning money for a cottage of their own. In five years, they earned two hundred *karbovantsi [dollars],* bought a small piece of the village pasture from the community for two buckets of whiskey, built a small cottage, and began living on their new homestead.

But it was very difficult to make ends meet in their new home. They worked hard for every *pood [forty pounds]* of grain and every armful of straw, and it took eight more years of unceasing labour as servants before Tetyana and Makar, although still poor, could finally say they were householders.

It was at this time that Makar inherited a *desyatyna [2.7 acres]* after his father died. Tetyana now felt as if she had a new lease on life; she worked still harder in their little field and strove even more diligently to improve their situation. A couple of years later, they already had piglets, ducklings, and various kinds of fowl; their garden bloomed with elegant roses and yellow gilly flowers; and icons gleamed behind glass. There was only one thing missing in the cheerful household of the assiduous housewife—the irrepressible chatter of tiny towheads.

In the first six years of their married life, God had sent them two daughters; but it was not possible to look after children properly while working for others, and the little girls died in infancy. At the time, Tetyana could not take the time to grieve for them, but now that she had her own little field and cottage, she often wept, recalling the tiny faces of her babies and praying to Holy Friday to bless them with at least one child.

And Holy Friday had listened to her prayers—they had been blessed with two healthy children, both with dark hair and rosy cheeks. Would she now have to leave them?

"O merciful God! O Queen of Heaven!" Tetyana groaned.

This time, Makar woke up. In the lamplight, he appeared quite young. He had never experienced the severe hardships that had precipitated Tetyana's ill health. Being a man, regardless of whether he was working for someone else or for himself, once he had completed his daily work, he could go to sleep early, have a good rest, and get up feeling refreshed and energetic in the morning.

Things were quite different for Tetyana; all day long she had to attend to many small but pressing tasks, and when night fell, there was still the spinning that had to get done and the tattered clothing that had to be mended, and she could not get enough sleep or rest. And so it continued day after day, and year after year, until her health was completely undermined.

"O Queen of Heaven! O Holy Saints! Oh, it's so hard to breathe!" Tetyana groaned once again.

"Why are you groaning, old woman?" Makar asked with a yawn.

"You're sleeping like a dead man! There's no one to fix my pillows," Tetyana said reproachfully.

"Well, how are you feeling? Better or worse? Oh my goodness, look at all the blood! Where does it all come from? There's so much blood . . . Oh my!"

"Is it the first time you've seen it, or what?" Tetyana said angrily. "Move the pillows over this way . . . no, no, not like that . . . over here . . . Gently, now!"

"Oh, the grief that you cause me—I just can't seem to please you. If only I knew whether you were going to live or die, but as it is . . . who can tell . . . There's just no end of trouble with you!" Makar said, moving away from his wife's side.

Tetyana wanted to reply, but could not muster the energy. During the brief time it had taken for her husband to adjust her pillows, the last traces of her strength had vanished. Now, propped up on a pile of pillows, she was watching Makar with a sorrowful look on her face.

But Makar walked around the room a few times, drank some water, glanced out the window, and went outdoors to see how the heifer was doing.

The blizzard had abated somewhat, and lamps were now lit in a few of the cottages. Makar put some straw under the heifer, shovelled the snow away from the door, and reluctantly returned to the cottage. He did not feel like sleeping, but there was nothing for him to do before dawn. Without taking off his sheepskin coat, he sat down on the bench and fell deep into thought.

He had long ago become accustomed to the idea that he would soon have to bury his wife. But as to what would happen to him after his wife's death—how he would take care of two children and the household by himself, how he would do the work that, at times, the two of them had not been able to handle—he had not given these matters any thought as yet.

"What is to be, will be!" he thought. When the time came, life would point the way, people would offer advice, and it would become clear to him how he should live and what he should do— if he should live out his life alone, or look for another wife.

There was only one thought that troubled him—where was he to get the money for his wife's funeral?

In their fifteen years of unceasing labour, they had managed only to build a cottage to live in; they had not had time to think about death. But the unexpected guest did not ask the householders if they had prepared anything to greet her with, if they had put away enough money for the whiskey, the food, and the new abode— the coffin; she knocked on the door, crossed the threshold, and was mercilessly drawing ever nearer to the ill woman.

And what would he do when death claimed his wife? Where would he find the money to bury her and pay for a funeral service for her soul?

"Oh, if only Tetyana could hang on at least for another week!" Makar sighed heavily. "There's a market in town next week, and I could sell the sheepskin coat for six *karbovantsi*, add the three *karbovantsi* that she has saved for the taxes, and bury her without a problem."

It was true, of course, that there was also the heifer in the pen— should he sell it? The heifer was carrying a calf that would be born towards Easter, and then it would be a cow. It's easy to say: "We've a cow in the yard." But it's not easy to attain such good fortune.

On the day when the calf bawled in the pen for the first time, all the farmers would know that Makar had finally freed himself from the lowly position of a powerless wretch. In the springtime, he would no longer have to run around, bowing and scraping to everyone in the hope that someone would agree to harrow his field; he would yoke up his cow together with that of his neighbour and go out into the field with his own plough and his own harrow.

But if his wife died, he might have to sell the heifer.

Hoping that his wife might be able to advise him, he asked her what she thought.

"Sell the heifer?" Tetyana boiled over with anger. "So that's what you intend to do? We cared for the heifer, nurtured it, and now you're going to sell it! Hasn't your heart had its fill of aching as you watched our children stare longingly at the neighbours' milk pots? Why, you'll be dead before you scrape together enough money to buy another heifer."

"Well, I'm only asking for your advice. How am I to bury you if you die before the end of Lent? I won't get anything for the sheepskin coat before the regular market day," Makar spoke up.

"So you're already planning to sell the sheepskin coat? I didn't even wear it to church, because I was saving it, and I caught a cold because I went to the market-place in just a jacket; I saved my money, a *shah [halfpenny]* at a time, to buy it, and now you want to sell it at the market. Just wait a bit, don't be in such a rush! You should be trying to figure out how to buy some medicine at the pharmacy for your sick wife, instead of being in such a hurry to get rid of our belongings, to sell the heifer. Don't get your hopes up—I won't die that quickly. It doesn't matter that you aren't concerned about helping me—I'll keep on living just to make life difficult for you."

"Oh Lord, am I supposed to worry about helping you? Anyone would get tired of looking after a sick woman for two months. I have to keep the fire going myself, and do the cooking, and do everything myself . . . and, in addition, I'm supposed to call in all the doctors and woman healers from all over the world! If only God would take you away or something! This is very tiresome."

"Tiresome? I lost my health because of your poverty! If I weren't with you, I wouldn't be lying here like a log. You liked your wife only when she could still work, but once she became ill, you're ready to throw her in the garbage. But watch out! The same evil hour may strike you, and then you'll remember your Tetyana, and you'll be sorry more than once, but it won't do you any good," Tetyana quietly reproached him.

"Am I blaming you? You're lying there, so go on lying there. You caught a cold, got sick, and can't work—I'm not reproaching you for that . . . All this may be more difficult for me to bear than it is for you to just lie around," Makar replied, and he stretched himself out once again on the sleeping bench.

"It's easy for me to lie here? The household is going to ruin—is it easy for me to watch this happen? On the pegs over there, the unwashed sacks with soil in them are going to fall apart from the mildew—and I worked for a half share to get the hemp to make those sacks. In the root cellar, the cucumbers have turned mouldy, and the cabbages have rotted—and I took both the cucumbers and the cabbage with the understanding that I'd work to pay them off.

"Oh, Lord! If only my illness would let up for at least a day, so I could put things in order in the root cellar! The mice are sure to have eaten the hemp by now. Other women probably lit their lamps before dawn—they're spinning already, and I'm the only one that's lying in bed."

"You've spun enough in your lifetime—you're finished now!" Makar muttered, turning over on his other side.

"Why are you saying 'you're finished now'? Maybe I'll get better, maybe the Lord will still let me spin enough for a shirt or two!"

"It will have to be in the next world!" Makar blurted out, covering his head so he would not have to hear any more of his wife's reproaches.

But Tetyana did not see him do this; everything that had been simmering in her heart during her lengthy illness, everything that she had thought about and quietly endured during the past two months began to seethe now—it all came to a boil and sought to escape from her aching breast.

"You know only too well how to hurt and blame me, but when I die and you take another woman—then you'll see what kind of a wife she'll be, what kind of a mother, and what kind of a worker in the household. I didn't begrudge either my health or my peace of mind to acquire a corner of our own, but she won't even try to preserve the little that there is. I managed to scrape together enough for a cottage, and a heifer, and a sheepskin coat, but she'll waste it all, spend it all, throw it away, and ruin it, because she won't know and won't see how hard I had to work for it," Tetyana wailed, breathing heavily and pressing her aching chest with the palms of her hands.

Makar did not reply because he had instantly fallen asleep.

Tetyana, however, did not fall silent. Calming down a bit, and interrupted at times by a fit of coughing in the middle of a word, she continued talking. And the more she spoke, the more her eyes blazed and her temples flushed. Far from tiring her, it seemed that this final confession was infusing her dying body with a life-giving strength.

Moving on from reproaches and recollections of her past life—a life filled with paucity and unending drudgery—Tetyana considered her present condition and glanced boldly into the future.

Oh, she would not die. She could not die as yet—she had children, a new dwelling, her own little cow; no, it was impossible to even think about death! She had to live; she had to save from ruin all that she had earned at the cost of her own health and thirty years of labour. She had to go on living. Even now, after this night, she felt much better. If it weren't for the sweating and the coughing, she would already be seeing to some of her work.

And this tiny glimmer of hope that she might go on living crept imperceptibly into Tetyana's heart and grew stronger by the moment. She was sure that in another hour she would be well, that in a short time she would abandon her hard bed, and that the work would fly once again in her strong hands.

Finally, comforted somewhat by these thoughts, she fell asleep.

II

She did not sleep long.

As soon as it grew light outside, someone walked up to her bed, squeezed her nose, and began touching her hands and feet.

She opened her eyes.

Before her stood old Granny Horpyna and, a little farther off, a few other women. The heavy odour from their boots and sheepskin coats, and the cold wind that blew through the open doorway made Tetyana cough. Weakened, and scarcely breathing, she looked away from the uninvited guests and turned her head to the wall.

Horpyna leaned her tall thin body over the sick woman's head and peered into her eyes.

"Her eyes are clouded over, and her lips are sunken," she said worriedly to the women who were standing by quietly, waiting to hear what she had to say.

"Her hands are quite cold, and there's hardly any warmth left in her at all," she added, taking off the quilted covering.

"You should change her shirt and wipe off her pillows," said a young soldier's wife, dressed in high-heeled boots and a wadded blue cotton jacket.

"Why disturb her? When she dies, we'll have to change her anyway," Horpyna said; however, she tore off a rag from an old shirt, dipped it in some water, and began wiping the blood from Tetyana's lips, face, and pillow.

Tetyana groaned.

"Wipe her behind the ears," said an older woman, blind in one eye, as she drew nearer.

"Her hair is all tangled—I'm afraid I'll pull it," Horpyna replied.

"But she doesn't feel anything any more; give it to me—I'll wipe it off."

"What do you mean she doesn't feel anything? She's still groaning," Horpyna said, grabbing the rag out of the hands of the partially blind woman, who had begun pulling it towards herself.

"Don't bother her now; she'll die, and then we'll wash her up properly," Stepanyda soothed the aggrieved woman.

"Maybe she's already dead?" Motrya, one of the older women, inquired in a soft whisper.

"She hasn't died yet, but she'll die quite soon—first there's a warm breath, and then a cold one. Come a little closer, kinswoman Khrystya, and take a look." Horpyna also spoke in whispers.

Khrystya placed her palm over the mouth of the sick woman. "You're right—first there's a warm breath, and then a cold one. Poor Tetyana will die very soon; let's hope she has time to give her final behest before she goes."

"It's absolutely necessary that she give her final behest—that she leave instructions regarding her husband, her children, and her household," Motrya picked up the conversation.

"Of course, we have to ask her about everything. Tetyana, hey Tetyana! Maybe you could give us some instructions?" Horpyna once again approached the sick woman.

"Don't disturb her! See—she's opened her eyes and shut them again. It's probably difficult for the poor thing to breathe, and you're all fussing about instructions," the soldier's wife interjected.

"Well, are we to ask you or someone else what to do with the cattle when she dies?" the partially blind woman asked the soldier's wife.

"What cattle are you talking about? How many are there?" the soldier's wife retorted.

"Well, there may not be very many, but she got them through the sweat of her brow. The woman worked all her life—she denied herself food and drink—and is she now supposed to let others decide what is to be done with her cattle?" Motrya spoke indignantly.

"What's there to talk about? If we don't ask her, she won't tell us, and then she'll blame us from the other world that we didn't do things properly," Stepanyda added.

"Tetyana! Tetyana!" Horpyna was already addressing the sick woman once again. "Why aren't you telling us anything, why aren't you advising us? Tell your husband—should he keep the heifer, or sell it? Should he take care of the household himself, or should he look for another mother for the children?"

"I'm not dying yet," Tetyana could scarcely muster her strength to reply.

"Oh, how can you go on living, dear sister, if your liver is completely rotted!" Horpyna sighed.

Tetyana turned away.

"You don't want to die? But what can be done about it? When your time comes, you can't bribe death to stay away; death does not pass anybody by when the appointed hour comes—neither a rich person, nor a poor one, a happy one, or a wretched one," Horpyna said.

"Is there some kind of medicine that might still help?" the soldier's wife inquired.

"What kind of medicine can there be—her face has already turned black," the nearly blind woman said in an irritated tone.

"Doesn't Makar have enough expenses as it is? His wife's about to die, and he doesn't even have the wherewithal to bury her, let alone waste money on medicine," Stepanyda said.

"God's will—that's all the medicine there is!" Motrya added.

"Come now, sweetheart, tell us—how is Makar supposed to live? What should he do without you? Should he sell the heifer, or maybe the sheepskin coat? Or should he borrow money from the bank?" Horpyna asked Tetyana.

Tetyana gestured at the oven bed, where the children were sleeping.

"She wants us to wake the children," the soldier's wife said.

"No, her gesture didn't mean anything; she's just annoyed."

"Shhh!" The soldier's wife exhorted them. "The woman's dying, and you're starting to quarrel."

"Come on, Tetyana dear, tell us exactly what you want us to do, so that we all know, and so you won't be blaming your husband afterwards, and so your soul won't be grieving—should the heifer be sold, or not?" Horpyna kept asking.

"Nothing is to be sold . . ." Tetyana hardly managed to say, and two tears, the size of peas, rolled down her face and fell on her shirt.

"She doesn't want anything to be sold," the women seized upon her words.

"And how do you want your husband to live? Should he look for a housekeeper after you die, or should he try to manage by himself?" the partially blind woman came up to her.

Teryana once again gestured with her hand. The woman did not see the gesture, and asked her once again.

"But you can see—she made a gesture as if she wanted to say: 'It's all the same to me—let him live as he sees fit, as long as he raises the children properly,'" Khrystya replied for Tetyana.

"Merciful God knows why she gestured, what she has in mind. If only she would tell us, it would be better," Motrya observed.

"Oh, oh, oh, Queen of Heaven, and Holy Mykola, God's saint! Is our dear little cuckoo still alive, and has her poor little head been blessed?" asked an old woman who was just entering the house; she was very pious and had gone on pilgrimages for twelve years in a row.

"Farewell, then, farewell, dear little sister! Forgive me, forgive all of us, my little dove! Don't take any anger against us into the next world; pray for our sinful souls before the throne of the Lord!" she continued speaking as she approached Tetyana's bed and bowed down to the ground before the dying woman.

"My dear little children, my little lapwings!" she turned to the children. "You have no idea, my orphans, what kind of fate awaits you. Come and receive your mother's blessing—let your own dear mother bless you, so that good fortune may be yours!" the old woman said anxiously.

The little girl began wailing at the top of her lungs and started to climb down from the *peech*, but the little boy, holding a *pyrih [turnover]* in one hand and a piece of *knysh [stuffed bread]* in the other, pressed himself still more closely to the oven.

The old woman went up to the *peech*, pulled the boy away from it, and placed him beside his sister by their mother's bed.

"You'd better come up to your wife as well, Makar; you may be the one most guilty before your wife. Let her bless you," the old woman turned to Makar, who had just walked in.

Makar obediently walked up to his wife. "Forgive me, Tetyana!" he said, and, for the first time since his wife had become ill, he started to cry.

Only now, in these last few moments of her life, did his heart beat painfully; only now did he fully comprehend the misfortune that had befallen him. It was not only a long-suffering worker, a workmate, who was leaving him; the only soul who was close to him in the whole world was departing from him, and no one could ever replace the heart that had beat, ached, and rejoiced together with his for almost twenty years.

"Forgive me, Tetyana!" he said for a second time, falling down to his wife.

Tetyana's face grew contorted, and she opened her eyes wide. "The door . . . to breathe . . ." she groaned.

"Open the door wider! Uncover her!" the women said anxiously.

"Oh, Lord, how difficult it is for her to breathe!" Khrystya sighed heavily.

"What else could it be but difficult—her liver is all rotted!"

"Bless your little children and your husband, dear Tetyana!" the pious old woman drew near once again. "Look, Tetyana—your husband and children are standing before you!"

Tetyana glanced at the children . . .

"Bless them, my little dove!" the old woman said again, lifting the feeble hand of the sick woman.

Tetyana gathered together all her strength, stretched her hand a little farther, and blessed her children and husband with the sign of the cross.

The women quietly began wiping away their tears.

"Oh, how heavily she's breathing! Like a fish out of water," Khrystya said, peering at Tetyana over the shoulder of the soldier's wife.

"She's dying now . . ."

"Oh, let me out—I'm afraid!" the soldier's wife rushed to the door.

"And she didn't give any instructions!" Motrya reminded everyone.

"She still hasn't given any instructions?" Horpyna, who was only now coming back into the cottage, asked in surprise.

Having become convinced that Tetyana would die before evening, she had left the others with the dying woman while she herself had gone to her farmstead to get a cast-iron pot for the hot water.

"Not a breath came out of her mouth—she was silent the entire time," Motrya said.

Horpyna set the pot down on the bench and peered into Tetyana's eyes.

"She's almost gone! How could you let such a thing happen? There were so many of you here, and you didn't find out anything? If only she'd come to for a moment!" Horpyna said anxiously, and she squeezed Tetyana's nose in an effort to make her revive for a moment and give the desired advice.

But there was no reply. Tetyana sighed for the last time, and her soul flew like a gentle breath out of her aching chest.

"She's dead! It doesn't matter now if you ask her or if you don't—she won't say anything." Horpyna said, and she closed the eyelids of the dead woman.

"May the heavenly Kingdom and eternal peace be hers!" the pious old woman made the sign of the cross and prostrated herself before the icons in the corner.

The other women also turned to face the icons and began praying for the repose of the soul of Tetyana, the newly departed servant of the Lord.

"Do you have any *pyataky [nickels]*?" Horpyna turned to Makar.

Makar pulled a kerchief out of the trunk and, untying a knotted corner in which there were two *karbovantsi* and some small change, gave Horpyna two *pyataky*.

"Is there any hot water?" one of the women asked.

"She has to be washed while she's still warm, because later it won't be possible to move her arms and legs," Motrya observed.

"Don't worry about the hot water—I filled two iron pots and shoved them in my oven at dawn. Take off your coats, my good women! Makar, take out the shirt and skirt she put away for her funeral, and get ready to go to town to buy some whiskey and kerchiefs. And you, Motrya, tell Harasym to inform the *batyushka [Russian Orthodox priest]*," Horpyna started giving out orders.

Harasym agreed not only to inform the *batyushka*, but also to make arrangements for the funeral—to haggle with the priest over charges for the Holy Gospel, the church banners, the priest's assistants, and the horses. This was not an easy task, for it all depended on the mood of Father Ardalion. And the priest's mood depended upon many circumstances, but mostly upon the "character" of the devils that he had to chase out of his "possessed" parishioners.

At times, the evil one turned out to be such an obedient, meek, and even stupid little devil, that it was enough for the priest to exert himself and shout "I curse you" and "I exorcise you" three times, and the little demon would put its tail between its legs and flee into regions unknown.

At other times, however, the devil was so stubborn and evil that the priest would break into a sweat as he exorcised him, and it was only after a full hour of curses—profanities that made your hair stand on end—that the unclean spirit would leave its victim. But then a new grief awaited the priest.

Chased out of his first refuge in a confused state of mind, the devil, without giving it much thought, would jump into the wide belly of the priest and begin to settle in there as if he were at home in hell. It was in vain that the priest would try to drown the fiend in brandy—the unclean spirit floated to the top like a feather and revealed itself in most inappropriate words, and even in some offensive "acts."

For a long time, the parishioners had been both amazed and angry, but when they heard about the situation from the priest himself, when they finally figured out that it was the evil spirit that was uttering profanities through the priest's lips, and that it was the wicked devil that was ruling his heart, they calmed down and patiently awaited the time when the demon would tire of behaving capriciously. It's true that some unkind soul finally made all this known where it mattered, and the *batyushka* was removed a couple of years later.

At the time that Harasym walked into the priest's living room, however, the *batyushka* was struggling with the devil from Solopiya, a woman who had been brought to him three days before the death of Makarykha. From the look on the face of the *matushka [wife of a Russian Orthodox priest]*, the tear-stained eyes of the servant, and, most of all, from the smell of whiskey, Harasym realised at once that the situation with the unfortunate Father Adralion was no joking matter.

Harasym had to wait for a full hour in the kitchen before the priest finished eating his dinner and deigned to see him.

"What do you want? Why have you come?" Father Adralion asked Harasym.

The unfortunate Harasym glanced obliquely at the priest's nose and sighed.

"Why have you come?" the *batyushka* shouted a second time.

"Makarykha has given up her soul to God, and so they're begging your Grace most humbly to come."

"Which Makarykha is it? What's her family name? Which Trokhymykha is it?" the *batyushka* interrupted Harasym.

"Makarykha," Harasym corrected him.

"Her family name! I'm asking for her family name!" the priest shouted in an enraged voice.

"Her family name . . . her surname? Well, let's see . . . what is it now . . . well, may the Lord forgive me, I've forgotten it!"

"You've forgotten it? How could you have forgotten it?" the *batyushka* yelled still more loudly. "Have you come to the tavern to buy some whiskey? Get out of my house, you drunkard! You've drunk a whole quart, and now you've come to your *batyushka* with empty hands!"

"I can swear, *batyushka*, that I haven't had so much as a drop in my mouth. And there isn't any whiskey at home either . . . Unless I . . ."

"Go away! Get out!" Father Ardalion stopped Harasym; he wanted to stamp his foot at him as well, but stumbled instead.

"My dear Adralion! Adraliosha! Don't get angry!" the *matushka* said timidly.

"My good man," she said, turning to Harasym, "isn't it Hrebenyuk's wife who has died?"

"Yes, yes, that's it!" Harasym rejoiced. "She's the one—it's Hrebenyuk's wife!"

"So, that's the one—Hrebenyuk's wife!" the *batyushka* said sternly. "But where's the child? Where are the godparents?" he shouted out of the blue.

Harasym was dumbfounded.

"Where's the infant?" the *batyushka* shouted more loudly.

"Adralion, the man is not asking you to christen an infant—he's asking you to bury a woman. Hrebenyuk's wife has died, sweetheart," the *matushka* interceded on Harasym's behalf.

"Aha! So Hrebenyuk's wife has died?" the *batyushka* finally figured things out.

"Yes, yes indeed . . . Hrebenyuk's wife died today . . . We're requesting you most humbly to bury her."

"I don't want to bury her! I don't want to, and that's the end of it! And you're to tell them this—that the *batyushka*, Father Adralion, does not want to bury Hrebenyuk's wife. Where did she prepare for confession? In the monastery? So, let the monks bury her. How am I to know how she confessed? Maybe she sat in a tavern instead of going to church! I don't want to bury such pigs.

"My church is in ruins, my assistant is almost dying of hunger, and you give away your *midyaky [copper coins]* to the monks? How much do you give your *batyushka* for performing church ceremonies? *Shahy [halfpennies]*! But as soon as I set a fee of ten *kopiyky [pennies]* to hear the confession of your souls—that are repugnant to God—you all went to the monastery for confession! Since that's the way it is, I don't want to bury you."

"Your Grace, my dear *batyushka*, please don't be angry at the newly departed; maybe she really didn't have any money for the confession. Show a divine mercy and bury her without any anger."

"And how much will I be paid for the funeral?" Father Adralion asked somewhat more pleasantly.

"Well, as you know, they're poor people—they'll show their gratitude in the best way they can," Harasym said cautiously.

"I won't accept anything less than two *karbovantsi*, and that doesn't include the Holy Gospel, the church banners, or my assistant. And have them send good horses for me—do you hear?"

"I hear you, I hear you, *batyushka*! Just don't be angry at what I have to say—bury her for a *poltynyk [half a dollar],* show some divine mercy, the people are poor . . ."

"Have you come to the marketplace to bargain?" the *batyushka* yelled so forcefully that the panes in the windows rattled. "Two *karbovantsi*, and not a *kopiyka* less!"

"Well then, let it be two *karbovantsi*, but let it include the Holy Gospel, the church banners, and your assistant . . ." Harasym bowed down low before him.

"So, you're still bargaining? Get away from here! I don't want to bury any of you. May you all perish like dogs! Go to the monks. Forward march!" the *batyushka* became even more enraged.

"When do you want the horses to be sent?" Harasym asked gloomily.

"So, you're asking about the horses, but you're not saying anything about the money? Rest assured that I won't bury her on credit! It doesn't concern me in the least that this Hrabenko, or whatever you call him, is being devoured by poverty. And you tell him that. You hear?"

Harasym heard it all too well. Moreover, he also saw that Solopiya's stubborn devil had barely begun to act capriciously, and if he, Harasym, continued his conversation with the priest, then the evil spirit would add a measure of wheat, a quart of whiskey, or some coloured eggs to the two *karbovantsi*, and so he did not contest the matter any further.

"I hear you, I hear you," Harasym replied humbly and, bowing down low to the *batyushka* and *matushka*, he retreated hastily from the room.

III

Ivan Kryvorotko harnessed his old nag and drove up to Makar's cottage. All that Makar had to do was get in the sleigh and drive to town to make his purchases, but he did not do this for a long time; he wandered about the yard and the cottage, looking at length in all the corners, as if he were searching for something.

"What should I take to town with me? What should I sell?" he asked himself, as he looked in the empty stable for the tenth time. But no matter how hard he thought, or how long he looked—it was only the sheepskin coat and the heifer that alternately came into his mind and stood before his eyes.

"The sheepskin coat—the heifer! The heifer—the sheepskin coat!" resounded in his head, and his heart kept growing heavier.

He could not bring himself to sell the sheepskin coat—his wife had not worn it even to church because she had been saving it for their daughter . . . but he felt even worse about selling the heifer.

"Have you become lost in the forest, or have you lost your head?" Ivan shouted at him.

"Right away, I'm coming right away," Makar said and, in despair, finally grabbed the sheepskin coat and sat down in the sleigh.

The people had already begun dispersing from the marketplace, but, nevertheless, quite a large group of women and men gathered around Makar, who held the new sheepskin coat in his hands. They all wanted to hold it and examine it from all sides; and they all wanted to buy it, but they offered him only what they could afford, and it was so little that Makar angrily grabbed the sheepskin coat from them and continued on his way.

Farther up, another group of people surrounded him. They also looked the coat over carefully, asked about it, swore to God that they were giving him as much as they could—and offered him even less for it than those in the first group.

Completely infuriated with the impoverished buyers—and even more so with Tetyana for not waiting for the market day to die—Makar returned to the sleigh. There, the old grey mare was attempting to chew an armful of straw with her toothless gums.

Makar poked her angrily in her sides, and shouted for no reason at all: "Stand still, damn you!"

He tore the straw out of her mouth, hit her with a corded whip, and turned the shaft around to go home.

He was sure that no one in the hamlet would come to his assistance, because they, like he, had an extra *kopiyka* or two only in the autumn, before the taxes, and the lords did not care about anyone except themselves. Nevertheless, he had not dared to give away the sheepskin coat—the coat that had been so hard to come by—for half of what it was worth.

"It will all turn out somehow or other . . . The people will come up with something or other . . . After all, Tetyana won't remain unburied," he consoled himself, as the mare slowly hobbled home.

"Maybe the *batyushka* will bury her without asking for any money, and then I'll be able to make a coffin with the money that we saved; and, as for the rest—it will be as God sees fit!"

But, at home, the bad news about Father Ardalion awaited him—the *batyushka* would not hear of taking less than two *karbovantsi* for just the funeral rites.

Makar, completely at a loss as to what he should do next, sat down dejectedly by the table and lowered his head on his folded arms.

What could he do? Where could he get the money? He did not have any in the bank. Could he turn for help to Afanasiy Petrovych Karpenko? Well, that miser would not lend it to him simply for a "thank you."

It looked as if he would have to put up his land as security, even though agreeing to the terms of repayment would mean that he would have to work all summer for nothing.

"Where can I go? Where can I get some money?" Makar asked himself for the tenth time, as he looked at the women keeping watch over the lifeless body of his wife.

And truly, the women seemed to be vying to outdo each other in showing their respect in various small ways to Tetyana's body.

While her body had still been alive, every one of these neighbours, even though they would have been happy to do something for Tetyana, simply had not had the time to make things easier for her. Moreover, there were times when they really did not know what they could do to help, and so, while she had been ill, they felt that only the woman healer, or perhaps, to some extent, the doctor, or to an even lesser extent, the doctor's assistant, could help the ill woman; most of all, however, they felt it rested in the hands of the merciful Lord.

From the moment, however, that the Lord accepted Tetyana's soul, and she closed her eyes forever, the distinctions between women healers, doctors, and ordinary people disappeared, to be replaced by the obligations, well-known to everyone, of the living to the dead.

Tetyana, while still alive, had both friends and enemies; Tetyana, as a corpse, was the same for everyone—her soul cast off the chains that had forced her to sigh quietly at times, to lament loudly at other times and, at still other times, to do evil unto people who were bound in the same earthly chains as she was.

Tetyana had finished her journey—thorns would no longer prick her feet, and she would no longer covet the possessions of others as straw to be spread under her bloodied feet; no one would stand in her way any more, no one would push her around, and she, in turn, would no longer shove a neighbour into the gutter.

However, this body and these heavy chains were not an illusion or a figment of the imagination—God had decreed that her body be born, grow, live, and fall ill, and, because of this, over the course of her life, it had often been necessary to act against her conscience; and now, the soul, even though it had issued from the body, had not abandoned it—for three days it would hover near it, look at it, and watch carefully what kind of final respects people would pay it.

The women did not begrudge their work, but the pious old woman was the most anxious of all to see to it that the newly departed was properly prepared for the other world. She did up the shirt herself, adjusted the skirt, and put on the head-dress.

Sitting here among these preoccupied women, Makar forgot about his own grief for a moment; he even forgot that they were busying themselves with his dead wife.

"Why aren't you going into town?" Horpyna asked in surprise, as she carried in a pail of water.

"I have nothing to go with," Makar replied, raising his troubled head.

"But you have two *karbovantsi*, don't you?"

"What good are two *karbovantsi*? I'll pay the *batyushka* and his assistant, but there's nothing left over to buy anything."

"But you can't get by without a coffin," the partially blind woman said, and she sounded angry.

"No, I can't," Makar replied sadly.

"It's time to make the coffin, but you don't even have any boards," she reminded him.

"I know it's time to build a coffin, but I don't have enough money . . . Maybe I should buy the boards and try to get some money somewhere else to pay the *batyushka*?"

"But you need more than boards, don't you? You don't have any linen cloths, or candles, or honey, or whiskey," she reminded him again.

"Go to Karpenko right now and ask him to lend you five or six *karbovantsi*. And take the sheepskin coat with you—you can't sell it because your deceased wife told you not to, but you can use it as security," Horpyna advised him.

"Karpenko won't lend me the money—I asked him once before, and he wouldn't," Makar said.

"If he won't lend you any money, we won't go out to steal some. You can't be blamed for what can't be helped. If you can't get hold of some money someplace, the deceased will forgive you. What's to be done, if there's no money to hold a funeral dinner? We'll pray for her soul and leave!" Motrya said from the *peech* where she was filling a sack with dry fodder.

"Go to see Karpenko right now," Horpyna advised him for a second time, obviously disagreeing, along with the other women, with Motrya's advice to pray for Tetyana's soul and depart.

"Karpenko has just come home from the city; he probably sold his wheat," Khrystya contributed to the conversation.

"Bow down low to him, ask him politely, and he might at least take pity on the orphans," Horpyna added.

Makar placed little hope on Karpenko, but he obediently rose to his feet and walked out of the house.

In the meantime, the women finished dressing the newly departed, lifted her up, and laid her out on the bench. At that very moment, a golden ray of the winter sun broke through the window near the bench, sparkled on Tetyana's brocade head-dress, leapt into the house, and landed on the group of women who were standing, as if turned to stone, by the deceased.

Not a word or a sigh escaped from the lips of the women, but strangely enough, at this moment, they were all convinced that there are times when people can understand one another without speaking, that there are moments when the souls of the living are united without the assistance of their bodies, and that, right now, an unknown power bound all of them beside Tetyana, pierced them, constricted their hearts, and was reflected in an indistinct but single thought: "We are all human beings and the same end awaits us all—the grave."

And all unkind recollections, and all unkind wishes faded under the influence of this thought; and something that was even more pure and angelic than the smile of an innocent child flitted across the usually gloomy face of the partially blind woman.

"Oh, my dear sisters! I haven't fed my child yet!" Motrya was the first to come to her senses.

"And I haven't prepared any dinner!" Khrystya remembered.

"Let's all go home—we've finished tending to the deceased, and Granny Horpyna can stay to do whatever else needs to be done. We'll all come again towards evening," the pious old woman said.

"We should ask Granny Horpyna if she won't find it depressing to stay here by herself," the partially blind woman said with some concern.

"Go on, go on—I'm not afraid. And there's no time to dwell on things, because there's a lot to be done," Horpyna assured the women, who promptly rushed home where their hungry children, and their cows and pigs, impatiently awaited them.

Horpyna really did not have any time to be sad. Makar was relying completely on her; he entrusted the baking, the cooking, the children, and the heifer to her care. In addition, Horpyna willingly took still another obligation upon herself—to find some money for Makar in case he did not get any from Karpenko. She could not rid her head of the words that Motrya had uttered so casually—"we'll pray and then we'll leave."

According to a well-established tradition, not a single villager departed from this world without the help of Granny Horpyna. At times, she had to do something to help the sick person live a little longer, and at other times—to help such a person die; but after death came, Horpyna positioned herself by the *peech* and demanded the best food provisions from the relatives, so that people would not speak ill afterwards about the funeral dinner.

Makar had not yet put anything into place, and this troubled Horpyna. What was she going to serve people if Makar did not buy any honey, or suet, or oil? Would they actually have to do what Motrya had said—pray and leave?

"It looks like I'll have to make the rounds of the village myself to try and borrow some money," she said worriedly to herself, as she peered impatiently through the window to see if Makar was returning.

Finally, Makar came home.

"Well, did you get any money?" Horpyna rushed up to him.

"He wouldn't give me any," Makar replied gloomily.

"He wouldn't? What did he say?"

"He said: 'I won't lend you any money. And I won't take the sheepskin coat as security. If you need money, sell me either the sheepskin or the heifer, and then I'll be protected, and you won't have to think about returning the money.'"

"How much is he offering?"

"Three *karbovantsi* for the sheepskin coat, and ten for the heifer."

"Ten *karbovantsi* for the heifer?" Horpyna cried. "May he wander the earth forever after his death, damn him! It's such a fine heifer, and he wants to get it for ten *karbovantsi*! Just wait a while; I'll run around the village, and maybe I'll scrape together ten or more *karbovantsi*," she said, dashing out of the cottage.

Makar sat down on the long bench. His recent conversation with Karpenko confirmed even more strongly his view that those who find it difficult to live, find it still more difficult to die.

But Motrya's advice also did not leave his mind: "We'll pray for the newly departed and then we'll leave—may the deceased forgive you."

And truly, would not Tetyana—who had gone without enough to eat or drink so many times, who had suffered so much grief, who had not wanted to spend an unnecessary *midyak*, who during the whole time of her illness had not satisfied her desire to drink a shot of whiskey—would not that Tetyana forgive him now, after her death, if he buried her without whiskey, without linen cloths, and without a funeral dinner?

Makar glanced at his wife.

Washed and combed, Tetyana was lying in a white shirt and a new skirt. Her tightly closed eyes and sealed lips did not alter the customary expression of meekness on her face; it was her hands, folded on her chest, that made a far stronger impression on Makar. It was only on an important church holiday that she folded her hands as she sat under the window and chatted with her neighbours.

But was not today an important holiday for her as well? If that were the case, what had her life been like, what had her ordinary days been like?

He recalled how she had stood with him before the altar. People had brought them together and seen to it that they were united on the *rushnyk [embroidered linen ceremonial cloth]* without asking them if they were in love; there was not a single word about true love, not a single pledge . . . Nevertheless, her face flushed with health, she had looked boldly into the eyes of her groom; her strong body had stood without wavering, and not a single doubt flashed through her mind—she was confident that she could do all that life demanded of her. She knew she would be able to help her husband—the man with whom God was uniting her at this moment—and all that she asked of the Merciful One was good health.

And later, appearing a little tired and pale, but no less confident, Tetyana had hired herself out as a cook in the manor.

"Will you be able to bake bread twice a day?" Makar asked her in a whisper in the office.

"Whoever wants his own home and table, has to be able," she had replied cheerfully.

And for five years in a row, she had baked four *poods* of bread every day.

And then, even paler, she had stood beside the tiny coffin of her first daughter. Her face was sad, hot maternal tears streamed from her eyes, and her heart grieved and ached for the little body of her daughter; but then the master's cow began to bawl under the window, and Tetyana hurriedly dried her tears and rushed outdoors with a milking pail—"there's no time to cry, if you want your own home by and by."

Finally, she was in the dwelling she had so long desired—her own home. The new little white cottage gleamed in the sun, clean as a tear; the windows appeared to be smiling, and the young cherry trees peered right into the house with their fresh green blossoms. But why had the number of wrinkles increased on the housewife's face? Why were her dark eyes clouded over? Why was her tall, supple figure stooped?

Yes, she had become stooped, and she did not straighten out, but Makar had not noticed that then. It was only now, when death stretched out her body to its full length, and when he saw the unusually calm face of his wife, that Makar realised how dearly Tetyana had paid for that cottage, the orchard, and the fallow heifer, and what a burden of daily troubles his wife had carried.

And was this body—worn out from work and ravaged by neglect and illness—not to be accorded the proper final respect? Was it to be thrown into a hole like a useless rag, covered with soil, and, because of five or six *karbovantsi*, deprived of the kind remembrances of the people? Would he let it come to pass that his wife's soul would wander over the earth, wishing for a proper funeral and a commemorative dinner, that she would grieve as painfully in the next world as she had in this one? May the Mother of God forbid it!

"You toiled, you exhausted yourself on this earth, my wife—live in abundance and find some peace after death!" The words slipped involuntarily from Makar's lips. "You did not want me to sell anything, Tetyana, but I will sell both the sheepskin coat and the heifer in order to hold a funeral dinner for you," he added, rising from the bench and kissing his wife's forehead and folded hands that were as cold as ice.

"I barely managed to get three *karbovantsi* from the villagers—there's nothing but poverty in this wretched village." Horpyna interrupted Makar's thoughts about his wife. "It used to be hard to live, but now you can't even afford to die in a Christian manner. Have you heard that the *batyushka* has added on another *chetvertak [a quarter]*? I've just come from Priska's kinswoman, and he asked her to tell you that he wants another *chetvertak* in addition to the *karbovantsi*."

"Thank you for the money, but I'll manage without it somehow!" Makar responded, walking away from the bench.

"Take them—you'll find some use for them!" Horpyna advised him.

"Those three *karbovantsi* aren't enough in any event . . ."

"I know they're not enough. So where are you going?"

"To Karpenko's," Makar answered from the porch.

Harpyna stuck a *karbovanets* under her head covering, tied the smaller coins in a small knotted cloth tucked under her waistband, and set to work again by the *peech*. Now she was confident that Makar had come up with an idea, that the funeral dinner for Tetyana would be held properly, and she began to prepare bottles, a little barrel, and small pots for Makar when he went to town. And indeed, in a short time, Makar came back with Afanasiy Karpenko; the latter wanted to have a look at the heifer, to check it out for any defects.

Horpyna rushed outdoors.

"Look here, my good man, her horn is cracked!" Karpenko stated accusingly, pointing to something on the horn.

"So what?" laughed some men who happened to come by just then. "Are you going to milk her by her horns?"

"It's nothing to laugh at, my good people! Even though I won't be milking her by her horns, it is clear that the heifer is not in perfect condition."

"How much is he giving you for the heifer?" a neighbour asked Makar.

"Eleven *karbovantsi*!" Makar sighed.

"Eleven *karbovantsi* for such a heifer?"

"Have some fear of God, Afanasiy!" Horpyna could not restrain herself.

"He's giving only eleven *karbovantsi*, and he's still finding fault with the heifer," added another man.

"I'm not finding fault with her; I'm only saying that the heifer is not in perfect condition."

"It's too bad that I don't have the money, because if I did, I wouldn't let you get this heifer," someone spoke up from the group of men.

"I'd give twelve *karbovantsi* for her right away if I could," another man said.

"There are many who are willing, but few who are buyers," Afanasiy faced the men. "Even as a group, you can't afford to buy the heifer, but you want to crawl into my pocket to manage my business matters. And as for you, Makar," he turned back to address Makar, "if you want to strike a deal with me, reduce the price by a *chetvertak*."

"Is it because of the horn, or what?" Makar asked.

"Yes, because of the horn . . . either go down a *chetvertak*, or spend a day or so working it off."

"May you wander the earth forever after your death!" Horpyna shouted so the whole village could hear. "Such grief has befallen Makar, such a terrible thing has happened to him, but you don't have any fear of God!"

"It's all God's will—it so happens that Makar has to sell his heifer, and it so happens that I can buy it, and I'm not offending our Merciful Lord in any way. I came here at your request, Makar, to buy your property, but if people are going to be insulting me in your yard, then I'll go away with God's blessing and remove myself from sin without any more trouble," Karpenko said, reaching for the gate.

"But why are you angry, old man? I didn't say anything to you. If you tell me to work off the damaged horn, I'll do it. Take out your money, take the heifer, and may God be with you," Makar stopped Karpenko from leaving.

"That's fine with me," Karpenko agreed. "But find a better rope to lead her with, because this one is badly frayed."

Makar ran to find another rope. Karpenko pulled a handkerchief from his shirt and began counting out the money. The men surrounded him and silently watched as he took out the most tattered bills.

Untying the heifer, Makar passed the rope to Karpenko. The new owner extended his hand from under the hem of his cloak, took the rope, crossed himself, and led the heifer out of the yard.

For a long time, Makar, his eyes filling with tears, stood and watched as the heifer receded in the distance. And when his eyes turned away to fall on the empty manger, his last hope of becoming a true householder, of owning a cow and a draught animal, vanished completely from his heart . . .

IV

They buried Tetyana on the third day. Even though the deceased had no kin, there were kind people who turned out to grieve over her grave.

The pious old woman spoke so touchingly about her "little neighbour," that even some of the men furtively wiped away a tear or two.

Makar cast the first handful of soil on the coffin. "This heavy soil will fall on your chest, my wife, but an even heavier sorrow is falling on my heart. It will be sad for you to lie all alone in your grave, but it will be still sadder for me and the children to live without you. We'll have to wear unwashed shirts, and go to bed hungry . . . And your little orphans will no longer hear any words of respect, or advice, or kindness," Makar stated, and he peered with infinite sorrow into the bottom of the deep hole where his wife's coffin gleamed whitely.

The women began wailing.

"It's not proper," Father Adralion began admonishing them, "to weep over a grave. Death is sent by God, and there's no reason to cry over corpses."

The women quieted down and began to cover the coffin with handfuls of frozen soil. In a short time, they filled the hole, raised a high mound, dug in a wooden cross, and went to have dinner at Makar's home.

Immediately after dinner, Father Adralion and his assistant drove off, and most of the people followed them. Only a small group of women remained for the night to watch for Tetyana's soul.

The villagers, completely satisfied with the funeral dinner, thanked Makar and Horpyna and went off to their homes and their work. Makar also left the cottage to go to his cattle enclosure; he opened the door, glanced in, shut the door, tied it with a rope, walked up to the manger where the heifer always stood during the day, and sighed heavily.

What was it that pained his heart most at this moment? Was it his now deserted cottage or the empty yard that caused him the most pain? He himself could not say which it was, but he understood only too well that now he no longer was the master in his own home, or a true father to his children. The end had come, not only to his modest hopes, but also to his independence.

He could not manage the small children by himself; he did not know how to do housework or cook—so he would have to find another wife. But who would be willing to spend her youthful years with an impoverished widower, no longer young, with two children?

It would have to be an older woman who would settle in his home, and she would rearrange their lives in her own fashion. She would reproach the children for every shirt she had to wash, for every piece of bread she baked for them; and he would not be in a position to change anything that she did, for truly, what means did he have to pay this stranger who agreed to work for someone else's children in someone else's home?

If only he had a cow—then, at least, this woman would not be able to look down upon him as a pauper; she would not dare to reproach him about his poverty, his stale bread—she would see him as a householder. Oh, why had he sold the fallow heifer? The people could have dispersed without having some whiskey; the neighbours could have called him whatever names they wanted to for not holding a funeral dinner—he would not have cared, because now he would have been spreading hay under his heifer, and he would have felt himself to be a master at least in his own yard!

And, once again, anger against his wife stirred in Makar's heart.

Why could Tetyana not have held out for at least another week, until the market day? He could have sold the heifer for twenty *karbovantsi*, held the funeral dinner for six of them, and bought himself a smaller heifer with the other fourteen.

Oh! Tetyana had known how to work, but she had not known how to die. She had left behind orphans, and she had ruined the farmstead!

"You should come into the cottage to be with us!" Horpyna interrupted Makar's unhappy thoughts.

"It's stuffy in the cottage; I'll stay outside," Makar replied and, taking the rake from the porch, he went to spread the straw.

Horpyna went back into the cottage. On a *rushnyk* in the icon corner stood a dish with *kanun [spiced diluted honey]*; on the table there were *pyrohy [turnovers],* headcheese made out of whitefish, bottles of whiskey, a bottle of brandy, a wheaten *palyanytsya [flatbread],* and a shot glass.

No one touched any of the food or liquor, however, because Tetayna's soul had to taste them first.

The children, pale from weeping, tired, and sleepy, sat on the *peech*, taking care not to fall asleep inadvertently and thereby miss the moment when their mother, transformed into a fly, would return to say her farewells.

The little boy kept tugging at his sister's sleeve and asking: "Isn't that mummy's soul—that dark spot that's moving from the beam to the wall?"

"No, no—it doesn't fly during the day; when it turns dark, and they light the lamp—that's when it will fly in. Go to sleep now, Sydorko; I'll wake you when I see the fly," Odarka tried to persuade her sleepy brother, hugging him tenderly.

"I don't want to sleep; I want to see the fly; I'm going to sit up until they light the lamp and mummy flies in," Sydorko fought to stay awake, staring straight ahead with his sleepy eyes.

Finally the winter sun set, and Horpyna lit the lamp. Sydorko leapt to his feet.

"O-o-o-oh! It's her soul!" he joyfully called out, pointing his finger at the black head of a nail.

"Shhhh . . ." Odarka gave her brother such a good tug that he sat down once again. "I'm telling you—it's not time for mummy to fly in. When it buzzes, I'll wake you. Lie down, cover yourself, and sleep!" she continued, and Sydorko did not struggle any longer.

"Well? Has he fallen asleep?" Motrya asked Odarka.

"Yes, he has," the girl replied, and she pulled the blanket up over him.

"The poor dear departed!" Horpyna sighed. "She left behind her children, her homestead, her husband—and she had to work so hard for everything!"

"A human being is like a fly—a wind blows up, and no one even remembers about you," Khrystya spoke up.

"She was such a young woman to die! She wasn't even forty, was she?" Stepanyda said.

"It doesn't take a long time for one of our sisters to find death— she catches a cold or exhausts herself with work, and it's all over. It's our villagers who are the worst off; the doctor says: 'It's too far to your village;' and the assistant doctor has no time—he simply can't keep up with all that has to be done," Motrya added.

"Oh, God help us! A lot of good those assistant doctors are! Why, he gave me, and you, and our kinswoman Yavdokha some kind of red powder to take, and all that happened is that we got nauseated from it!" Stepanyda said.

"Oh, my dear doves! Neither the doctor nor the assistant doctor could have helped Tetyana, because she died because of her anger—the deceased was a wrathful woman who couldn't control herself. There were times when she yelled at Makar with such fury that she'd foam at the lips and faint. You heard her, didn't you, kinswoman Khrystya, when she flew into a rage at the whole village?" the partially blind woman turned to Khrystya.

"For some reason, I don't recall that," Khrystya replied.

"That's the kind of memory you have! It's not that I'm judging her—let the merciful Lord judge her in the next world—but she really was very wrathful . . . Last year she almost beat me up, I swear to God, because the children shook some plums off the trees in her orchard," the partially blind woman continued.

"Oh, sisters, sisters!" the pious old woman admonished them. "It isn't right to criticise the dead; her soul is hovering over us— it hears everything, sees everything, and is afflicted with sorrow. It's a great sin to speak ill of a newly departed person!

"It has pleased the Lord to let me live for a long time in this world, and I've learned a few things from others, and I'll tell you, if you like, what I heard one time from a woman in Kyiv.

"There was once a widow, said this woman from Kyiv, who spent her entire life in misery, grief, and sorrow; because of other people, she was burdened by many sins, her heart was agitated, her health was ruined because of her poverty, and she began to implore God to let her die.

"'Lord!' she said. 'Send someone for my sinful soul, so that my misfortune won't torment me, poor widow that I am.'

"And so the Lord sent an angel for her soul. Rejoicing and cheerful, her soul flew out of her body; it wanted to abandon the earth instantly and fly to God to bow before Him.

"'Your time has not yet come, and so I won't let you in to bow before Him,' the Lord's angel said, and he blocked the door before the soul.

"The soul, remaining in the house, flew around its body and examined it.

"In the meantime, some women came to sit with the body. And they were sitting there, just as, God give us good health, we're sitting now, but they were speaking ill of the newly departed one, and not remembering her kindly.

"One of them said: 'She took my *chetvertak* with her into the next world.' A second one said: 'She didn't return the flour she borrowed from me.' And a third one said: 'She yelled and swore at me in such and such a manner.'

"And the widow's soul hovered over them and, alighting on them, it wanted to say: 'Forgive me, dear sisters! Forgive me, dear neighbours! I had neither a *chetvertak*, nor any flour, nor any malice in my heart when I upbraided you; it was my misery and my poverty that made me take what belonged to others and to speak angrily to you.' But it couldn't say anything.

"The unfortunate soul kept circling and circling, and finally it once again began to implore the angel: 'Permit me to enter heaven,

O Angel of God. The reason that I implored God for death was to leave people far behind.'

"'Your time has not yet come!' the angel replied for the second time, barring the cottage door. The soul once again had to fly around and listen to the women's conversation, and all the women did was berate her and criticise her.

"The soul groaned still more heavily and beat itself against the ceiling beam in its grief; then it flew into the bosom of the dead body, settled in right next to its heart, and fell silent. And such sorrow seized the messenger of the Lord that he leaned over the widow's body and began to cry.

"The women rushed up to the body and found that it was all damp with tears. And those tears did not dry even when they buried her—and they placed the widow, still sprinkled with the angel's tears, in her coffin."

"Don't criticise others, and you won't be criticised!" Khrystya added her words to this story.

"I wasn't criticising her, was I?" the partially blind woman responded angrily.

"Of course you were!" Motrya said.

"Just look—they're going to begin quarrelling! It would be better if granny would tell us another story. I've never been in Kyiv in my whole life, but they say it's beautiful there! Were you in the Monastery of the Caves this year, as well?" Stepanyda directed her question at the pious old woman.

"How could I not be? I was in both the more distant caves where the saints are laid out in their coffins, and the ones closer in; I went up to every saint, and I prayed earnestly at all of the coffins. And oh, the things that I heard, and the things that I saw during my trip—and, indeed, in all those times that I was in Kyiv!"

It was so pleasant to listen to her clear, silvery voice flowing evenly like a current between sheltered banks, when she spoke about Kyiv, the Monastery of the Caves, the end of the world, the righteous, and the martyrs.

Before the eyes of the mesmerized listeners clearly arose the golden domes of the temples of God, Christ's agony, the lives of the righteous, and the infernal sufferings of sinners. Large numbers of people gathered in Kyiv from various countries, from various lands, and not a single bit of information, not a single bit of news or a mention of olden times that this living current of pilgrims brought with them, disappeared from the memory of the pious old woman.

Minute after minute flew by, hour after hour, but the old woman still had not finished narrating all that she knew.

The older women began to doze, and the younger ones moved in closer to the pious old woman, but she did not notice any of this and kept on talking without a pause.

"*Koo-koo-ree-koo-koo [Cock-a-doodle-doo]*!" an old rooster crowed lustily in the porch.

"*Koo-koo-ree-koo-koo*!" another enfeebled rooster belatedly responded somewhere in a reedy voice.

"Oh, dear mother of mine! The roosters are crowing. It's midnight already!" Motrya jumped to her feet.

"Maybe the soul has been here already, and we missed seeing it," Stepanyda said worriedly.

"Oh, no," Horpyna observed, "I was looking at the wall the whole time—there wasn't anything there."

"You probably weren't looking carefully enough," the partially blind woman said reproachfully.

"What do you mean—I wasn't looking carefully enough?" Horpyna was offended. "Is this the first time that I've watched for a soul? Why, when Katya died, I was the first to see a chrysalis on the wall, and when Ivan died, the place was filled with people like a church, but I was the first one to see the fly."

"Maybe it won't come at all?" Khrystya spoke up.

"How could that be? Why would it, God forbid, not come?" Horpyna asked in astonishment.

"If it doesn't want to appear as a chrysalis, then it will change itself into a fly; but it definitely will come today," the pious old woman said.

"And if it doesn't want to be a fly, it will appear as a woman," Motrya added.

"Oh no! That kind of thing—O Mother of God, Queen of Heaven preserve us—doesn't happen," observed the pious old woman.

"What do you mean it doesn't happen? What about Tkachenko's wife when she died? She came back to look after the children for a whole year. The children would come out in the morning—Tkachenko's neighbour told me about it, and she swore it was true—and they'd be all combed, washed, and fed. 'Who combed you, who washed you, who fed you?' the people asked the children. 'Our mother came, heated a pot of water, washed our heads, baked some *pyrohy*, and boiled some noodles,' the children said."

"Oh, may God be merciful! It's too depressing to even hear about such a thing! It was the evil spirit that was carting her here from the other world, because a Christian soul turns only into either a fly or a chrysalis, and it flies in for only a moment," Horpyna stopped Motrya from finishing her story.

"Oh, Lord! How sorry I am for the unfortunate Tetyana!" the partially blind woman sighed unexpectedly.

"Why feel sorry for her? Did she experience any happiness in her life, or did she rest for so much as even one day?" Motrya inquired.

"But that's why I feel sorry for her—because she died without knowing any happiness or peace. You don't feel sorry for someone who dies when she's been on good terms with fate all her life— she was born into this world by her mother for a reason, and she did not live in vain. But when it comes to us, and to Tetyana— why were we born, why are we living, and why must we die in agony?" Stepanyda asked Motrya.

"To gain the Kingdom of Heaven!" the pious old woman replied for Motrya. "A poor person has fewer temptations, fewer enticements—and fewer sins."

Stepanyda silently shook her head; she recalled very well how one time her brother had stolen a tree from the forest to heat his cottage that had remained unheated for two days; she also knew that if he had found a *karbovanets* in his pocket at the time, he would not have chosen to steal it. But she did not dare contradict the old woman.

"There's no reason to feel sorry for Tetyana—she's folded her white hands, and closed her dark eyes—she's fallen asleep, and found eternal peace. It's Makar and the children who are to be pitied," the old woman Kuzmykha spoke up for the first time that evening.

"Yes, of course, Makar is truly to be pitied—he lost both his housewife and his prize posession in a single day," Motrya agreed.

"There isn't much of a problem as far as the housewife is concerned; the widow Stolyarykha is among the first ones who would get married, even today. 'I'm so tired,' she says, 'of reaping with a sickle, that no matter what old reaper came along, I'd marry him.' It's easier to get a housewife than a cow. It's such a pity about the fallow heifer! It's as if Makar raised it for his own grief!" Horpyna said.

"Makar won't take Stolyarykha," the partially blind woman spoke up.

"Why not?" the women asked.

"She's ugly, and her mouth is twisted," the partially blind woman replied.

"Oh, when spring comes, and Makar sees his neighbour's freshly plastered cottage, and when he sees that all the people are mowing and sowing in their gardens, and his cottage is the only one that's still dark and deserted, and his garden is the only one with weeds growing in it, he'll be ready not only to take Stolyarykha as a wife—he'll be glad to take even one of us!" Stepanyda laughed.

"You come out with the dumbest things, there's no denying that! As if there were no women uglier than I am! Take a look in the mirror at yourself!" the partially blind woman was offended.

"But I was just joking, they . . ."

"Hush now, my good women!" the pious old woman interrupted Stepanyda. "Listen—there's a fly buzzing someplace."

They all fell silent at once and listened intently.

"I can't hear anything. You're probably tempted to taste the *kanun*," Kuzmykha spoke up, still half asleep.

"As if you could hear it! You've banged your nose on the table three times so loudly that the echo resounded throughout the cottage, and you expect to catch sight of a fly!" Horpyna said, staring raptly at the kitchen walls.

"There's the fly! It's on the *kanun*!" Khrystya pointed.

"Call Makar inside, Stepanyda! He's gossiping out there with the men," said Horpyna.

Stepanyda slammed the door as she walked out, and little Odarka jumped to her feet.

"Wake up, Sydorko! Mummy's soul has flown in; it's sitting on the *kanun*!" she started waking her brother.

Sydorko lifted his head, scratched himself, and squirmed down under the blanket once again.

"Sydorko! Hey, Sydorko! Mummy's flown in! Sydorko! Get up!" Odarka, almost crying, began shaking her brother.

"Don't bother the child, my daughter—let him dream about the holy angels! Come here yourself and look at the soul of your dear mother," the pious old woman turned to Odarka. "Your mother would be happy to come close to you, just as the mother lapwing would be happy to embrace her little lapwings, but she is not free to do so; it's not within her power. She's turned into a fly and flown here for a minute, and then she'll fly away once again from her orphans.

"Kneel, my daughter, and pray to God that the holy angels will show her the road to His throne, and that the holy archangels will defend her sinful soul before those who serve God."

The women crossed themselves, and Odarka knelt beside the pious granny and bent down low, touching her forehead to the floor.

Makar entered the room, and all the men came in after him. Everyone took a spoonful of *kanun*. The fly flew to the *pyrohy*, and everyone ate one of them. All the men and women tasted whatever food the fly settled on. The hour was late, and the food was well prepared, and so the women enjoyed a tasty supper.

Makar, however, could not stop thinking that he was devouring his heifer, and so he could hardly force himself to bring the glass to his lips.

"Don't worry, Makar! Don't be downhearted! The world isn't confined to your window. God willing, we'll hold the forty-day commemorative service for your wife, and then we'll marry you off. You can't care for the children without a housewife, and we have just the right woman for you quite close by—whether it comes to washing clothes, or washing the dishes, or working out in the field—she'll do as much as two Tetyanas," Horpyna said.

"For the last while, Tetyana, may the Kingdom of Heaven be hers, was simply not capable of working," Motrya added.

"For two months, she didn't do anything at all. She'd try to sweep the floor, but she couldn't even do that," Makar agreed.

"That's what I mean! But even the devil won't take Stolyarykha!" observed Horpyna.

"Yes, you're right about Stolyarykha—she's a really good worker!" The men picked up on the idea.

Makar recalled a short fat woman of forty-eight, with small slanted slits for eyes, thin, tightly compressed lips, and a big hooked nose—and his heart contracted painfully; he sighed involuntarily.

"You don't love her, or what?" Motrya asked him. "The time has long gone when you can be picky—take the one you can get!"

"She won't marry me," Makar replied gloomily.

"Yes, she will!" all the women said at the same time.

The fly seemed to buzz more loudly during the last few words; it fluttered its wings and rose to the ceiling, where its buzzing and wailing filled the room; then, after flying down to touch the head of the sleeping Sydorko, it vanished forever into the great unknown . . .

Fate

(1901)

Hey, which one of you is saying: "There is no fate"? Who's saying: "Fate is just a myth"? Is it you Okhrim? My goodness, but you're a strange man! What do you mean "there is no fate"? What do you mean "fate is just a myth"? You'd do better to ask me about it if you want to find out the truth. People may or may not have seen her—fate, that is—but I saw her many a time with my own eyes, and I know very well what she's like: how big she is, the colour of her hair, her nature, and where she lives.

You don't believe me? I haven't seen fate? Oh, yes I have! I carried her around in my arms like my own child, I lived under the same roof with her, I drove her around in my wagon.

Ah! What sceptics you all are! So, you're saying that I'm lying? That my eyes are clouded by whiskey? Oh, sure, with whiskey. That's what my Khivrya says: 'with whiskey,' but just you go ahead and try drinking even a whole keg of whiskey—will you see fate? Go ahead and try it! Cyclops, red mice, headless roosters, devil's mushrooms, you know, will teem before your eyes; they'll be on your pillows, on the walls, and leaping all over your shirt, but as for fate . . . fate won't even wiggle her finger, and she won't drop in, because that's not her nature—that's the way it is!

And just think about this as well—what kind of a drunkard am I? I'll down a shot or two after work, and even then, it's more because of all my troubles, because you'll never rid yourself of those wretched troubles, or overcome them until the day you die.

Let's take, say, this nag . . . never mind that it cost me twelve *karbovantsi [dollars]*—it's a living creature, it wants to eat. You have to think of something, use your wits, figure out how to support it, how to feed it. Or take the children! Our daughter got married and moved to another village to live with strangers, Khvedir is in the army, Andriy is a servant, and Stepan stays at home all the time to do the work—do you think all this was easy for a father to endure? Why, even now—we're driving along, chatting, but my heart feels like there's a snake writhing in it, and my head's buzzing—it's weary and full of sorrow—and it's all because of those troubles.

Because of my grief I'd like to toss back an *os'myna [eighth of a quart]*, I really would . . . but the damned old woman didn't give me so much as a *shah [halfpenny]*—would you believe it? The fiend went and locked the chest. Oh, what misery!

Aha! You're still going on about fate? You really got interested, didn't you? Well, if I don't get *a chvertka [fourth of a quart]*, I won't tell you. Each of you just has to pull a *pyatak [a nickel]* out of your pocket, but I'd find it easier to roll a stone up a hill than to talk about that fate. You're agreeable to a *chvertka*? Good! Let the horses trot along at their leisure for a while—we're not hurrying to a wedding . . . we'll toss enough of these hempen sacks in our lifetime.

Okhrim! Stop wasting matches—here's a flint for you. You light your pipe too, Stepan, so they won't worry about you back home. And you, Andriy, come sit on the sleigh as well. Now then, my brothers, listen how I first came to see fate.

People say you can see her on the Feast of Melanka on New Year's Eve—and it's true. Well, there was one time we happened to get a good job on that very day—we hauled some barley to the train station. We got there quite early and figured we'd get home before the sun set; but by the time we unloaded the sacks, and by the time the landowner paid us, it was turning dark. We had a bite to eat, some of us might have even drunk an *os'myna* or two (well, that's the custom, you know—it was winter!), and then we set out for home.

I also joined the caravan. I kept driving and driving, and then, quite unexpectedly, I fell asleep. Well, when I woke up—my horse was standing on the edge of a ravine, and there wasn't a soul around, no one at all . . . just the level, white steppe—and that's it. I felt depressed and somewhat uneasy. I raised my eyes to the sky and observed that the moon—full and bright—was winking and smiling at someone.

"Aha!" I thought. "It's winking at me; it's rejoicing that it's not alone in these steppes, and the poor thing wants to talk to me."

I doffed my cap and smiled amicably, but just as I was about to say: "Good health to you, O Brother-Moon," I heard something go: "Tee-hee-hee," right by my sleigh.

I turned around, took a look—and turned cold with fear. No farther away than you are from me, Okhrim, a strange looking girl was skipping and hopping along. Her light shirt was torn down the back from the collar to her heels, a tuft of fur was dangling at her side, and her tiny feet were up to their ankles in the snow.

She hopped along, twirling a rope in a circle, and the moon's rays penetrated right through *her*, as if they were shining through crystal.

O my brothers, I was scared at first, really scared—there's no use denying it—I wanted to sit down in the sleigh and flee to only God knows where, but then I got to thinking: "It's such nasty weather—the cold and the snow—and the poor thing is hopping along barefooted."

"Hey," I said, "sit down on the sleigh, my daughter, I'll take you home."

"I don't want to."

"But why don't you want to?"

"You won't listen to me."

"Oh, you little kitten," I said. "Who listens to you, my little ragamuffin?"

"Davyd Moysiyovych and Avram Duvydovych listened to me."

"So you're Jewish, or what?"

"Pamfyl Tymofiyovych and Nykyfor Semenovych listened to me," and *she* hopped away.

"Who are you?" I shouted after *her*.

"Fate!" The wind carried her reply to me.

"Well now!" I thought. "If you truly are fate, I won't let you get away; I've longed for you for a long time, I've waited for you to come from every which way, I've placed all my hope in you— you won't escape from me!"

I lashed my horse once, twice, and finally managed to catch up to *her*.

"Hey, there," I said. "My dear fate, don't run away, don't hop through the snow—you'll weary your legs; get into the sleigh."

She didn't want to.

I jumped down from the sleigh and grabbed her shirt. "I won't let you go," I said, "until you tell me where you're running, why you don't want to come to me."

She tugged at her rags once, then a second time, but *she* could see that *she* didn't have enough strength.

"I'm looking for a place to stay," *she* said.

"So you're a servant?"

She burst out laughing: "A servant! What a thing to say! They're my servants. I pay them."

"Who are *they*. Who do you pay? Where do you live?"

"I paid Davyd Moyseyevych and Pamfyl Tymofiyovych, but they're dead now."

"Well, that's fine!" I said. "May their memory be eternal, may the earth rest like a feather on their graves . . . Come to my place now; pay me."

"I don't want to."

"Why?"

"You're just like that cobbler."

"What cobbler?"

"The one that tore my shirt."

"Which one is he?"

"Crooked Khvedir."

"I know that cobbler—he stitches really fine boots . . . Don't jerk—anyway, I won't let you go until you tell me why Khvedir tore your shirt."

"Because of paper soles," *she* said.

"What do you mean, paper soles?"

"Like I said—paper soles," *she* snapped at me and tried tugging her shirt out of my hands.

I didn't let go.

"I won't let go," I said, "until you tell me everything about those soles."

She didn't want to tell me—*she* really didn't want to, but *she* must have been worried about her shirt; *she* frowned and said: "I ran in to see Khvedir, and he was hammering soles on some boots. I sat down beside him and said quietly: 'It would be better if you used soles made of thick paper; Tymofiy Tymofiyovych was able to build himself two stores by using paper soles.' But he just grabbed me by the collar and chucked me outside . . ."

"Oh, that Khvedir's a fool," I said. "Now, if only it had been me . . ."

But *she* had already vanished—as if the earth had swallowed her, as if *she* had evaporated like steam. Oh! I was really angry. Imagine—to have fate in your hands and to let *her* go!

I lashed my horse a third time—and he tore off so fast that I lost my breath, and my heart fainted, but he just kept on going. We flew like the wind, and New Year's carols were echoing over the wide steppe. From one direction came the carol: "Oh, the bells rung out in Jerusalem;" from another direction came the sound of young men and women singing: "Oh, in Lord Danylo's manor yard."

And my horse carried me onwards, without stopping for a moment. We leaped across a ravine, passed a forest, drove on ice over several tilled fields—and then my horse suddenly came to a dead stop in front of a house.

I crawled down from the sleigh, took a look . . . Oh, my God! I was at Maksym's. By what roads my horse had brought me there, from which direction we had driven up to the house—well, you can strike me dead, but I can't tell you. Where that ravine was, or that forest, or that river—I don't know to this day.

"Praise the Lord," I thought, "that I finally made my way to a man I know; at least I can celebrate the holiday in someone else's home."

But oh, my brothers, what a misfortune—I couldn't find the door. I circled the house, groped all the walls, went over the entire house with my hands, from the thatch to the ground—there wasn't a door anywhere. It looked as if I'd have to jump in through the roof! I came up to a window, knocked once—they didn't hear me; I knocked again—no one heard me. Well, it's understandable— there was a lot of noise, singing and dancing! I grabbed a staff.

"Well," I thought, "I'll knock the pane out if I have to—but I'll let them know that I'm here."

I lifted the staff, took aim—but I couldn't hit the pane; I took aim again—I still couldn't. Well, may God's power strike me down! What was going on?

But then the door opened; a mummer dressed as Melanka was leaving the house. I saw where the door was—and tried to rush to it. It was no use. I couldn't budge from the spot. Something was holding me by the shoulder, restraining me. I turned around— *she* was hanging on to my sheepskin coat, and there was no way that I could free myself.

"Let me go!" I began pleading with *her*.

"Sure, I'll let you go" *she* said, disappearing like a flash into the house . . .

And once again I couldn't see any door. I understood why *she* was deluding me—*she* didn't want me to see Maksym.

"You lied to me," I said. "You're smart, but I'm older—you won't fool me. May I turn to stone standing right here, but I'll find out what your intentions are, what your plans are."

I stood by the window and watched. Maksym was sitting by himself—his wife was nowhere to be seen—holding his older son on his knee. Three smaller children were sleeping under a blanket on the floor, and *she* was perfectly still, hiding herself among some pokers.

"Will you buy some steers at the market, daddy?" the little boy asked.

"No, I won't," Maksym replied.

"Why?"

"There's no money; old lady Bondarykha hasn't paid me yet."

"But why does Uncle Spyrydon always have steers, and cows, and money? He's a weaver just like you . . ."

"Well, my son, he must either be a better weaver than I am, or his fate must be better." Maksym sighed heavily.

"What kind of fate does uncle have?" the son asked.

"A hardworking one."

"And what is your fate like?"

"She's a lazy one."

"Find yourself a hardworking one as well," said his son.

"I'd be happy to do that, but I don't know where to look for her; even though I keep calling and calling her—she just doesn't come."

"Well, what if I call for her up there. Will she come?"

"Go ahead, shout, shout all you want to—today is the very day that she roams the earth!" Maksym laughed.

The boy leaped down from his father's knees, jumped up on a chair, and shoved his little head into a niche by the oven bed: "Hey," he shouted, "hardworking fate, come to live in our home."

And just them Lukyna walked in the door.

"And here she is—our fate!' laughed Maksym, pointing at his wife.

"Yes, it's our fate—may even our worst enemies be spared a fate like ours! I don't know if we're forbidden to have one, or if we're sinful in God's eyes—we just don't have any fate, and that's that," Lukyna said, almost in tears.

"What's wrong?" Maksym asked. "Where were you?"

"I was just at Khrystya's, and I came away with enough grief to last me through the holidays and the rest of the year, and for all the years to come."

"But what happened?" Maksym inquired.

"Old lady Domakha came," she said. "She said she'd come expressly to pick up her cloth. Well, Sydir brought her the cloth, and he had done a terrible—a really terrible—job of weaving it; but she doesn't see well, so she paid him the full amount up to the last *kopiyka [penny]*, and even thanked him. 'Tomorrow,' she said, 'I'll stop by at Maksym's; if he's begun working on my weaving, I'll pay him all the money in advance.'"

"You don't say!" Maksym said in alarm.

"As I live, it's true!" Lukyna said.

"What did you say to her?"

"I was so upset," Lukyna said, "that I didn't say anything."

"Ah, woe is me! It would have been just what we needed to buy the steers," Maksym exclaimed.

"Well you can go on moaning or you can stop—it won't help. You should have listened to me when I told you to stop working on Bondarykha's cloth, and to start on Domakha's."

"But you see," Maksym said, "I wanted to be fair—to do the weaving in the order that it was brought to me."

"So now you'll know what's fair, and in what order it should be done—you'll be left without steers this year as well," Lukyna said.

"Oh, my cursed fate! You think, and you agonise over how to do things best, but it turns out for the worst!' Maksym exclaimed passionately. "You work and work without laying down your hands, but you never see an end to the unfortunate hour. So, because the holiday, coming today and not tomorrow, prevented me from starting on Domakha's weaving—does that mean we'll be left without steers for another year?"

"If only you could at least start the weaving," Lukyna said, "so that Domakha could see the warp—then the money would be ours."

Maksym fell deep into thought, so deep that he appeared to turn pale. Lukyna said her prayers, bedded her son down on the floor, and climbed up on the *peech [a large clay oven with a sleeping area on top]* to sleep.

I moved my eyes over to *her*. Oh, my God! Even now, when I recall it, I have to hold my sides in laughter. If only you could have seen, my brothers, the kind of comedies that *she* began to stage.

Maksym was sitting at the table leaning his head on his hand, and *she'd* take one step away from the pokers and then dart back again into a corner; then *she'd* come closer to him again, peer into his eyes, and then dash back as fast as *she* could, and all the while her face kept changing—once *she'd* be happy and flushed, and then *she'd* turn white with fear . . .

Then I looked around—the bobbins had begun to move on the loom. Oh! One ball of yarn was already in Maksym's hands; he spun that ball, unwinding it and winding it up again, and *she* kept saying to him ever so quietly and carefully: "Begin the weaving with it—you'll finish the warp by morning, and you'll have the steers."

"But it's such an important holiday," Maksym said softly to himself.

"God will forgive you, your wife is asleep, and you'll have the steers." *She* was speaking more boldly now, and drawing nearer and nearer to Maksym.

I glanced at Maksym—his face was black with sorrow; he remained silent and looked obliquely at that ball of yarn.

"Well," I thought. "You've come to a dead end? Just wait! He'll give you a blow on the head as well."

But then . . . up rose my Maksym; he rose to his feet . . . and headed straight for the loom. Ah! May the power of God strike me down! He began laying down the wool for the warp . . . May I not live to see the evening if I'm lying! I saw it with my own eyes—he was laying it down. He kept at his work, but the wool kept breaking, and breaking, and it barely moved . . .

"Why, this must be our wool from the year before last; Domakha's yarn is strong," Maksym realised, and he instantly began rewinding the yarn back on the ball.

But *she* seized him by the hand: "Thread it," *she* said, "thread it without giving it any thought—Domakha doesn't see too well, and you'll make even more on the weaving than Svyryd did."

Well, what do you think? He didn't say so much as a word to *her* in reply. The work, my brothers, raced on! Never in my life have I seen someone weave that swiftly. He was threading the yarn, and *she* was unwinding the ball and tying the knots in the warp.

"Just look," I thought, "it's no wonder they say that the devil rocks a rich man's cradle. With such a helper, Maksym will also be able to set out on a rich man's path in life."

But suddenly my Maksym leapt to his feet! He tugged at the warp, tore it into pieces and ruined it.

"You won't lead me into sin, damn you, no you won't!" he yelled, increasing in size until he reached the ceiling. I've seen a lot of big, strapping fellows in my lifetime—why, even Okhrim here, may he enjoy good health, is not a small man—but I've never, from the day that I was born, seen a man the size of Maksym that evening. His arms became as long as pitchforks, his fists were as big as my head, his eyes as large as apples, and his hair stood straight up like bristles . . . He yelled, swung his hand—and fate, together with the warp, landed beyond the gate.

She stood by the fence and looked confused for a moment, but only for a moment. I didn't have time to say a single word to *her* when *she* ran off, and I took off after *her* once again . . .

I ended up in some village—it looked a bit like Matyashivtsi, and a bit like Mykolayivtsi. I glanced up . . . and *she* was already darting about under the windows of a cottage. *She* looked into it—and left; peeked into another cottage—and something there didn't appeal to *her* either. *She* ran up to a third, a fourth, and then hopped down the entire street like this, until *she* came to the village gate.

"Where are you running, you madwoman?" I asked.

"To Lord Nadiyenko," *she* flung at me, and took off like the wind, like a tempest.

"Well," I thought, "it's great that you've come up with this idea—you'll be heading directly for my house."

You all know where my house is? Yes, indeed, it's right next to the lord's manor yard.

I looked—and I was by my own house. I left my horses in the middle of the yard and set off as quickly as possible for the lord's house. I looked—and *she* was already there, skulking under the windows. *She* prowled around for quite a while and then fastened onto one window where a light was shining.

She fastened herself to it, clutched the frame with her tiny fingers, and pasted herself to the glass.

I stood beside *her*—looked, listened . . .

Oh, my brothers, I'd almost forgotten about that *shkalyk [flask]*, but I've just thought of it again—it's got me right in the heart. Would I ever like to drink an *os'myna* right now!

Oh, and the lord probably would have wanted to drink one even more than me if he had been convinced earlier as to how effective that *shkalyk* is against a wife's rebukes. I've had to accept my share of grief from my wife, and I've had to suffer much because of her in my lifetime, but never once has she plagued me like the lady plagued the poor lord on that night.

What, you may ask, did she do to him? Well, she didn't do anything at all—she just stood before him and flapped her tongue, and flapped her tongue . . .

He'd get up, sit down, roar at her, and plead with her—but no, she wouldn't quiet down and didn't stop for even a moment. The sweat began to roll off him, and spots appeared on his cheeks, but she just carried on—she didn't stop talking.

What, you may ask, was she saying to him? Oh, my Lord! Is it possible to remember everything said by a woman—and, God help me, an educated one at that—over such a long time period of time? I could tell by the man's face that she was rebuking him about their poverty. Now there's grief for you! Almost three thousand acres of land, forests, groves, a household like theirs, so much wealth—and it still wasn't enough.

"By God," she said, "I'm always living in penury, in poverty, in anxiety because of you." And there she was, sweeping the floor with the tail of her silk dress. "By God, right now in Petersburg there are all sorts of balls, musicians are playing, comedies are being staged, but I'm being devoured by boredom because you don't have the money for me to go to Petersburg. By God, you don't know how to enjoy your wealth; you don't know how—you just have no idea—how and where to acquire money."

"Be patient for a little while," the lord begged her. "You know that I haven't paid the hired workers yet or sent money to the bank, but am I to blame? I can't get a loan, and I can't sell the grain, because the crop turned out to be very light this year."

"Ivan Ivanovych's grain isn't any heavier than yours, but he still managed to sell his," the lady fumed.

"I don't know how he managed to get rid of his grain. He just got lucky," the lord sighed.

"He probably got lucky because you think he's a fool. You'd do better not to think of yourself as such a great intellect, and maybe your fate wouldn't go berserk!"

"Oh, fate, my fate!" the lord groaned.

And *she* just shook all over . . . Before the lord could take another breath, *she* was already at his side; there *she* was, my brothers, pressing closely to him, caressing him, kissing him . . . and just this close to saying: "Here I am."

"Well," I thought, "you've finally hopped to the right place, you've finally found a person to your liking; you'll probably spend the winter here. I may as well go home to sleep."

But I hadn't even reached my house when I heard something go whoosh and run off into the garden. I recognised *her* at once.

"Can it be," I thought, "that you're not satisfied there either?"

And then, blink! And I stopped . . . Where do you think I was, my brothers? By the bed of our buyer. May the power of God strike me down if I'm not telling the truth. Yes, my horse was standing right by his pillows.

She was hovering near the buyer, whispering something in his ear. And he leaped out of bed as if he'd been scalded.

"Surka, hey, Surka! Is it you who's telling me to go to Lord Nadiyenko to buy his grain?"

"Leave me alone—I'm sleeping!" his wife growled at him.

"I keep hearing a voice, and it's saying: 'Get up, take out your money, and go at once to see the lord!'" said the buyer.

"Have you gone mad? What voice? You've examined that rye three times already, and all three times you've said that it's no good."

"Yes, I did look at it, and I did say that, but now there's this voice . . . A telegram must have come saying that the price of rye has gone up. Get up!"

And then we all seemed to be in the lord's yard once again; the buyer was there, and *she* seemed to have grown healthier—*she* was running, skipping, and kicking up little lumps of snow with her feet . . .

That was the time, my brothers, that was the time when I saw piles of money. The buyer covered the entire table with *chervintsi [gold coins]* and paper money. Never in my life have I seen so much money, and I'll probably never see the likes of it again. It wasn't only me—even the lady clapped her hands in delight when she looked at the table. She sat down beside the lord, hugged him around the neck, kissed him, and cooed: "Luck's on your side, my darling; you're so lucky."

"Oh, my" I thought. "No matter where you look, it's the same all over; it doesn't matter if you're among peasants or lords—if a man gets lucky, if fate smiles at him, then everyone finds him adorable."

Why, I myself once sold a couple dozen unhatched eggs, and for the entire day—would you believe it?—I didn't hear a nasty word from my wife. For the entire day she didn't say a contrary word, or look askance at me, and I myself . . .

Gosh, but you're an impatient bunch! Just wait a moment! I'll tell you more about fate right away . . .

Well, the lord sat down at the table, arranged the paper money into piles, and said: "This pile is for my wife for Petersburg, this one is also for my wife, and this one is for the workers."

He finished with the paper money and started on the gold. He counted off one pile: "This is for the taxes," he said; then he took what was left and counted it: "Ah! Woe is me!," he exclaimed, "there isn't enough to pay the rent."

"Add some wild oats from this year to last year's crop, and you'll have enough for the rent as well," *she* jumped up to the lord.

"What? Add wild oats to the oats? Fool the buyer? I'd sooner tear the heart out of my chest than stoop to such vileness," the lord said passionately.

"So you listened to me about the rye, but you won't listen to me about the oats?" *she* wailed at the top of her lungs and walked dejectedly out of the room.

"Fate, my little darling!" I said to *her* then. "Listen, come to my place! I'll listen to you, I'll cater to you, I'll obey you as if you were my mother . . ."

She stopped on the porch, looked all around, and dried her eyes. "Pick up a sack of wheat," *she* said, "and take it home."

Never in my entire life, my brothers, had I stolen anything, and there were never any thieves in our family, but now . . . May God forgive me—I walked up to the granary, picked up one of the sacks that was ready to be taken to the mill, and lugged it home.

I walked along and kept looking behind me; no, *she* hadn't lied—*she* was running after me.

We entered the stable, and I poured the wheat into the bin; and then *she* started laughing so merrily, so good-naturedly, that it became more cheerful in the stable, and I myself felt that I'd never know any grief in my entire life. And I had no fear of hunger, or cold, or taxes—as if all that had ceased to exist.

And I had good reason to feel this way—from that time on, my life truly took a turn for the better. I began to have good luck everywhere, my brothers; I sowed and ploughed only half as much, but the number of my sheaves doubled.

Why, you may ask, did this happen? How am I supposed to know?

We'd go out into the steppe at night. "Fate, where is my stack of sheaves?" I'd ask.

"Begin," *she'd* say, "with the lord's."

And I'd begin . . . Life was good; there's no denying that! The only bad part of it was that I couldn't get my sleep at night. All the villagers would be sleeping so soundly that they were snoring, but I'd be holding counsel with fate.

"Where, dear fate," I'd ask, "should I go? What should I do?"

And *she* would have already thought of something, and there'd be enough work for the entire night.

I'd harness the horse, seat *her* down beside me, and off we'd go to the lord's storehouses, his haystacks, or into the forest— wherever an opportunity presented itself . . .

In the morning, people would just be stirring in their beds, but I'd already be home from town, having brought with me the money I'd made and the things I'd bought—I was all finished with my work.

"That infernal Stepan is one lucky fellow—his fate isn't sleeping; his fields yield well, his horse is well-fed, and his children aren't going hungry."

"My fate," I'd say, "has returned, my brothers." And I wasn't lying. *She* was taking care of me, *she* was protecting me, *she* was guiding me, *she* was counselling me. I may or may not have fallen asleep at times, but *she* never so much as dozed off.

But then Great Lent came along. One time I went into town, sold something for a tidy sum of money, bought my wife a kerchief, shod the horse, drank an *os'myna*, and came home in a happy mood . . . but not at a good time. My wife tore strips off me, my brothers!

"And how long, and until when, you robber, thief, drunkard, are you going to be roaming around at night? How will God let you partake of Holy Communion?"

"But, I'm not doing anything, am I?" I protested.

"Come to your senses, you drunkard. Think about what you're doing!"

"Are you going to forbid me to listen to fate?"

"What fate? Has whiskey clouded your eyes, or have you lost your mind?"

"The fate," I said, "the fate that helps people build stores, and fill their treasure-chests with silver and gold. Just wait a year or two, and you'll see what a rich person I'll be."

"You're lying, thief! You're lying, drunkard! Would fate want to have anything to do with you?"

"Do you suppose," I said, "that she's picky? All she wants is someone who'll listen to her."

Well, you know my Khivrya, don't you? She gave me a good tongue-lashing, spit in my face, and didn't want to hear me out. So, I spit on her as well—she's a madwoman—and left . . .

But even though I walked away from her—her words fell on my heart like seeds from that wretched pigweed. I railed at her, the damned old woman, but I felt, I really did feel, those seeds taking root and sending out shoots until it hurt. It really pained me, honest to God! And my head was spinning, as if I had a hangover. I'd begin counting the sacks, hay, or chickens that I'd stolen over the winter—and I'd see the priest with the communion chalice before my eyes; I'd begin counting the money I'd made selling things—and my thoughts would turn to the Final Judgement . . . In a word—there seemed to be no way out!

I kept wandering aimlessly about the yard, and then I went to the tavern—there was no liquor store yet. I drank an *os'myna*, then a *shkalyk*—they had no effect on me. I just couldn't rid myself of the picture of that Holy Communion and the Final Judgement. It also became awkward to look people in the face . . . well, you know . . .

I returned home and went straight to *her*. "My dear fate!" I said. "Isn't it time for us to stop roaming through other people's fields and granaries? They say, you know, that there once was a fate that walked in the master's footsteps in the steppe, gathering up the ears of grain that he dropped—so you do likewise. I have a little bit of wheat—sow it with your little hands; walk over the field with your tiny feet, and gather the ears of grain together. And you'll see, in ten years or so, we'll accumulate a lot of capital."

Well, did *she* ever look daggers at me. "Capital from ears of grain! By now, even the ashes of that distant ancestor of mine who gathered ears of grain have all blown away, and you're rubbing her into my eyes?" *She* turned away from me, pouted, and became still angrier; then, putting her fists under her head, *she* shut her eyes . . . and fell asleep.

I managed to get by, one way or another, for the first week or so. Then on Monday, we were out of hay. I dashed up to fate— *she* was fast asleep. I went and borrowed an armful. By Thursday, I'd also borrowed some flour; on Saturday there was no fuel for the stove . . .

"Where's your fate, Stepan?" the people taunted me.

"Where? Sleeping!" I said.

They laughed, made fun of me . . .

"Laugh, go ahead and laugh!" I thought. "Spring will soon be here, God willing, and then we'll sow the wheat, and when *she* awakens . . ."

Well, with people's help, I managed to get by for another few weeks, but then I really got worried. What was I to do? My wife was reproaching me, my children were crying, my nag's ribs were sticking out—I could see that it was no joking matter—and so I hired myself out in the manor yard.

One day I got permission to go home for a visit; I walked up— and saw the yard filled with guests! Well, my brothers, they were appraising the horse, everything I owned, whatever could be sold to cover unpaid bills at the village store. They had pulled outdoors every trifling article they could lay their hands on, every item of Sunday dress or any spare clothing that was lying around. They had pulled it all out, piled it into a heap.

Khivrya grabbed our children in her arms and placed them there as well. "Here! Appraise the children too!" she screamed.

The children were crying, the people were shouting, my wife was raging—oh, it was such a terrible misfortune! It makes me sad just to recall it. I seized my head in my hands—I didn't know if I should beg the children to stop crying, or make my wife stop screaming, or plead with the people; I dashed off to see *her*—*she* was still fast asleep.

I ran back out to the people. "Gentlemen, my good people!" I said. "Don't touch the horse, don't touch these rags. I'll sell my wheat and pay off my debts without any problem."

Well, the people left, and I was thankful for that; my wife settled down, my children stopped crying—and I began to load the wheat.

I loaded all of it, to the very last kernel—and I saw that there wasn't enough to pay off the debts. I got worried then, really worried. I reproached myself, scolded myself: "May you lose your mind, you old fool; you stole and you stole, but you didn't manage to get enough to pay off your debts."

Then I looked up—*she* knew just what to do. *She* lugged in a full load of sand in the bosom of her shirt.

I wavered a bit, thought about it, thought about it some more, and then waved my hand in agreement. "Pour it in," I said.

She poured that sand into the grain. I tied up the sacks and loaded them on the wagon; *she* sat down on top of them—and off we went. We were already approaching the town and had just started driving on a sandy road, when a beggar came towards us—he was returning from the monastery.

He came abreast of us and greeted us. I gave him a *shah*. The beggar pulled out his wallet, put away the penny, and put the wallet back into his pocket—but instead of slipping into his pocket, the wallet fell on the ground. Well, what do you think? No sooner had that wallet hit the sand, than *she* had already picked it up and was shoving it into my hands.

I sat down on the sand, opened the wallet, and saw the money in it. Just then along came Maksym Barabolya.

"Good health to you," he said. "There's nothing like having fate—money grows even in the sand. How much have you got there?"

"Two *karbovantsi*, and a few *shahy*."

"It's enough," he said, "to have a drink to cure a hangover." And off he went.

I finished counting the money—two *karbovantsi* and twenty-seven *kopiyky*—closed the wallet, and didn't know where to hide it. Just then I heard: "Bong! Bong!" The bells were ringing in a church, and then: "Bong! Bong!" even more loudly. I grabbed the wallet and ran as fast as I could after the beggar.

"Here granddad," I said. "Here's your wallet; be careful not to lose it a second time."

And I still can't understand, even now, if it was because I saw the crosses on the holy church, or if it was because of the joy I felt that I had not permitted my soul to sin by hiding the wallet, but I doffed my cap then and there, and began bowing and prostrating myself.

Oh, if only you could have seen fate at that moment! If only you could have peered into her face. It seemed to become overcast, to darken. *She* looked at me as if with lightning bolts, shook all over, and turned away from me without making a sound.

I weighed out the grain for the buyer, emptied the sacks, and he paid me what was owing; I tied my horse to a post, and ran in there—you, know, to the tavern—for a moment. I walked out—well, it's no use lying—some villain dragged me out of the tavern and threw me under a fence. When I woke up, I had no horse, no cap, and not even a *shah* to my name.

Oh, sure, go ahead and laugh! It's fun to laugh at another person's troubles, but my very soul flew out of me by the time I arrived home.

I came up to our fence, walked around it, and peeked into the yard, but I was afraid to approach the house—where had I squandered my horse Bulavy?

And just then I heard my son Stepan yell: "Stand still, Bulavy!"

Praise the Lord! The horse was at home . . . It was *she*, fate, that must have taken care of things and sent the horse home, even though *she* was annoyed with me. I thought I should thank *her*.

I walked into the stable, darted into all the corners, in all the grain bins—*she* wasn't there.

The next day, at about noon, I harnessed the horse and drove over to the buyer's house. But he no longer was anywhere nearby; he had gone, I was told, to that contractor who delivers food, boots, and things like that to our soldiers in Turkey.

"And where," I asked, "is fate?"

"How should I know?" Surka replied in surprise.

I went to the storehouse where I had poured the grain yesterday and called out for *her*—*she* didn't reply.

I didn't see *her* for twenty-two years; I didn't know where *she'd* gone, who *she'd* taken up with. And then . . . You know, don't you, how hard up I was during Great Lent this year?

In the first week, my Khivrya had to borrow grain, and by the last week, people were no longer willing to give her any more. Orthodox Christians were happy to see the holidays approach; they plastered their walls, coated them with white lime, sewed, and prepared themselves, but as for me, on Monday of the Holy Week, I was enveloped in such sadness that I didn't know where to go or what to do.

First, I was annoyed that I would have to go to confession during the last week along with all the drunkards; second, I had nothing to confess; third—I knew that there was not a speck of flour left for the *paska [braided circular Easter bread]*. And to make matters even worse, my wife was in a rage. And somehow you have to endure, as best you can, so much trouble all at the same time.

On Holy Thursday, even before dawn had broken, my wife was already yelling at me: "Go to the train station, go on! Maybe you'll at least earn enough for a *paska*."

I didn't want to go—Lord, but I didn't want to go. First, the neighbour was celebrating a christening; second, I was thinking: "What good will it do if I earn fifty—or, if I try very hard, even sixty—*kopiyky* at the station? I'll give the the priest the money for the confession—and there'll be nothing with which to bake the *paska*; if I buy a *paska*, I'll have nothing to wear to church and bless the *paska,* because there's no heel at all on my right boot, and all five toes in my left one are waving hello."

But there's no way you could plead your case before the cursed woman; you couldn't convince her—she just kept repeating: "Go!"

I went.

I was still a good distance off when I heard the iron engine hissing, whistling, and groaning.

"I hope I'm not late," I thought.

I hurried to reach the vestibule. It was no use! You couldn't even get near it. More than that! Even an apple couldn't drop into it—there was such a crowd of people. By the vestibule stood a coach as big as a granary, with golden designs on it, and decorated all over with little nails. Six identical horses were rearing and kicking up their heels. Behind the coach there were as many as three phaetons with four horses harnessed to each one. Then, two people sporting gold buttons walked out of the station—they looked like officers, but they had no epaulettes. And they were leading, my brothers, a hoary old gentleman in a long coat that almost reached to his heels.

"So," I thought, "it must be the archbishop." And I shouted: "Let me through, my good people, to receive his blessing!"

And the people said to me: "It's our buyer, our buyer who's come. Our buyer has returned from Turkey . . . He's already built one sugar refinery someplace, and now he's going to build the second one here, not far from our village."

I took another look—yes, it was him, our buyer. My God! It was my acquaintance.

"Mr. Buyer, Mr. Buyer," I dashed up to him.

But I didn't get there in time; they'd already seated him in his coach. The coachman struck the horses—and off they went. I ran after them . . . caught up with them, jumped on the iron step, grabbed the golden mirror in the door, looked into it, and froze. Oh my brothers! Our buyer was sitting on a velvet cushion with his eyes shut, and next to him . . . Who do you think it was? Fate! The very same fate, in the very same shirt that Khvedir had ripped a long time ago. *She* was sitting by the buyer and playing with some *chervintsi.*

"My dear fate! My darling dove!" I shouted to *her* in a voice that didn't seem like my own.

But *she* just shoved me in the chest: "Can't you see, you stupid fellow, that he's sleeping?"

I fell smack into a puddle. I lay there and couldn't get up, and *she* stuck her head out of the coach, laughed, and even stuck her tongue out at me.

Oh, but I was furious! I made a dirty gesture and raised my hand up high: "Here, eat it!" I yelled in a resounding voice. "Even though I'm lying in a puddle, at least I'm not your servant, you tattered slut!"

Look over there—do you see how many bricks they've hauled there? Our buyer is going to build a sugar refinery there—and that's where *she* lives . . .

Behind the High Wattle Fence
(1902)

Evening was approaching. The sky was still bright, but in the west, where the sun was glowing like a red-hot ember, a dark wall was slowly rising. The uppermost edge of the wall already blazed with stolen flames, but the sun, with an unhindered view of God's world, lovingly fixed its gaze on a steep hill. In an instant, yellow and white cliffs reddened and sparkled, a grove caught fire in the golden rays, a river—like a rosy ribbon—wended its way below it and, from the summit, a well-trod narrow path gleamed whitely like an unwound roll of linen, as it ran downwards through the grove.

On this path, steeped in the evening rays, walked an older man— a man who was not so much old, as weary. The sun's rays bathed him and gilded the yellowing leaves and grass; the old man, however, did not see anything; gloomy, deep in thought, and indifferent to the caresses of the sun, he paid no attention either to the radiance or to the beauty surrounding him. His right hand rested in the bosom of his shirt, while in his left he carried a drill and a smoothly hewn spigot.

A grimy, threadbare shirt, patched in a few places and ripped in a few more, flapped about him without clinging to any part of his emaciated body; his heavy cotton pants—also unlaundered for a long time—hung to the ground and covered his twisted and gnarled bare feet right down to his heels. From under a reddish lambskin cap—ruined long ago by the sun and bad weather— peered a gaunt, sallow face marked with a number of deep furrows. Thick eyebrows hung over his eyes, and a dense, grey, unkempt beard covered his chin and descended unevenly to his chest. Clumps of equally untidy grey hair fell down his sunburned neck and covered his waxen, transparent ears.

The old man would have looked like a corpse if it had not been for his sharp and gleaming small grey eyes. At times, those eyes grew dim and dull. In the very next moment, however, they would blaze again, and then the old man's piercing gaze penetrated the entire grove down to the river surrounding the hill on three sides, or glanced uneasily backwards, staring intently at the summit, at the sprawling village that he detested, and his own homestead.

There was not a soul in sight. He was fortunate—he was alone in the grove that was enclosed by a planted hedge of prickly bushes. And he would be all alone down there, by the river; he would not see a single one of his enemies—and those enemies constituted an innumerable horde. The entire world was a hostile field, with as many enemy encampments as there were people.

He did not have the strength to contend with them, and no one had the power to conquer them. They did not fear retribution of any kind, for they were evil, cunning, and deceitful. They did not arm themselves with swords and muskets to engage in honourable battle, nor did they, like murderers, carry sharp knives; they secretively nursed their evil intentions in their fierce hearts, wove snares for the truth in the darkness of their conscience, forged chains out of flattering words, and attacked unexpectedly, in broad daylight. They did not allow anyone to live in peace. The great, joyous gift of life that the Lord granted even the tiniest insect, they reduced, through their fighting, quarrelling, and wickedness, to an oppresive state of atonement.

Does anyone truly control his own life? Had "they" allowed him to be the master of his fate? They had ripped him to shreds and destroyed his possessions, his heart, and his soul, as they saw fit; and they would have kept on abusing him if he had not learned to despise them. They had ruined his life and, more than likely, were already preparing chains and snares for Hapka as well. But no, their work and their efforts were in vain. The old man's granddaughter would not experience an orphan's life; she would not eat bread that was buttered with curses, nor would she have to curry favour with the enemy . . .

The old man stopped in the middle of the path to catch his breath. The trip from the summit, where the old man's yard, enclosed by a high wattle fence, was situated, was not a long one, and until quite recently the old man had sped down it in less than ten minutes; today, however, it seemed as if the path would never end. His feet were trembling, his heart was fainting, his lips were parched, and the twenty or thirty steps that were left seemed to him to be the length of a tilled field.

If the thoughts and emotions that were bearing him along on their wings had deserted him for even a moment, he would have collapsed right here, almost on the threshold, and perhaps he would never have regained consciousness. Fortunately, however, his mind and his heart were on good terms—they supported each other like true brothers, and encouraged each other like the best of friends. If his thoughts grew dim—his heart, incensed with a burning hatred, contempt, and loathing of people, hastened to assist his mind, agitating it; and if his heart calmed down and stopped rattling for even a moment—painful memories of past misfortunes were ever ready to upset his repose and evoke bitter feelings once again.

Mykyta did not like to share his memories with anyone. He furtively nurtured every tiny seed that had ever fallen into his heart, and he himself plucked the flowers when they came into bloom; he elaborated every thought until he perfected it into a smooth link for the chain that he had begun to fashion in childhood; he surreptitiously concealed every incident in that treasure-house in which he had tucked away his first adversity. At the time, he had been only fourteen, a young boy who lived with his guardians—his Uncle Kuzma and his Aunt Horpyna.

When Mykyta was three, his father left him a good-sized field, a well-cultivated garden, a large cottage, a couple of steers, and a dappled mare; on her deathbed, his mother increased her six-year-old son's inheritance by giving him a silver cross from the Lavra Monastery in Kyiv and some well-meaning advice: "Do not bother people, do not argue with them, do not covet what belongs to others, and do not take advantage of the misfortunes of others."

With the inheritance from his father and the legacy from his mother, it should have been possible for Mykyta to have a good life.

Unfortunately, however, his Uncle Kuzma was appointed as his guardian. To make matters even worse, this same Uncle Kuzma was related through marriage to the village head and, to further compound the problem, the village secretary, Anton Stepanovych, was the godfather of his child.

As soon as Kuzma took over Mykyta's inheritance, there were problems and money shortages—the field no longer yielded crops, the garden was overrun with weeds; the steers became ornery, the mare became restive, and when Aunt Horpyna decided she wanted a new house, the orphan's cottage was torn down. Within a couple of years—the orphan's cottage, stable, steers, and mare vanished; a year later, the land was sold and, finally, the entire farmstead was transferred to Uncle Kuzma on a bill of exchange—sealed with more than one bucket of whiskey—that amounted to not all that little, and not all that much: a hundred *karbovantsi [dollars]* in all.

Divested of his patrimony in short order, Mykyta did not think about it for a long time. The people remained silent, and even though the children badgered the orphan boy about his old nag, he was taciturn by nature and disinterested in gossip, and did not pay much attention to what they were saying.

Time flew by, and his father's farmstead, the steers, and the mare vanished from his memory like a dream, an illusion. Mykyta became inured to the indigent fate of an orphan and learned to be thankful for the scraps of bread he was given. He became accustomed to staying out of harm's way, distancing himself from trouble, and ignoring the blows he received from his aunt and her children, and, all the while, he thanked God sincerely for the kind people who had not allowed him to die like a homeless waif.

But then there came that unforgettable day, that never-to-be-forgotten day—the Feast of the Transfiguration. At dawn, a rumour spread through the village that the village head and secretary had been arrested because of something to do with "public money." All the villagers, to the last person, raced to the district office; fear for their hard-earned *shahy [half-pennies]* even drove in people from hamlets that were farther away. Mykyta herded his uncle's cattle home at noon, and then he too ran to the district office with the other boys.

The huge village common in front of the office had long since been filled with people and carts. The people were buzzing, shouting, and arguing; here and there, curses and reproaches resounded. The people called to mind the "great," "holy" truth, stretched their arms out to it, blessed it and, it seemed, were prepared to stone the betrayers of this truth—the thieving head and the secretary, Anton Stepanovych.

Mykyta stood by the mill, his eyes devouring this incensed, infuriated, and terrifying crowd. He understood their grief and sympathised with them, for they had been robbed, misled, and wronged by their own kind—fellow peasants—and he listened intently to the loud words being spoken. And truly, there was much to listen to, and much to see.

The memory of the people was awakened—a memory lulled to sleep either by wariness or by drinks that sealed questionable deals—and the stagnant mud of endurance into which the public was accustomed to cast all sorts of filth, became agitated. All the old evil deeds rose to the surface, and even matters that it seemed no one could possibly have heard of, let alone remember, were recalled.

Misfortune united enemies, and the people, hitherto powerless, dejected, and seemingly indifferent to everything in the world, suddenly raised their heads, muttered, experienced new power, and came to life the moment the thief placed his hands on their wallets. The assembly, its anger fierce and focussed, reacted violently and demanded that the head and the secretary answer for their actions, but they were no longer in the village. At that point, all the pent-up anger was transferred on to the heads of their cronies and helpers.

At the fore of these cronies stood Uncle Kuzma. Someone made an accusation against Kuzma; the gathering picked up on it and spread his infamy over the entire village common, flinging mud at his discredited name. Curses, name-calling, and rebukes showered upon him like dried peas falling out of a bag. Everyone was talking noisily, everyone was inflamed, and everyone hurried to publicly reveal everything that he knew about Kuzma.

Mykyta was visibly upset—it was his uncle they were defaming, the one and only righteous person who had welcomed him, an orphan, into his home. The peasants were passing judgement on the person before whom they had bowed only yesterday. Neighbours were consuming the neighbour who only recently had been a most welcome guest in their homes . . .

And his uncle was putting up with this terrible condemnation! He had said something in reply to the assembly, but he had spoken so timidly and so softly, that not a word had reached Mykyta's ears.

"And where are the orphan's cattle?" someone shouted in a voice that carried through the entire village common.

"His land, cottage, steers, and horse—what have you done with them?" another voice chimed in.

"Thief! Swindler! What have you done with Mykyta's patrimony? What have you done with the orphan's wealth? Answer us—the community is asking you," an elderly man—known to all as Maksym the drunkard—spoke up.

"You dogs! Why are you barking? You madmen, why are you on the attack? Have you all forgotten that it was here, in this very spot, that you drank four buckets of whiskey paid for by the orphan's money?" Aunt Horpyna's voice rang out like a bell.

"What have you done with Mykyta's cattle?" the assembly roared. "You bought the field, the garden, the steers for a hundred *karbovantsi* . . . you built a house on the posts from the orphan's barn . . . you traded the orphan's mare to the gypsies! Do you think we don't know? Do you think we didn't see it, or hear about it?"

"And what about the sheepskin coat, and the heavy woollen coats, and the clothing?" Maksym recalled.

"What have you done with the clothing? Are you going to tell us that Mykyta wore it out?"

"Mykyta! Where's Mykyta? Let him show us his threadbare shirt! Let him tell the community how his uncle took care of him!"

"There's Mykyta! He's over there! Bring him here, to the assembly!" Maksym shouted across the village common at the top of his lungs.

"Mykyta! Where's Mykyta?" the community picked up the refrain. "Bring him here!"

Frightened, Mykyta stepped back.

"Mykyta, go on! The assembly is calling you," one of the young fellows shoved him from behind.

"Do you hear, Mykyta? They're calling for you. Go, and Uncle Kuzma will give you back your dappled mare," another chap pushed him.

"Give the community another four buckets of whiskey, and they'll even recall your father from the other world!" Panko, the pockmarked leader of the young fellows laughed uproariously in his ear.

Mykyta leaped up as if he had been scalded and ran as fast as he could towards the grove. A few moments later, however, he came to his senses and, remembering that the cattle were still in the enclosure, went home and drove them to pasture.

All this had happened a long, long time ago. Panko, the ringleader, no longer walked this earth, but his laughter still rang in Mykyta's ears. No, it was not the young leader who was laughing; the entire community was laughing with his lips, that vast crowd of people who had sold their consciences for four buckets of whiskey, robbed an orphan of his fate—ruined it and shredded it to pieces—and called to mind Uncle Kuzma's perfidy only when they realised they could use that orphan's misfortune to seek revenge on behalf of their own pockets.

It was then, at that very moment, that he should have cursed the entire nest of human vipers, run away, and hidden himself from his enemies, but his young heart had not been able to hate properly—it only became terrified, and contracted more powerfully in his chest. And so, he continued to live and suffer— a stranger among people who were alien to him.

Up to the age of sixteen he restrained his heart, lived in fear, kept his distance from people, and continued working for his uncle and aunt; it was only when he turned seventeen, that he abandoned the cursed farmstead. It all happened rather unexpectedly.

One day, dejected and despondent, Mykyta sat by the river, staring at his paternal farmstead where strangers were now living and working. The sun was setting, and it looked as if some really bad weather was brewing; the cattle were returning home from the fields—it was time for him to hurry home so that within the next hour he could herd his uncle's cattle into the barn and the sheep into the pen. His hands, however, lay limp. They did not want to work for the benefit of people who were loathsome to him, and Mykyta did not budge from where he was sitting.

Just then, a fisherman, Omelko, was returning home. The wind was raising high waves on the river, and the tiny boat was plunging into them time and time again. The old man, however, handled his light craft with the greatest ease, as if he was not even aware that he was directing it against the wind and the current.

He was a powerful, sturdy man, as if hewn out of stone. Bareheaded, white-haired, dressed in white, and all alone on a tiny boat amidst the wide expanse of an enraged river, he bore almost no resemblance to the people who comprised a meek, easily frightened herd—known as a community—that were always ready to have still another drink at the expense of the misery of others. He was so unlike all those "uncles" and "old men" that Mykyta was accustomed to seeing, that the young man decided then and there to become a fisherman and, as soon as the craft touched the shore, he ran up to Omelko and begged him to take him on.

"Keep on growing where fate has planted you," the old man, having heard his urgent pleas, advised him.

Mykyta smiled bitterly. "My fate planted me over there," and he pointed at his patrimony, "but my uncle yanked me out of the soil and threw me down by the roadside. Take me with you on the river, where people won't walk and trample on my heart. Now that they've turned me into a person who must work for others, I'd rather work for you, granddad, than for my enemies; since they've taken away my field, I'd rather splash about in the water than shed my sweat on someone else's field . . .

"Take me, granddad! You'll see—I won't cause you any trouble, and one day I might even come in handy."

Omelko hesitated for a while, thought about it, and finally accepted him—not as a son, and not as a worker, but more as a companion to whom he promised a share of his earnings.

Mykyta never returned to his uncle's home; he did not even want to go back to pick up an extra shirt. And so, just before dawn, with only the clothes on his back, he set out on his first fishing trip.

Five years flew by like five happy days—the river, the fish, the net, the Holy Scripture on Sundays, brief questions and short replies regarding the fishing or the Scripture read by the old man, and not a word about human matters, not a hint about quarrels and problems . . . It was a safe, quiet, leisurely, and happy life. But his heart was not content—it rested for a while, grew bolder, and then made itself be heard and, in doing so, it confused his mind, and his fate fell prey to evil enemies.

Not far from Omelko's cottage lived Odarka, a dark, sharp-eyed young woman, who was a soldier's widow. She sometimes came to Omelko's home to buy fish, and before Mykyta realised what was happening, he had fallen in love with her.

At that time, his Uncle Kuzma paid out a hundred and fifty *karbovantsi* to him, and the old man, Omelko, gave him another hundred. Mykyta purchased a small piece of land and a cottage near the grove at the edge of the village, bought a boat and some fishing tackle, got married, and extended his hand to happiness; but happiness eluded him, and people pushed him far, far away.

Mykyta had made a mistake—his irrepressibly cheerful young wife was not a suitable partner for him.

Having had a delightful childhood, she had grown up into a headstrong girl and young woman. Not having experienced any misery in her life, she did not foresee that her star would ever dim, even for a moment, and so the cautious and distrustful Mykyta never ceased to amaze her. And his urgent pleas—that she "not go to visit people" and "not entice all sorts of people to their home"—made her angry. Accustomed to being among people from childhood, she liked the village. The neighbours and the village streets attracted her in the same way as the river and the reed-banks attracted Mykyta, while a new dress fascinated her more than the bright stars.

Before long, the young couple realised they differed in temperament, as if they had come from different countries; as yet, however, they did not quarrel, and Mykyta, placing great hope on the usually submissive nature of women, expected the same behaviour from Odarka. But Odarka's best friend, a young married woman called Paraska, whom Mykyta had always loathed, did not see things his way. She had put quite a bit of effort into Odarka's wedding, and she clapped her hands in amazement when she found out that Mykyta was not a man, but a ferocious animal.

"And you're going to submit to him? You're going to become a nun? You're going to hide yourself away from people behind stone walls? May he not live to see the day! Let him build a nest for himself and the devil in the reeds, but don't you submit to him, don't indulge him!" she advised Odarka.

Odarka, however, did not have the nerve to start quarrelling, and so it was a long time before Mykyta knew that a termite was gnawing away at the foundation of his dwelling.

"Tell me, has Paraska been over to see you today?" Mykyta sometimes asked when his wife seemed out of sorts.

"Why would she drag herself over here?" Odarka would reply. At the same time, however, she would blush furiously, as if Mykyta had greatly insulted her.

Eventually, one Sunday, Odarka, dressed as if she were going to church, set off somewhere. Mykyta waited patiently until dinnertime; then, not having eaten, he took his fishing tackle and went to the river. He came home towards evening, but his wife still had not returned. He would have given a great deal to have someone give him the slightest hint as to where she might be, but he felt ashamed and uncomfortable asking. And so, Mykyta resolved not to wash his dirty linen in public, but to lay low and wait for his wife.

It was night before she came home. Mykyta attacked her verbally, but the young woman could not look him in the face, so he left her in peace.

The next Sunday, Odarka once again started to leave the cottage to visit Paraska, but Mykyta made her come back. The young woman sulked and grumbled for a while, but then settled down. Paraska, however, made the rounds of the village, cursing the bitter fate of her friend. She did not leave out any of her friends, kinswomen, relatives or in-laws—she visited every one of them and made them all feel sorry for Odarka.

The womenfolk became concerned about the unfortunate fate of the hapless young woman; they pitied her, for she was wasting the years of her youth, and her beauty was withering away in vain . . . Advisors and helpers appeared out of nowhere and, as luck would have it, Paraska's brother—with whom, in her youth, Odarka had whiled away the hours listening to the nightingales' song—returned home from the army. Before Mykyta fully realised what was happening, black crows had settled on his house, and evil people had torn his wife from him and thrust her into the embrace of a good-for-nothing soldier.

Forsaking Mykyta, and abandoning their two little children, born a year apart, Odarka slipped out of the village. Impulsive and trusting, like a fly entrapped in a web of evil advice, she perished in the embrace of her advisors, like a poplar entwined in curly hopvines. A butterfly singed to death in the flame of the illusory happiness that her lover, the community's darling, had promised her, she died a homeless derelict in the city. But neither her death, nor Mykyta's misfortune, satisfied the ravenous enemies sharpening their claws for their children.

It was difficult for Mykyta to care for small children, but he managed to raise them. Marusya, dark, nimble, and cheerful—like her deceased mother—busied herself by the stove and took care of everything. Ivan, a spitting image of his father, assisted with the fishing. The neighbours no longer dared to stick their noses into Mykyta's business, and no one attempted to give him any advice. No one disturbed their peace, and the father of the two grown children could have considered himself fortunate—if his fate did not lie, as it always had, in the hands of other people.

"I won't be able to rid myself of people; it's inevitable that the unfortunate hour will come when I'll have to see my children go away to live in a stranger's home, or else I'll have to sully a corner of my cottage with someone else's child," Mykyta sighed. And as time went by, his sorrow grew and intensified.

He worried most about Marusya. Deeply concerned, he watched over and hid her from peoples' eyes in order to keep her at his side as long as possible and ensure her a good fate in life. But he did not save his daughter! She was just seventeen when one of the young fellows, Stepan, saw her by the well, took a liking to her, courted her, and took her away to the village.

Mykyta almost lost his mind. And, from that moment on, his luck abandoned him—he no longer had any success on the river; either his nets would tear, or the line would break, or bad weather would catch him unawares.

He would go out on the river, take his fishing net in his hands and be ready to place it, when he would recall that his Marusya was in a stranger's home in a village that was alien to him; he would recall that he had torn off a piece of his heart for people who had begrudged him a crust of bread; he would recall his wife, and he would forget about the fish. He would stand up in his boat and remain standing, as if turned to stone, until the waves carried his boat far into the willows. Coming to his senses, he would look around, grab an oar, turn the boat around, lower his fishnet, and then—without warning—either lose his willow fishing basket or go past the nets without shaking them.

And it was all in vain that Marusya boasted about her wealth, her husband, and mother-in-law—her cheerful chattering did not bring him any joy. He did not believe in happiness conferred by strangers, and when Marusya swore that it was true, he shook his head sadly and warned her about the trouble that might befall her.

"But where would that trouble come from? Have I ever harmed anyone, daddy?" Marusya asked in astonishment.

"Did I ever harm anyone, or did your mother?" Mykyta sadly countered. "People, my daughter, are like a raging fire, or like floodwaters in the spring—they don't bother finding out if you're innocent or if you're to blame, but whoever they attack will experience much woe."

And even though no cloud had passed, as yet, over Marusya's head, some kind of trouble—unclear, unknown, and because of that, still more terrible—soared powerfully on rustling wings before Mykyta's eyes, bared its teeth like the gang leader, Panko, and danced the *hopak [a lively folk dance]* like his wife's lover, the soldier. And trouble really did come. Before long, Stepan came home drunk from town and beat Marusya. Running home in tears, Marusya showed her father the welts on her arm.

Mykyta almost dropped to the floor. Red hoops whirled around the room, a cold sweat covered his forehead, and his heart momentarily stopped beating. His cup of grief overflowed when he saw the terrible marks on his daughter's body.

"May the enemies choke on my grief," Mykyta thought as he revived and rushed to the door.

But Ivan had beat him to it. Proud and independent, and raised by his father to value personal honour and family loyalty, the young man sped like the wind to punish his brother-in-law for the ill-treatment of his sister.

Mykyta crossed the threshold, glanced at his departing figure, and thanked God sincerely for such a son.

A day went by, and Ivan did not return, and when he did come home, he was bruised beyond recognition. Severely beaten, his overcoat soaked in blood, covered with straw and thistles, and so pale that his face was almost black, he scarcely managed to reach the sleeping-bench; he toppled over on it, and never raised himself from it again.

His son had been murdered, but Mykyta was not able to punish the murderer. The young man was killed in the village, but no witnesses could be found. No one had seen anything, and no one had heard anything—it seems that the brothers-in-law attacked one another in the barn and did not ask for help from anyone.

Having outsmarted and duped the court, the enemies laughed at the judges, but they did not fool Mykyta. He developed an even more intense hatred of people, and if it were not for his faith in the righteous judgement of God, he would have sought to revenge himself fiercely against the hostile village.

Ivan was buried. Mykyta did not shed a single tear, nor utter a single word. But at night, after the villagers had fallen asleep, he went to the grave, embraced it with his arms, and shouted despairingly: "Son, O my son!" And the grove shuddered, the ravine groaned, waves rose from the very depths of the river, and the stars flashed.

That terrible groan, however, did not reach Marusya's heart. It was already defiled, debased by her love for the murderer, and at the very moment when the father was cursing his fiercest enemy, the daughter was praying for him.

People convinced Marusya that Ivan was to blame for what had happened, that it was he who had first raised his hand against Stepan, and that the Lord had punished him for his wicked intentions against his brother-in-law. Marusya listened gladly to what they had to say, clinging to the slightest detail that could justify her husband's actions; she grieved for him, and her heart soared ever closer to him.

Finally, there came a night when Marusya abandoned her father and fled back to Stepan. It was then that Mykyta cursed her and her progeny to the seventh generation.

He got himself a fierce dog, bought some willows, and fenced himself off from the world with a high wattle fence.

Now it seemed to him that he no longer had anything more— either on this earth or in his heart—that his enemies could covet. The green grave of his son, his curse on his daughter, and his hatred of people—this was the entire treasure that he had acquired in his fifty years of living, and it was meant to last him for the rest of his life.

The people had truly known how to wound him.

One day, when Mykyta was returning home from his son's grave, a woman, gasping for air, ran out to overtake him.

"Mykyta! Go quickly to Stepan's home!" she shouted at him. "Marusya is having a difficult childbirth; she lifted a sack of wheat and ruptured herself."

Mykyta hesitated for a moment; but then he recalled Ivan and his curse, and, picking up speed, set off on a short cut to his own yard.

"Mykyta! For the love of God! Where are you going? Don't bring a sin down on your soul—remove your paternal curse from your daughter!" the woman said.

Mykyta chose an even more direct route to his home.

"Mykyta, have mercy on your daughter! She's your blood, your very own child! Don't wait until it's too late! It's childbirth! It's the Last Judgement!"

Mykyta reached his homestead, entered the yard, and locked the gate.

"May you yourself be cursed by God and people!" the woman yelled as she ran off to help the woman giving birth.

Mykyta stepped into the house, sat down by the table, and fell deep into thought. For three whole years he had found comfort in the thought that the people could no longer cause him any grief, that he had already done penance in the extreme, that he had freed himself forever from the claws of his enemies, and that there was nothing left in the whole world that could move his heart or add to his suffering.

Now this thought no longer comforted him. He called to mind all the medicines and other things that people used when they ruptured themselves; he pictured Marusya lying in bed, and his heart responded to the suffering of the daughter he had cursed—cursed seven times over.

Despite the pain in his heart, however, his resolve did not waver, and he did not go to see her.

After giving birth to a daughter, Marusya died the same night. Mykyta attended the funeral and paid for another requiem for the repose of her soul.

"It's too bad, it's really too bad about the young woman!" the priest sighed, as he took off his ecclesiastical stole. "She should have lived for a long time yet."

"And she would have lived, if it hadn't been for the people," Mykyta responded gloomily.

The priest cast a sideways glance at him.

"A sack of wheat on her back when she was pregnant—that's all the thanks she got from the strangers for whom she renounced her own father," Mykyta added, and he gave Stepan such a piercing look that the latter involuntarily lowered his eyes.

And so, another four years went by. Exactly how they went by, Mykyta did not really notice. The days alternated with the nights, and the nights with the days; the earth adorned itself with flowers, then slept in the chains of winter; the river flooded the wide lowlands, and then receded within the boundaries of its own current. But to Mykyta it seemed like a single, endless day.

He never went into the village—he sold his fish in town—and the villagers appeared to have forgotten about him. There was only a single path that led from the village past his cottage to the river, and even it had become overgrown after a trench was dug around the grove. Everything around him fell silent, as if it had all turned to stone, and his own life would have passed as in a dream if it had been possible to calm his heart. But it did not allow itself to be lulled to sleep—on the contrary, under the protection of the surrounding quietness and peace, the bitter seeds planted by people sprouted even more luxuriant flowers. Every day, a new bud opened its petals; every day the roots of grief grew deeper, and his poisoned heart yearned for hatred—not sleep.

During these years, Mykyta experienced the heights of hatred, and when his heart finally was unable to absorb a still larger measure of that feeling, he began to feel an aversion to people. The human form, voice, look, words—everything seemed to him to be infinitely repugnant, and a human being—a lump of filthy mud, too revolting to touch.

To avoid going into town, he began to make do without flour and salt; to avoid contact with people, he would turn back halfway to his destination if he saw someone approaching; to avoid contact with sin, he stopped attending church; to avoid uttering a single superfluous word, he dumped whole nets of fish back into the water or gave them away to dealers at half price.

There was just one tie that he found bearable to maintain with the rest of God's world—the old woman Khivrya who was deaf in both ears and who for many years had woven ropes for his nets. It was only to her that Mykyta could make himself go, and even then, he went only rarely, when he absolutely had to.

As it happened, four years after Marusya's death, he had no choice but to go Khivrya during the harvest. Almost all the corners of his nets had rotted; he did not have a scrap of bread in the house; he had burned the last drop of kerosene; and he had no money to pay for the annual requiem for the repose of Marusya's soul.

Mykyta, choosing a time when all the working people were in the fields, went to see Khivrya. To get to her home, he had to go past Stepan's yard. On his way there, he did not even glance at the odious house; but on his way back, he was forced to stop by the gate because, stretched out on the pathway, lay a little girl, sleeping soundly. A moment before him, a cart had sped down the road, and the little girl's tear-stained face was grimy with dust;

countless flies had settled on her tiny nose, chin, and open mouth, and burrs adorned her tangled, uncombed hair.

Mykyta looked at her, spit in disgust, and had already walked past her when something unexpectedly occurred to him, and he turned back and waved away the flies with the skeins of thread he was carrying.

The little girl opened her eyes, gaped at the terrifying, unshaven old man, and began crying uncontrollably. Not a single soul responded to the child's bawling, and Mykyta realised she must be an orphan.

He spit a second time, and continued on his way home. But his peace of mind was disturbed by the little blond head, the terrified child's widely opened eyes, the cart, the dust, the flies, the mad dog that had run through the grove that morning, and the people who were indifferent to the tears of the orphan.

During the past four years, he had not, not even once, remembered about his granddaughter or inquired about her. But now, he could not stop thinking about this disgusting, ragged, neglected child, this last drop of his blood, the final sprout of his unfortunate lineage.

The more he thought about her, the more convinced he became that his evil enemies were deriding him, and that neither the deep ditches, nor the high wattle fence could protect him from the people; even though they did not have the power to topple the old oak, they knew how to destroy its youngest sprout.

And so, one evening, the villagers saw someone's figure flash by Stepan's house. At that time, Stepan was enjoying himself at a wedding with his wife and her children, while Marusya's orphan was wailing alone in the locked house. On the second evening, just after dusk had fallen, a figure once again crept up to a window. And on the third evening, Stepan himself saw this figure and ran out of the house. Near his window he saw Mykyta.

"What do you want? Why are you skulking about under my windows? If you have something to say, then come into the house," Stepan said and, giving in to a feeling of fear, grabbed hold of the wooden peg on the door to open it.

"I won't set a foot into your foul house as long as I live, but give me Hapka," Mykyta said.

"Hapka? Who will look after her at your place?"

"Give her to me. She'll perish in your home," Mykyta insisted.

Stepan hesitated. It was true that Hapka was somewhat in the way; she was often the cause of quarrels with his wife, who had two children of her own. All the same, he loved his daughter and was sorry to give her away.

"Let me talk it over with my wife," Stepan said after a brief pause.

"Give her to me—she'll perish as a homeless waif," Mykyta spoke for the third time, handing over a thick shawl that had belonged to his grandmother.

Stepan took the shawl, stood a little while longer, thought things over, and went into the house to consult with his wife.

A short while later, Hapka—protected by a blanket from the wind and flies, and sheltered from people by a high wattle fence and her grandfather's bitter experience—was fast asleep on her grandfather's bed.

The little girl almost never returned to the village from this cottage. Ahead of her lay the greatest good fortune that her grandfather could think of for her—the fate of a righteous nun, a life of continual prayer in a quiet harbour behind nunnery walls. Mykyta had carefully planned how to nurture and rear the orphan.

The little girl's ninth birthday passed, but she still did not know the village, nor did she often see people. Her grandfather's house, the grove, the river, and, on a distant hill, a large building with a cross and gold stars on its azure roof—this was her whole world. Her grey-haired, pensive grandfather and the pale, pious nuns were her entire family; the shaggy dog, Pokot, and a spotted cat—her only friends; and her grandfather's words—her sole instruction.

It was only here—in the monastery and in the cottage by the grove—that you could save your soul, because out there, beyond the high wattle fence, lived strangers, and they were the cause of all the evil on the earth.

God was merciful, the sky was bright, the earth was righteous, every creation was a blessing of the Lord, but people, slaking their desires, had turned it into a hell for themselves. Their voracious souls could scarcely accommodate the sins they were raking in with both hands; their fierce hearts were overflowing with jealousy; their wicked thoughts did not drown in their heads; their lips were befouled with lies; and their tongues were desecrated by profanities. They had spread manure and slime on the living image that the Lord had given them, and had dressed themselves in the skin of the enemy.

You had to avoid people like bloody mire, keep them at a distance, shun any contact with them, so that you yourself would not be defiled—this was what Mykyta taught his granddaughter, and she listened gladly to what he said, peering intently into his deeply sunken eyes, in which an animated spark flared time and again, and she sincerely believed that not even an echo of the iniquitous world could reach into her grandfather's sheltered home.

At last, Mykyta attained some peace of mind—he had become the master of his granddaughter's fate, if not of his own. His will was no longer being shattered by the wiles of his enemies; his every word was falling on fertile soil, and his every thought resonated with a sympathetic note in the heart of his wise and obedient granddaughter.

Everything was coming along as it should; but, unfortunately, Mykyta neglected to inquire of God how long he would remain living on this earth—if he would have enough shoring for the foundation that he had begun to raise, because death does not grant time to anyone. And so, perhaps at the very moment when Mykyta's happiness in having attained his goal was at its zenith, death was already sharpening its scythe to ruin—no less so than his evil enemies—the work he had accomplished in the past five years.

A month had gone by since death sent him her first harbinger— an illness struck the old man's head and legs. All the same, for a long time he did not give any thought to death, and he relied on God's grace to his granddaughter and on the fact that he was not all that old yet.

Today, death had given certain signs that made her presence known—the dry oak table had creaked three times during the night; in the evening, a screech-owl had moaned by the window; and at midnight, his deceased mother had visited him. There could be no doubt that his final hours had arrived . . . And once again all his hopes were shattered, his fondest goal was perishing— inexorable death was extending her hand to remove the nun's hood from his granddaughter and make her homeless . . .

Mykyta sat up the whole night, searching for a way out, for a home for Hapka, a sheltered nook, but despite all his efforts, he could not come up with a more sheltered and quiet harbour than her father's cottage.

As soon as it began to dawn, he set out for Stepan's house. His trip to the home of his enemy-murderer was a difficult one, very difficult. The old man trudged along slowly, while his sorrowful thoughts rapidly wove terrible scenes, one after the other; the future life of the orphan appeared to him in all its painful, inevitable minutiae . . .

The sun was already quite high in the sky by the time he arrived. The gate was wide open, and the path from the gate to the threshold was neatly swept. Mykyta, however, did not dare to go directly to the house; instead, he stopped for a moment by the fence to at least partially subdue the feelings that Marusya's home awakened within him.

The cottage looked cheerful. The green yard teemed with chickens and ducks; by the new curb around the well, three children sat and played; a fourth child, still in swaddling clothes, was lying in the lap of the eldest girl. A stout young woman with a ruddy complexion carried out a bucket of slops, poured the contents into a trough, and called for Brovko. A fat, sleek dog leapt out of a stack of straw and rushed up to the trough. The mistress stood for a while by the trough, glanced in at a hog in the pen, and walked up to the children.

Mykyta felt a load lift off his heart. The house, the yard, the children, and especially the calm and friendly expression of the young woman made a far better impression on him than he could have hoped. He was already stepping forward and had almost reached the gate, when a scruffy white dog, lacerated and limping on one leg, appeared out of nowhere. Tucking his mangy tail under himself and lowering his bony back until he was almost pressed to the ground, he crawled past Mykyta's feet. Trembling with fear and hunger, and glancing all around and looking backwards, he lunged at the slops.

At that moment, the young woman turned around. Her face flamed; her eyes blazed. Jolted, as if she had found herself surrounded by ten wolves, she rushed up to the trough with curses and vile profanities, and struck the dog with all her might on the spine. Her cudgel broke in two, and the dog's howl reverberated through the village as he tucked in his tail and dragged his now completely useless leg beyond the fence. The young woman adjusted her head-dress, picked up the pieces of the cudgel, threw them into a pile of brushwood under the fence, and calmly, as if she never had harmed anyone, even in her sleep, walked into the house.

Mykyta did not approach that cottage. This cheerful dwelling, where only "one's own" could find refuge, now seemed to him worse than hell itself, and the crust of bread that this young woman was to give Hapka—someone else's child—after his death, seemed harder than a stone. Mykyta once again cursed the human nest of vipers and fled.

Far away from the village stood an abandoned windmill. A long time ago, someone's farmstead had been located in that spot; now there was no longer even a trace of the house, the cattle had eaten the trees, and only the mill, resold for the tenth time, remembered its original owners. Black, tattered, crooked, without either a capstan or arms, with a ragged rotten roof, it creaked and shuddered, and with every gust of wind leaned over more precariously.

For quite some time now, people had been demanding that the owner either sell the windmill for firewood, or pull down the eyesore. The miserly magnate, however, did not have the time to dismantle it himself, and demanded an outrageous sum of money from prospective buyers. And so the mill, complaining loudly to the screech-owl about its painful existence, remained standing all alone out in the steppe.

To Mykyta, drained and deeply perturbed, this lonely black skeleton seemed like a brother. He turned off the pathway and walked towards it. Next to the mill, an old stump was rotting away. Mykyta sat down on it and leaned against the skeleton's walls.

The skeleton creaked and swayed.

"You're creaking? Go ahead and creak! You'll creak for a long time yet before the wind takes pity on you and hurls you to the ground, and it's no use waiting for any human mercy—they'll delight in your groaning until they come up with an idea as to how they can profit the most from your pleas," the old man muttered to himself, dejectedly.

His head was spinning, his thoughts were muddled, the crippled, hungry dog swam before his eyes, every bone in his body ached and begged for peace, and his soul was searching for an answer to one burning question—where could he place Hapka? To whom could he entrust the orphan? And the mill, as if sympathising with Mykyta's distress, continued creaking and groaning ever more sorrowfully . . .

It was noon when Mykyta started out for home.

"Grandpa, how you've changed!" Hapka leapt to her feet when she caught sight of the old man on the threshold.

"Get dressed nicely and come out to the river when the sun sets," Mykyta replied to her. He sharpened a spigot, took a drill from the shelf, and went off into the grove.

By the time he finished climbing down the hill, the sun had rolled to the horizon, but it was easier to walk on the lowlands than on the smooth, slippery, winding path; the air in the valley was also fresher, and Mykyta picked up his pace. The tall, thick-stalked reeds stood almost motionless, and only the young aspens rustled in the calm air; but the rooks were already circling their nests in the tall willows and, disquieted by the coming storm, were loudly debating what they should do.

Mykyta looked all around, glanced at the setting sun where the clouds had stretched the darkest of tents, and headed straight to the clump of reeds where two boats were hidden. He went past the newer one, climbed into the old decrepit one, and spent some time working with his drill near the bottom of it; then he clambered out on the bank, pulled an oar out of the willows, cut some rushes, and spread them in the boat. Exhausted, he sat down to rest.

A moment later, Hapka showed up wearing a green skirt, flowered bodice, and white shirt. Her hair was adorned with mint and pink cloves and, flushed and boundlessly happy that her grandfather was finally going fishing again and taking her with him, she fluttered like a butterfly down the hill and rolled like a bright star over the green carpet of the bank.

"Granddad, granddad! You forgot to take your new fishnet, so I brought it," she shouted from afar. "How tiny this boat is!" she added, joyfully jumping into it.

At that very moment, the last ray of the sun faded. A light breeze came up, and the first lightning bolt flashed.

"Granddad, the rain will soak us! We should at least have taken our hooded coats," the girl said anxiously.

"Hurry and sit down," Mykyta responded, pulling abruptly on his oars.

The boat darted over the water.

"Aren't we going to the flooded area?" Hapka asked in surprise.

"Despicable . . . pitiless . . . murderers . . . assassins . . ." Mykyta whispered to himself, plying the oars more strenuously.

At that moment, there was another flash of lightning and a terrible crash of thunder.

The little girl crossed herself, then laughed: "Oh, the echoes roll so far over the water! Why, if you tried shouting loudly . . ."

"Sit still! Now then, your eyes are younger than mine—take a good look to see if there's anyone on the bank," her grandfather ordered.

Hapka leaned over the water and peered keenly at the bank. "No, there's no one in sight."

"Well, even if there were, it's all the same to me . . . I'm not afraid of them," Mykyta said softly, and he laid down his oar.

The boat tilted to one side, but Hapka, not wanting to upset her grandfather, did not say anything.

"There's no salvation for an orphan, my child. . . . The murderers will trample you, and stomp on you, and then they'll kill you. Pray, Hapka! Pray to the All-merciful One—we can place our trust only in Him; our only hope is His righteous judgement. . . . An innocent soul . . . an immaculate heart, a virgin's peace!" the old man spoke up in an altered voice.

Then he fell silent again.

"Granddad! Aren't you cold?" Hapka spoke up after a while.

"Pray to God, my little daughter," Mykyta replied, taking off his cap.

"Put your cap on, granddad—you'll get sick again," the little girl reminded him.

"Pray to God! It is in Him, the Merciful One, that I'm placing my trust!" her grandfather responded in a troubled voice.

"Which prayers should I recite?"

"Our Father," Mykyta ordered her, leaning forward with his whole body to hear his granddaughter's voice.

Hapka started the prayer. The clouds hung low over the river. A brilliant, jagged thunderbolt ripped the sky and slammed into the water.

The little girl started in terror.

"Don't be scared," her grandfather said sharply.

The wind strengthened, the rain came down in torrents, and the little boat spun around in the middle of the river.

"You're tired, granddad—look how the boat is being tossed about. Give me the oar, and I'll turn it around to the shore."

"Don't be scared," he said a second time, bending over to the bottom of the boat. He rustled about for some time among the rushes. The wind grew stronger, and the rain came down more densely, and in bigger drops.

"Granddad! Give me the oar, I truly can turn the boat more quickly into a sheltered spot!" the girl, trembling and soaked to the skin, pleaded urgently.

"Huh?" Mykyta responded, as if in a trance, and he rose to his feet.

The boat rocked.

"Sit down, granddad—the boat's really rocking," Hapka pleaded.

"Huh?" Mykyta responded a second time and fervently began making the sign of the cross over himself and his granddaughter.

Hapka turned cold with fear. Never before had her grandfather been afraid of lightning. There had been many times when storms that were much worse had caught him unawares on the river, but he had never panicked—he had just calmly steered the boat to shelter. Now he appeared to have gone mad with fear—he did not understand or hear anything, nor did he see that the boat was taking on a lot of water.

"Where's the scoop? I'll bail out the water. Granddad! The water's coming up higher," Hapka leapt to her feet.

"It's nothing . . . It's nothing. The rain is stopping. Don't be scared . . . Pray to God," her grandfather answered, composing his hands in prayer.

"Oh, it's gurgling here . . . There's a hole," the little girl finally realised, and she rushed to plug it. Mykyta shoved her hands away.

"Granddad! What are you doing?" Hapka asked in utter horror. "Let me plug it."

"Lord! Be with me, a sinner!" the grandfather whispered.

"I'm scared," Hapka sobbed, "just look at all the water in the boat . . ."

"Pray, my little daughter! An innocent soul . . . An immaculate heart . . . O Holy God! Holy Mighty One . . ."

The boat began to sink.

"Granddad! Granddad, I'm scared!" Hapka screamed heartrendingly as she disappeared under the water with her grandfather and the boat . . .

At that moment a man dashed out from behind a tree, ripped off his clothing, crossed himself, and flung himself into the water. Something seemed to be glimmering in the middle of the river. He rushed towards it and, a moment later, dragged the old man to the shore. Then he dove into the river once more and disappeared for a long time.

Mykyta rose to his hands and knees and leaned against a willow. He was cold, shivering, and spent, but neither the rain, not the cold water had doused the flame ignited in his heart near Stepan's cottage and fanned into a blaze by the mill.

He remembered well all the thoughts that had led him to this crime, understood his great sin, and—even though his heart contracted in burning pain for his granddaughter—he did not regret what he had done; his only fear was that she might remain alive.

But the person who had rescued him from the water and flung himself in the dead of night into an abyss to save a little girl had awoken a new feeling in his heart. Mykyta, holding his breath, fastened his eyes on the spot where the unknown swimmer had vanished.

Who was he? Who was struggling with death out there in the river to save someone else's soul? Who was it that attached such value to an old man's dying moments, to an orphan's life? What kind of a person was he? There were no people like that in the world. No, there were none, for everywhere there were only "strangers," and "enemies."

A minute went by . . . another one . . . To Mykyta they seemed as long as hours. It was quiet all around—not a sound, not a rustle. There was silence on the bank, silence on the river, and silence in the grove . . .

The cold breath of death was enveloping everything in ice; the soaked ground was enticing his wasted, dying body, and only his heart was rumbling dully in his breast and asking: "Who is that swimmer swaddled by the fog? From where did he come? Where are those wonderful countries where people give up their soul for the life of an orphan?"

Finally, there was a splash, and then another one; now the splashing was closer, the reeds snapped, and the swimmer walked out on the bank. In his arms he carried something tiny, dark . . .

It was Hapka.

Mykyta glanced at his dead granddaughter and, lifting his eyes to the swimmer, he raised his arms in boundless despair, with unspeakable regret.

The man carrying the lifeless Hapka was Yakym, his nearest neighbour, the one from whom he had closed himself off with a high wattle fence . . .

How Lepestyna Got Some Kerosene
(1897)

In all my life, I've never had anything as bad happen to me as happened last week on Wednesday evening, and even on Thursday morning—and it was all because of my husband . . .

O merciful Lord, O all-gracious God, how much suffering I've had because of him—the Queen of Heaven forbid! I've withered and wasted away; my nimble speech has been cut off like a thread; my keen memory has faded—and it's all because of him. I worry about things, try to do my best, try to look after everything, but he . . . all he wants is the glory of "running a household." Why, even on that day, he went off to the market, drove the oxen there in a terrible blizzard—and forgot to buy any kerosene.

"Why," he says, "didn't you give me a bottle for it?"

Well, may the power of God strike you down! Is my poor little head supposed to remember everything? Even so, I wouldn't have forgotten—I never ever would have forgotten—if it hadn't been for that Tsymbalenko, that despicable neighbour of ours. The devil had to drag him over to our place just as my old man was driving out of the yard.

Why did the devil drag him over, you're asking? He came to quarrel with me. I'd scattered a fistful of ashes across his boundary line, and he came charging over to wrangle about it.

"You've taken over all the neighbours' gardens," he says, "both to the left and to the right, and now you're closing in on me?"

Well! May you rule over your fingers like I rule over those gardens! I just threw out some ashes, and now I'm forbidden to do even that. He made me angry and got me all upset, and then he went home in a huff. And, because of him, I forgot all about the kerosene.

Evening came. My husband ate his supper, said his prayers, spread himself out on the floor, and fell asleep like a dead man. But I, you see, was supposed to sit down—oh, my poor little head—and spin as best I could without any light. And to make matters even worse, the moon was growing dimmer.

Well, I sat down by the window and didn't budge, but tears the size of peas rolled down my face. I was tired of living on God's earth; I had no desire left to work. No one needed me, and I didn't need anyone . . .

Just then, my in-law Solokha walked in. She greeted me and asked: "Why are you sitting here without a lamp, my dear little in-law?"

"It's like this," I said, "my husband forgot to buy some kerosene."

"Well," Solokha said, "go and borrow some."

"I don't want to bother the neighbours," I said. "God be with them! The way the world is now, the only time you don't have any trouble is when you stay in your own home."

"You're imagining things! No one is annoyed with you anymore. That misunderstanding took place way back when, and you're the only one still harping on it. Praise God, everything's as quiet as can be in our neck of the woods. Even the worst of enemies— your neighbours—are all related now through christenings or marriages. Tsymbalenko was a godfather for Katrya's child, and the two women, Stolyarenchykha and Babenkova, bought the lord's hemp in partnership and even hauled it home together on one wagon.

"It's only your cottage, my dear in-law, that's standing off to one side, as it were. You don't get together with anyone, and no one comes to see you. You sit here all alone, as if you were an orphan, and without any light, at that!"

When she said this, when she began to remind me what my life was like, and to talk about my unhappy orphan-like condition, I burst into bitter tears.

Lord, Lord! What has my life become? What have I, Lepestyna, become? It used to be that Lepestyna was the most sought after young woman in the entire village, but now she sits at home like a wormy mushroom. In the past, Lepestyna knew everything, even where the birds flew for the winter, but now she has no idea even as to what her neighbour plans to do. At one time, Lepestyna's every word was considered sacred, but now her tongue has been silenced . . . Yes, I've been gagged, broken, and threatened with jail. My husband's forbidden me to go out among the people, and he won't allow me to visit anyone . . .

My in-law left. I glanced down at the floor—there, sleeping and snoring, was my misfortune; there, sprawled over the entire floor, was my hapless fate; there, not hearing or seeing anything, lay my ill-starred hour.

And my sorrow suddenly vanished—he was fast asleep! Feeling as if I'd been reborn, I dashed out into the street.

I glanced around—the village was quiet, very quiet. Every cottage was lit . . .

"I'll go," I thought, "and borrow some kerosene."

I didn't want to go to Katrya's place—Lord, how I didn't want to go there. It wasn't so long ago that she had shamed me in front of absolutely everyone when she chased her clucking hen off the nest that I, without any evil intentions, had made up in a niche of my clay oven . . . I didn't want to go there, I'm saying, but I could hear that her infant was crying, and I'm the best of sorceresses when it come to bawling babies.

I strode boldly into the house.

"Good health to you on this Wednesday! Why is your child crying?"

"The Lord only knows why. It hasn't fallen silent since dinnertime, and it keeps thrashing around in its cradle."

"Someone's looked at it with an evil eye," I said.

"There's been no one in the house," said Katrya, "except for Tsymbalenko."

"There you have it—you found yourself a goggle-eyed godparent, and now you're surprised that the child isn't well! Can someone like that Tsymbalenko bring a child into the faith? Is he fit to do something like that?" I said, and I walked up to the cradle, blew on the child, licked its face, and uttered the words that need to be said to ward off crying. Oh yes, it quieted down a bit right away.

"Do you have any kerosene you could lend me?" I then asked.

"Do you think it's possible," Katrya said, "to keep anything on hand among such wretched people? I had a full bottle, but some villain tipped it over when he was stealing my suet."

"What suet?" I asked, because, as I could have sworn, I hadn't heard anything about it.

"Don't you know? Somebody took off with all the stomach suet—just as it was, in a bag. I'm thinking of asking a fortune teller about it."

"I'll be your fortune teller," I said. "I saw with my very own eyes how that wonderful godparent of yours, that goggle-eyed Tsymbalenko, carted off something on his back at night. It must have been your suet—it couldn't have been anything else!"

Her face flamed furiously. "You know," she said, "yesterday his biscuits were made with suet."

I went away with my empty bottle to see old lady Ivanykha.

I walked in and saw that old lady Voronykha was bragging how Granny Beznosykha had helped her with her infection.

"I'm thankful to Granny Beznosykha as well," I said, "May luck be with her. She saved me from a sudden death."

"When?" Ivanenchykha asked.

"You see," I said, "what kind of a neighbour you are? You live just across the garden from me, and yet you don't know that last Sunday I almost joined the ranks of the saints. If it weren't for Granny Beznosykha, I would have dragged a full bowl of beetles with me to the Holy Throne in that other world.

"You see, my daughter-in-law treated me to some *balabushky* [filled buns] and *pyrizhky* [turnovers], but as to what she filled them with—well, may she answer for that in the next world. On Sunday, after the liturgy, I ran in to see her. And she was so happy, absolutely delighted to see me. She set out some *balabushky* and *pyrizhky* in front of me and brought in a bottle of whiskey. I drank a shot of whiskey, ate a *pyrizhok*, thanked her, and went home. And that evening, I got terrible stomach cramps . . . Oh, it was awful! I drank some turpentine, and then some tar—but instead of feeling better, I felt worse and worse.

"My old man harnessed the oxen, put me in the sleigh, took a measure of wheat, enough cloth for a towel, and a bottle of whiskey, and drove me to Beznosykha.

"She looked me over and said: 'You've been poisoned, my darling, poisoned; beetles are already crawling around in your stomach. Stay with me for a day and a night, and I'll help you.' She cooked up something for me, steeped it in whiskey, and made me drink it.

"Well, did the beetles ever rise up in revolt! May the Mother of God have mercy, may the saints protect us. It's dreadful to recall it even now. They crawled around in my stomach, scratched for all they were worth, and then they started coming out . . . the entire night they just kept coming . . . and coming . . ."

"And we didn't know anything about it?" Ivanenchykha was astonished.

"That's my misfortune, that I don't have any good neighbours, even when something bad happens to me . . . Take you, for example . . . You're angry with me that I took of a bit of your garden for our stable, but do you think I knew what I was doing? Petrenko told me to do it—he swore that in our grandfathers' time, our land stretched right up to your pear tree."

"Well, he's lying!" Ivanenchykha erupted angrily. "Let the people say how far our land goes, and let him stop lying . . ."

"Do you think," I said, "that I can't see that he said it on purpose to annoy you and to get me, fool that I am, into trouble? But I've moved the stable, just like you wanted me to . . . Well, I just came for a minute to borrow some kerosene, and here I am, jabbering away . . ."

"Oh, I don't have any either," Ivanenchykha said. "Unless I run and borrow some . . ."

"No, no," I said. "I'll get some myself."

I left Stolyarykha's home, walked past my own cottage, and went to see old lady Petrenchykha, the neighbour to my left.

I walked in and greeted her. She invited me to sit down and didn't even mention the damage my boar had done to her potatoes.

"Thank you, my dear, but I don't have time to sit; lend me a bit of kerosene, and I'll be on my way . . ."

"Hand me the bottle," she says, "and I'll give you some. Yesterday my husband brought home a full metal container, and I've already lent out quite a bit—I poured a full bottle just for the Doroshenko family."

"But aren't you still feuding with old lady Doroshenchykha?" I asked. And I stood there as if someone had hit me on the head with a stick, as if a fog had spread out in front of me, because I don't like Doroshenchykha at all—Lord, how I detest her!

"Oh, no, not at all," Petrenchykha said, "I've already asked Doroshenchykha to act as a midwife for my Hapka."

"My, but you're good-natured, neighbour," I said. "You have a good nature, but a poor memory! Is it possible you've forgotten that she called you a goose?"

"When?" Petrenchykha attacked me.

"But didn't you hear?" I asked. "On the Feast of Jordan, when the water was being blessed . . . You walked into church, and she nudged Domakha and said: 'Look, the goose has come—her boots are red, and she waddles like a goose.'"

"I'm a goose? Well, just you wait, just you wait! She's in for it now! I'll show her what kind of a goose I am. She won't forget me in a hurry!" She was foaming at the mouth with anger.

"Hush," her husband began to calm her. "Why are you so angry? It's not you who's the goose—it's your boots that are like the legs of a goose."

But no. She became angry, infuriated; she ran around the house, flinging pokers and oven-forks, shoving the children, and railing against Doroshenchykha.

"So, I'm a goose, am I? And she doesn't like the way I walk! Well, at least I don't jump over stiles at night to meet the overseer. People have been saying for some time now that her older daughter resembles that knock-kneed Yosyf, but I didn't say anything . . . I kept quiet, as if I didn't know anything and hadn't heard anything, but now I'll shame her in public. I won't take pity on her shaggy grey hair—let her know what happens to anyone who slanders me!"

"Maybe I should come to see Hapka sometime?" I asked. "After all, I was a midwife for her first child."

And she clutched at me. "Come, do come—and I'll have a kerchief ready for you."

That was the sum total of our conversation. I sat for a little while longer, took the kerosene, and scurried home.

II

On Thursday, just as dawn was breaking, I heard something rumbling and thundering so loudly that the ground was reverberating. And the noise was drawing closer to my home.

"Holy, holy, holy! May the Holy Spirit be with us!" I prayed softly in my sleep.

Then I opened my eyes and saw that my cottage was filling up with people so quickly that there wasn't room to take a step.

The first one to run in was my daughter-in-law. She had run so fast that she was gasping for breath; her eyes were blazing, and she was hissing like a snake, hopping like a frog, and foaming at the mouth like a madwoman.

"When did I poison you? Tell me—when? Was it after the respect I showed you that you vomited beetles?" she yelled, almost leaping up to my bed on the *peech [a large clay oven with a sleeping area on top]*.

"Now, now, you fool! Come to your senses! When did I say that? Who's told you such a pack of lies?" I replied from the *peech*, quietly and amicably at first, because, Lord only knows, I really dread trouble.

But Tsymbalenko was already peering over my daughter-in-law's shoulder. He bared his teeth and stared at me with bulging eyes, as if he wanted to eat me.

"When, old woman, did you see me steal some suet?" he asked in his twangy voice.

"Go choke on your suet! Get away from me—may the devil take you, may the fiend get you! I didn't see your suet, and I didn't see your ugly mug . . ."

"No, it's no use trying to lie! I won't forgive you for this—you'll spend your old age rotting in jail!" that ugly man threatened me.

And then I heard my Omelko restraining somebody in the porch. Oh, woe is me—Petrenko was forcing his way in.

"When did I ever tell you to build your stable in Ivanenchykha's garden?" he shouted from the porch.

"When did I call Babenchykha a goose?" Doroshenchykha shrieked so loudly that my ears rang. "You yourself, you old witch, laughed at her in church, and now you're laying the blame on me?"

"Leave me in peace! Let me at least say my prayers!" I screamed at them, and I leapt down from the *peech*, because I could no longer just lie there, listening to them.

"Come on, let's take this so-and-so to the district office!" Tsymbalenko bleated through his nose.

"To the district office!" shrilled Doroshenchykha.

"To the district office with this old mother," my daughter-in-law added her two cents as she kept bouncing to the ceiling.

"Devour me, hack me to death, you thugs; drag me to the district office! I didn't say anything to anybody—and that's that!" I said.

After all, did I need any trouble?

"You didn't say anything? You didn't say anything?" they all attacked me.

"I didn't say anything!" I said, scarcely able to stand on my feet.

Well, you should have heard them all begin to scream and yell then, especially that Doroshenchykha.

"Deceiver! Liar! That's what she is! To the district office with her!"

Oh, did I ever become enraged!

"Get out of my house, you thugs, you villains!" I screamed as if I were herding sheep. And I yelled so loudly that the windows rattled.

And then I took a step and stumbled—and ended up spread-eagled on the floor.

Well, my lower back started to ache terribly, and I boiled over with anger—I had ripped a perfectly good shirt.

I grabbed a rolling pin and went at them.

And what do you think, my dears? All of them, to the very last one, fled like startled sparrows bursting out of a field of hemp.

I followed them outdoors.

"You'll have a long wait now for a kerchief from my daughter-in-law," Petrenchykha yelled at me from the gate, while making an insulting gesture with her hand.

"You'll remember that suet," Katrya shouted.

I felt as if I'd been stabbed with a knife, and thought: "Lord, Lord! It's me who'll end up getting all the blame."

"Just ask Petrenchykha, you slut, who your older daughter resembles!" I shouted after Doroshenchykha. "Ask me what she said about you."

She ran back from the street and came straight at me.

"What? What did she say? What?"

"She said that your husband is feeding Yosyf's children!" I flung at her, and then I ran after Tsymbalenko so that he could hear.

"Go ahead and ask Katrya, you goggle-eyed wonder, if the biscuits you made with her suet were tasty."

"What biscuits?" he wanted to know.

"The ones she ate at your place."

Oh, woe is me! Oh, my heavens! Did that Tysmbalenko ever glare at Katrya, and then he attacked her . . . And then along came Dorosh—and he attacked Petrenkova; Babenko went after Doroshenchykha, and Ivanenko laid into Petrenko—it's impossible to tell you about it, or to describe it . . .

They quarrelled, and argued, and yelled, and accused each other; and then they began to fight. The people could hardly pull them apart. And then they sued each other in the district office.

Well, almost two weeks have gone by since then, but all the neighbours are still quarrelling. And, as for that kerosene—well, may the devil take it, may the fiend get it! If I'd known the grief it would cause, it would have been better to be without any light for those few days.

And how was the good Lord able to spare me from getting the fright of my life? How could anyone who's still half-asleep survive an attack like that? A woman's quietly sleeping, dreaming about the holy angels, when suddenly, wicked enemies appear out of nowhere, confuse her and scare her—just like they scared me.

Moreover, you know . . . things almost got out of hand.

And if only I'd at least been able to light a lamp after all that. As it was, I came home that night with the kerosene, groped around the door, and couldn't find the latch.

I knocked once, and then a second time, but my husband didn't hear—he was sleeping the sleep of the damned.

That was when I got good and angry. There I was—running around, trying to get some kerosene in such cold weather and at such an evil hour, and there was he—not a worry in his head!

I grabbed a cane, struck the door as hard as I could, and that damned cane flew out of my hand and hit the bottle—shattering it into smithereens . . .

The Butterfly
(1903)

Ivan Ivanovych caught a butterfly.

It is true that this butterfly was much more interesting than those that, as a child, he used to catch in his father's small orchard. It was also true that it was already a trifle tired, but if one took into consideration the short and somewhat worn-out legs of Ivan Ivanovych, his twisted hands, and his feeble old eyes, then one would—along with his good friend, Petro Petrovych—pat him on the back and say: "Well done, Ivan Ivanovych, you're a great guy!" At least, this is what all the close acquaintances of Ivan Ivanovych did.

He accepted this affectionate gesture willingly, with even a degree of pleasure, and he never so much as alluded with a single word to his assistants—although he did have assistants. He avoided mentioning them not because he was, may God have mercy, in any way evil, underhanded, or malicious, but only because those helpers of his—like misfortune, grief, poverty, and death—were themselves taciturn and sullen and never sought any reward for their work, hiding themselves in dungeons instead . . . At least Ivan Ivanovych never saw them, and he was certain that he had managed everything using his own strength, and that he had caught the butterfly all by himself.

As he chased after the butterfly through orchards, meadows, forests and ravines, he could not get a good look at it and, except for its golden colour and its transparently thin wings that fluttered so joyfully whenever it flew away from the weary Ivan Ivanovych and alighted on one of its favourite flowers, he did not notice anything else about it. Therefore, when that butterfly ended up in his hands, and he looked into its eyes, something akin to fear seized his heart for a moment.

Ivan Ivanovych had never thought that the golden butterfly's gaze could be so direct, so stern; he had not supposed that such heavy, menacing clouds, like those that herald an approaching storm, could darken those tiny blue eyes that were so similar to the clear bright sky. Ivan Ivanovych had once observed a wonderful flash of lightning in the butterfly's eyes when it was imbibing the sweet nectar of a field flower, but he had not known that these same eyes could blaze with another kind of flame, a flame like the infernal fire of hell . . .

He had not known this . . .

But Petro Petrovych—a person who was most interested in all kinds of butterflies, beetles and insects, and who, in his day, had dried a large number of various tiny creatures and stuck them on stickpins, and even presented a delightful collection of them to Ivan Ivanovych on his name day—instilled an even greater fear in him.

He made the observation to Ivan Ivanovych that one always had to be careful with butterflies like this one, and that it was no easy matter to tame them and keep them indoors. It would be better if Ivan Ivanovych were to select a nocturnal butterfly for himself—a little grey one, a black one, or any other kind—as long as it was not golden, not such a delicate colour.

"A nocturnal butterfly," Petro Petrovych said, "does not see anything in the daytime; it sleeps during the day and awakens at night when the windows and doors are shut, when there is nowhere to fly. This one, however, will eagerly strive towards the light, the sun, freedom; it will beat against the closed windows—in a word, it will cause you distress.

"There is only way to tame the butterfly—one must remove the powder that covers its wings, but this is no easy task when you take its colour into consideration. I, for one, have never succeeded in doing this properly, even with the coarsest of wings; I would either scrape the wing so hard that the butterfly instantly lost its strength and died, or I would not see things too well, and the butterfly would fly away."

Ivan Ivanovych became alarmed, but he did not have any regrets—this golden butterfly appealed greatly to him, and as for how it could be kept, that question had to be resolved.

And so Ivan Ivanovych began to ponder the matter. To begin with, he ordered that screens be put on all the windows, that the doors be locked, and that they not be opened to anyone without first covering the butterfly with a silken head-dress that had been made specifically for it. As for the powder on its wings, after a few sleepless nights he came up with a splendid idea. First, he requested that a pair of eyeglasses be made for him, and that the glass in them be out of the ordinary.

"The glass is to be such," Ivan Ivanovych said to the optician, "that a mouse will appear like a watermelon, and my own fingernail like an entire field."

Those glasses were not easy to come by, and they were not cheap, but sooner or later, he did manage to procure a pair, and once, when the butterfly was sleeping, he came up to it with a concealed lantern, lit it abruptly, and saw in a flash what it was about the powder that gave strength to the butterfly's wings. It was like a fine, golden sand, and not all the grains reflected the lantern's light in the same way. There were brighter ones, some that were less bright, and some that were completely pale, almost whitish, and if he had some very fine tweezers or something like that, then Ivan Ivanovych could try, as an experiment, to remove a few of them.

The next day, Petro Petrovych fashioned such tweezers and presented them to his friend, and they approached the butterfly together.

After a lengthy argument between the good friends, and a brief dispute as to where to begin, from where to take off the first grains, they decided against removing them one after the other, so as not to leave conspicuous and aesthetically displeasing spots on the golden wings, but rather, to pick off the most brilliant ones first, then the less brilliant, and finally, if it were necessary—if the butterfly did not settle down—to take away the whitish grains as well.

The butterfly did not give in for a long time. The process was not too painful, but it tickled, and the butterfly began to flutter. Soon, however, realising that it was more painful if it moved about, it calmed down and became still. The first time, the friends removed only a few grains—and then they let the butterfly go. It rose up to the ceiling, flew around for a short while, grew tired, alighted, and fell asleep.

After some time, they removed some more of the powder, and a little later yet, still some more . . .

Ivan Ivanovych could not find enough words to praise his friend for his splendid invention—the tweezers. As an aesthete, an admirer of beauty and harmony, he was genuinely glad that no blemishes could be seen on the wings of the butterfly— that there were none of those unpleasant spots and sores that catch everyone's eye and, on occasion, create an unfavourable impression.

The butterfly was growing weaker; it no longer tried to rise up to the ceiling and only flew around in the middle of the room. Still, its wings did not hurt too much, and it had no reason to complain about anything.

Ivan Ivanovych, however, was walking on clouds. It was only now that the butterfly belonged solely to him; it was only now, when it had stopped soaring in flight, that Ivan Ivanovych could safely take delight in it all day long—without straining his thick, fleshy neck—for he no longer feared that it would fly away.

A portion of the butterfly's life flashed by. It forgot that there was a sun; that there were fields, forests, valleys; that there were fragrant flowers with an abundance of healing, life-giving nectar; that beyond that room there was a whole happy world; and that out there, somewhere, there was a sky. It grew accustomed to the light that found its way in through the window and to the flowers that Ivan Ivanovych placed for it on all the sills; it stopped yearning for the sky, for now even the ceiling was too high for it.

It lived as Ivan Ivanovych wanted it to live, and it began to think that this was how it ought to live; and the open window no longer enticed it.

But one night the butterfly had a dream—it saw itself in a small green orchard. Ripe red apples were hanging on the luxuriant leafy trees, branches were bending down low under the weight of heavy pears, and tiny, multicoloured flowers were sprinkled throughout the orchard.

A woman, all in white, was sitting on a low green bench in the orchard. She was holding a lute in her hands, strumming the strings, and composing songs as she went along.

In those songs, she called upon all people to unite, to work together, to strive towards the light, towards warmth. She challenged injustice to a duel and reproached people for days lost in dreaming. She sang:

"Look, O birds, insects, and people,
Look at the sun, at its rays.
There are many of you in the world,
And you all have a different fate.
But there has always been only one sun.
Lift up your tearful eyes,
Have faith in the sun—it will make you all equal,
As truthful as I—the holy truth—
It will not betray or deceive you.
Tear off your cataracts. Shatter your chains.
You are all equal—children of a single sun!
You are all of one blood! The whole world is yours!
  Fly to me,
  Gather into a single flock,
  And I will lead you to the sun.
  Your lost happiness,
  Your spent strength,
  Freedom, and hope—
  All these I will return to you . . ."

The butterfly rose up abruptly. It fluttered its wings a few times and was astonished—it had not felt such strength for a long time, a very long time. And it joyously began to sing as it flew out the window:
  "Your lost happiness,
  Your spent strength,
  Freedom, and hope—
  All these I will return to you . . ."

It was a beautiful morning. The sun had already risen high in the sky. Once again the butterfly sang out:

  "Fly to me,
  Gather in a single flock,
  And I will lead you to the sun!"

And it spread its tiny wings to fly far up into the sky, to the sun, to the light, to the warmth; but the fresh, fragrant air had already dazed its little head; its eyes clouded over, and a gentle breeze, like the breath of a child, seemed like a storm to it.

It flew in circles for a while, and then, its strength depleted, it dropped into a puddle made that morning by Ivan Ivanovych's gardener as he was watering the flowers.

As for Ivan Ivanovych, he never saw the lady dressed in white in his dreams, and he never heard her songs. He did not like the sun beating down on his head, he could not smell the fragrance of the flowers because of his catarrh, and he would not admit that the butterfly was flying to the sun of truth.

And so, bowing to his inexorable fate, and crushed by the burden of being Ivan Ivanovych, he collapsed into the puddle.

The Gloves
(1903)

Mykyta was running home as fast as his legs could carry him.

On the Saturday before Easter, stores always stay open late. This year, however, the city people, enjoying the calm, warm evening, kept the merchants up even later than usual, and Tykhin Semenovych did not dismiss his salesclerk until it was almost midnight.

Mykyta was hurrying to the Kyivan suburb of Podol, where his young wife was waiting for him, so they could go to church. He was certain that she had long since finished her work in their small quarters, and that, having tidied up the cosy living room and arranged everything on the table, she was already dressed and impatiently watching for him.

He imagined how happily she would greet him, how pleasant it would be to walk alongside her to church on this enchanting night, how wonderful it would be to break the fast and, of course, how proud he would be of her—his beautiful wife—the next day when they visited the other clerks, some city people, and the lords with whom they were acquainted.

Most likely, they would first visit Lady Lyubytska. His wife, Dunya, had lived at her place for almost seven years. It was there that she had learned to attire herself attractively, to speak with an unusual propriety, and to behave properly among people. It was on this lady's advice that Dunya had married him, and it was she who had given her the most presents.

Even the white dress that seemed to be woven out of silver, the one that Dunya had sewn for herself for Easter, was a present from her.

It was true that Dunya had spent almost half of Mykyta's monthly pay on the trimming for the dress, but was he to begrudge his dear wife five or six *karbovantsi [dollars]* for a bit of trim? Because of that little extravagance, he had been forced to ask for

an advance on his next month's salary, but it could not be helped—
he had to do what he had to do.

He had done it, and now the trimming was exactly the kind that
Dunya wanted, and had won the approval of the lady herself.

As the holidays approached, Dunya asked him to get another
advance. Mykyta acquiesed and gave her all the money, except
for two *karbovantsi* that he had kept to buy a new beret for
himself. Not too long ago, however, he had given her those two
karbovantsi as well, and now he did not have so much as a *shah
[half a penny]* to buy a candle for Christ's sepulchre.

An orphan and a servant from the age of nine, not very
handsome, and without any wealth of his own, Mykola could
scarcely have expected that, with his own two hands, without any
help from anyone, with his own strength, his own work, he would
succeed in securing such a reliable means of earning a living. At
the age of twenty, he had become the chief salesclerk in one of
the best stores in the city. And, when he turned twenty-five, he
married Dunya, Lady Lyubytska's chambermaid—a striking beauty
who, in Mykyta's opinion, did not have an equal among either the
chambermaids or the city girls.

She was his first love. He fell in love with her at first sight and
admired her secretly for a whole year, concealing his feelings from
others and from himself. He most certainly would not have dared
to confess it for a long time if Dunya, who noticed how he
alternately flushed and paled whenever he saw her in the store,
had not come to his assistance.

In the opinion of Lady Lyubytska, Mykyta was a suitable partner
for Dunya, both in terms of age and financial status. Moreover, he
had earned such a good reputation and such respect, among both
the merchants and the city people, that he could look forward to
a much better position, with higher pay than he was receiving at
Tykhin Semenovych's store.

Three months had passed since they were married, and those
three months seemed like three days. Every morning, Mykyta
leaped out of bed before sunrise. Carefully firing up the samovar
so as not to awaken his wife, who was accustomed to sleeping in,
he brushed his clothing, cleaned his boots, and carried in some
firewood and water. And, only when the samovar began to boil,
did he awaken Dunya and invite her to have a cup of tea with him.

After breakfast, Mykyta rushed off to the store, where he worked without a break until evening.

He had no idea what his wife did all day—what she did in the house, where and on what she spent his money. He demanded nothing but happiness from her, and this she gave him voluntarily, with her love, her affection, and her kind words.

Oh, in the past, life had not smiled upon him! Before now, he had known neither a warm home where he could truly feel himself to be a "real" person, nor a family, nor kindness from anyone. Up to now, he had known only his obligations to strangers; he had fulfilled these obligations and received, in return, respect and a few *karbovantsi*; but neither the respect nor the money warmed his heart. From his earliest childhood, he had been someone's servant or someone's drudge, and this was the first time he would be celebrating the great holy day in "his own" little home with "his own" wife, eating "his own" *paska [braided circular Easter bread]*.

He was almost home now; he could see the light in the window. Just a few more minutes, and Mykyta would be in his own house.

He found everything as he had expected. Dunya, having long since finished her household chores and run out on the street twice to see if he were coming, greeted him joyfully. How nicely she had fixed up the house! Where had she got those white curtains for the windows? And she had hung up some pictures as well. And the Easter breads stood so tall and even on the table! She had also baked a *mazurka [a special Easter pastry]*.

It was Easter! Easter! She was completely satisfied. Their house and their table were adorned no worse than that of the dignified Ivan Semenovych, the salesclerk in the hardware store, and despite the fact that he was paid more than thirty *karbovantsi* a month, his wife, the plump Priska, could not show off such fine Easter breads.

Dunya's dress was truly splendid. The silver threads woven into the material complimented her dark complexion, and Dunya was slender, with a wonderful figure. His shirt and boots were also ready. He dressed hastily, while she—ebullient and contented—chattered away without stopping for breath.

This week had caused her so many problems! She had not dared to bake the Easter breads herself; she had ordered them from an acquaintance who baked for others, and they had cost her dearly.

It's true, of course, that one could have had cheaper ones baked. Her neighbour, for example, had baked six, and used only fifty eggs, but would she dare to bring shame down upon her beloved Mykyta by treating his guests to an ordinary bread instead of to a real *paska*? The *mazurka* also had not been cheap, but it did not really matter. Easter came only once a year.

Then, all at once, she fell silent.

"What are you thinking about so hard?" Mykyta asked her.

"I'm trying to remember something," Dunya replied, sinking into even deeper thought.

"Tell me, what is it?" Mykyta inquired, somewhat upset by the strange look on Dunya's little face.

"You won't be able to find what I'm looking for, anyway," Dunya responded, hastily unlocking her trunk.

"But perhaps I will."

"You won't!" Dunya replied a trifle angrily, and she began to overturn everything in the trunk, rooting around to the very bottom. Not finding what she was looking for, she slammed the heavy, iron-clad lid of the trunk and, tucking up her skirt, clambered up to the storage area between the tall *peech [a large clay oven wih a sleeping area on top]* and the wall.

There were countless boxes, baskets, and bags there, with all sorts of ribbons, doilies, women's head attire, and pieces of cloth that Lady Lyubytska had thrown out at one time or another. Dunya emptied all those boxes and baskets, messed up all the ribbons and pieces of cloth and, becoming more and more agitated, began to turn things over on the bed.

Mykyta stopped dressing and watched every movement. For a long time, he did not dare ask her what she was trying to find, or what it was that she had lost, because he was afraid that he would make her angrier. But, finally, he could not hold back any longer.

"Is it perhaps some money that you've lost?" he asked carefully.

"Money? What kind of money? Where would the money have come from? There are only seventeen *kopiyky [pennies]* left from the twenty *karbovantsi* you gave me," she retorted scathingly.

Mykyta felt as if he had been stabbed by a knife! "Seventeen *kopiyky!*" he said to himself. How were they to survive for the two weeks after Easter?

"So what are you looking for," he asked, pretending to be unconcerned, as if he had not heard anything about the money.

"Gloves," Dunya replied, as she hastily straightened the pillows and quilt.

"What kind of gloves?"

"White ones," she answered, almost in tears.

"I don't think I've ever seen them . . ." Mykyta observed.

"What do you mean you haven't seen them? Don't you remember the wedding? Oh! I know, I know where they are! I've just remembered!" She clapped her hands joyfully. "Take the stool, Mykyta, and climb up to the shelf with the icons; they're over there, behind that icon."

Mykyta pulled up a stool and instantly found a small roll of paper.

"There they are! We've found them!" Dunya skipped with joy, her eyes began to shine, and her face became as happy and carefree as it usually was—it became the face that Mykyta found so attractive.

"Did you really need those gloves so badly? Couldn't you have done very nicely without them?" he asked with a smile, recalling the sadness that had enveloped Dunya when she was searching for the gloves.

"But don't you understand, my foolish one, that without these gloves the holiday would be totally ruined for us?" she responded with a question, smoothing down his new green and red polka dot tie.

"Would I dare to step beyond our threshold in this dress without gloves? Where would I hide my hands? They're so chapped and red! I'm embarrassed to show myself in public on an ordinary day with bare hands, and this is, after all, the eve of an important holiday! I also had to buy myself a pair of special shoes to wear with this dress," she added, showing Mykyta a foot shod in a new, delicate shoe.

The shoes did not appeal to Mykyta. His wife's wide feet seemed to spread out in them, and they appeared clumsy and inelegant; however he did not say anything to her. Nor did he ask how much she had paid for them. He was happy that his home was once again filled with joy, and that Dunya was cheerful and smiling. He hastily finished dressing and began to urge Dunya, who was painstakingly re-arranging her curls mussed during her search, to hurry along.

At last, Dunya smoothed her dress, threw a shawl over her head, and began to pull a glove on her left hand. It seemed strange and wonderfully gratifying to Mykyta that his wife, like a true lady, was standing in the middle of the room fussing with a glove; and he took pleasure in looking at her face, so happy and contented because of those gloves.

But now Dunya began to frown; she stamped her foot and turned away from Mykyta.

"Don't look!" she said, blushing furiously.

"Why is that?" Mykyta laughed. "Am I going to cast an evil spell on you, or what?"

"Don't be a nuisance!" she responded angrily.

"Why are you annoyed? You have your gloves now!" Mykyta laughed once again.

Dunya did not reply. And she walked away from him into the farthest corner of the room.

Mykyta, tired of standing, sat down on the bed and smoked a cigarette. Dunya continued fussing with her glove.

"Perhaps you're putting the glove on the wrong hand?" Mykyta finally suggested, recalling how a cook had once torn a glove to shreds in the store when she tried putting it on the wrong hand.

"Pull it on for me," Dunya responded, and she extended her hand, from which the fingertips of a glove were dangling.

"They won't go on," Mykyta said, visually comparing the wrinkled glove and his wife's big, broad hand.

"What do you mean, they won't go on?" Dunya asked furiously. "I wore them for our marriage, didn't I?"

"But now they won't go on. Believe me, they won't go on, so don't tire out your hands for nothing. Let's go to church; you can get along just fine without them."

Infuriated, Dunya yanked the glove with all her strength; it split and came apart in three places. Dunya tore it off, threw it across the room and, sobbing bitterly, flung herself, just as she was, in her new dress and shawl, on the bed. Mykyta did not know what to do or say to calm her. Her only response to all his pleas and exhortations was more tears.

What could he do? How could he help? Were the holidays truly going to be ruined because of those gloves? After all, very few townswomen wore gloves, and it was warm outside . . . Of what use were they? Mykyta tried to console his wife, but his words only made her more distraught.

What did it matter that not all the townswomen wore gloves? Had he forgotten about Sanka, Natalka, and Halka? Had he ever seen them with bare hands? In what way was she, Dunya, worse than they? Perhaps only in that she had married him! Oh, while she was still in service, she had not had the occasion to cry over something as trifling as gloves. Why had she married him? If it were not for the kindness of Lady Lyubytska, she would not have had a new dress for the holidays; she would have walked around like a tramp in rags, because her husband could not find the money to buy her gloves that cost only a *karbovanets*.

Mykyta just listened. Until this moment, it had never occurred to him that someone, least of all Dunya, could call him a bad husband. It seemed to him that up to now he had fulfilled all his obligations to his wife—he worked just for her and gave her all his money. But she was dissatisfied with him. Perhaps he truly was to blame in some way?

He was not at all sure if Dunya really needed those gloves, or if he truly were to blame, or if she had the right to reproach him and demand more from him—but what was the difference? He saw her bitter tears and felt in his heart that these tears would not stop even after the holidays. He saw that Dunya felt that she was unfortunate—or at least less fortunate than some Sanka, Natalka, and Halka—and this was enough; it was more than enough to make him unhappy.

Mykyta moved away from the bed and sat down by the table. On the table lay the huge key from the store—the merchant always entrusted Mykyta with a key, so that he could get into the store without having to wait for him.

Mykyta caught sight of the key, thought of the store, and simultaneously recalled the countless pairs of multicoloured gloves that were in it. Was he not being stupid? Why was he worried? Would it be so difficult to go there—to the store—take a pair of gloves for his wife, and in that way find peace and recapture the happiness that had been destroyed so unexpectedly? The guards knew him, and he could tell his employer everything that had happened, or, perhaps, he would not say anything at all; he would borrow a *karbovanets* from someone after the holidays and pay for the gloves then. It would be very easy to do this.

"Dunya! That's enough crying! Let's go! I'll get you some gloves from the store," he said happily.

Dunya instantly fell silent. She rushed up to kiss and thank him. She vowed she simply could not get along without the gloves, and she pleaded with Mykyta—her "dear one," her "beloved husband"— not to be angry with her, all the while hastily wiping her teary eyes with a wet towel.

They set out.

There were no guards nearby. Dunya sat down on the steps, and Mykyta unlocked the store. He walked in, closed the door behind him, lit the candle that he was taking to the church service, and took the box with the gloves down from the shelf. He went through everything once, and then a second time; he examined every pair but, except for a few black pairs that would not go with the silver dress, he could not find a single pair that would fit his wife's hands.

All the church bells were ringing, and the sound echoed in the high-ceilinged store. Mykyta heard first one group of young people, and then a second one, run past the store to listen to the priest in Podol after visiting all the other churches; he could hear people hurrying to the church to have their *paska* blessed. People continually drove and walked past the stone walls of the store, while he searched and searched for gloves without finding any.

Something akin to despair was squeezing his chest; he recalled Dunya, her tears, and his heart fell and grew cold . . . All at once he saw a pair of pale yellow gloves on the shelf. He looked at the size and almost shouted with joy—it was exactly the size he needed.

Five or six minutes later, blissfuly happy, they were standing side by side in church. They attracted the attention of almost all of the residents of Podol.

Immediately after the service, Mykyta and Dunya walked up to his employer to exchange Easter greetings with him. The merchant invited them to his home to break the fast. Mykyta would have preferred to go home, but such an unusual and unexpected favour could not be refused, and so he agreed. As for Dunya—she did not have to be asked twice; it was as if she had forgotten all about her own *paska* and *mazurka*. She was certain that she would amaze not only the merchant's guests with her attire, but also his daughter-in-law Halyna, who took great pleasure in elegant dresses and was prepared to go to great lengths to obtain them.

And Halyna truly did like the dress, the trim, and the delicate and fine shawl; but she was most interested in the gloves—they were exactly the colour of her yellow dress. She had chosen a pair like that for herself, but they were a little brighter, and if Dunya would not mind exchanging gloves with her, she would be most grateful.

Dunya happily agreed, because her yellow gloves were a little too dark for her white dress.

It was only now that Halyna remembered that she had left her gloves in the store. She simply had to have them, and she rushed up to Mykyta. She was not sure where she had left them—Mykyta would have to look throughout the store, but he must examine them carefully, for she had marked them in a special way. And so that Mykyta would understand exactly where to look for the mark, Halyna took Dunya's glove and turned it inside out.

"But these are the ones I marked," she said in surprise, pointing to a small round circle on the glove.

"Show it to me!" the merchant cried out.

Halyna showed him.

"You're right—they're yours," the merchant said. "They were lying by themselves, off to one side on the shelf. How is it that Halyna's gloves have ended up on your wife, Mykyta?" he asked his salesclerk.

Mykyta blushed furiously, but he was certain that it would not occur to anyone to accuse him of some wrongdoing. He was just about to tell them what had happened, but when he looked at the merchant the words died on his lips.

He knew his employer. In the six years he had been with him, he had learned to read his every gesture. He knew what every glance and every word meant, and the twisted smile on Tykhin Semenovych's face told him all he needed to know. He had seen the very same smile once before, quite some time ago, when Tykhin had caught a small boy shoplifting and chased him out of his store.

"Get out, you thief! Get out of here, you ugly thief!" he had said as he pushed the boy out the door and, all the while, he had kept on smiling.

Could it be that Tykhin Semenovych, Halyna, and all these guests who were breaking the fast together considered him to be a thief? What about his honourable name? And the fifteen years of irreproachable work he had done among strangers? Could it be that all this was forgotten, and that a pair of gloves had clouded their eyes? Could no one remember anything except this unfortunate incident? Did no one see that it was he, Mykyta, who was standing before them?

"So you gave your wife, your dear little wife, a small present, is that it? Is that right? Instead of a *pysanka [multicoloured Easter egg with intricate designs]*, you gave her some gloves?" the merchant smiled, but he kept the gloves in his hands.

And those gloves grew larger and larger. Mykyta could no longer see anything except them, not even his wife who was standing somewhere close by. There was nothing left of the years he had spent in service; there no longer was any happiness or grief in the world; there was nothing at all—only those pale yellow gloves.

Mykyta wanted to smile, to laugh, to relate in an amusing manner the anecdote about Dunya's tears and his distress. But something unusual was happening; everything was growing dark, his heart was fainting, and he was covered in cold sweat.

In the eyes of the merchant and all the guests he could read the judgement that was being passed on him: "Thief!"

"Well, our Mykyta has been caught—caught like a cat with the bacon," the merchant joked, "and all because of his young wife!"

"But I didn't steal them . . . I . . ." Mykyta finally began to say, but he himself was surprised how strange his voice sounded, how difficult it was for him to speak.

"Forget it! Forget it! There is no one alive who has not sinned. In honour of the great holiday, I forgive you and God forgives you. Let us drink a toast to the human race, my brother! Come on, come closer to the table! Halyna, pour him a full glass! Treat him to the yellow wine: it's the right colour. Ha-ha-ha! It's the colour of your gloves," the merchant interrupted what Mykyta was trying to say, and he pulled the young man by the sleeve towards the table.

"Tykhin Semenovych, you mustn't think that I . . ." Mykyta made a second attempt to vindicate himself.

"That's enough, that's enough about that! After all, don't I know you?" The merchant once again interrupted Mykyta and thrust a full glass of wine into his hands. Mykyta took the glass and drained it, but it only made him feel worse.

He had to go quickly, very quickly, into the fresh air, home, anywhere—just to get away as far as possible from all these people, from these gloves.

They set out for home.

Along the way, people continually stopped and exchanged Easter greetings with them. Mykyta responded and answered their questions, but it seemed to him that it was not he who was talking, it was not he who was exchanging Easter greetings, but someone else, someone who had taken on the task of speaking and laughing for him. He was not connected in any way with these people who were talking with him, or with the holiday, or with the city. It seemed to him he was bound with a steel chain to a pair of gloves, and there was nothing in the whole world that was as salient as the question: what did the merchant think about him now? Did he, or did he not, consider Mykyta a thief?

Back there, in the merchant's house, and during the first few moments that he was out on the street, Mykyta was certain that he had understood the significance of both the merchant's smile and his words, but, little by little, under the influence of the fresh air, his certainty began to fade, and he leaned towards the pleasant thought that the merchant had truly made light of the incident. It was Dunya who supported him most vigorously in this thought; she did not act at all like the wife of a thief as she merrily exchanged greetings with passers-by.

"Shall we go to see Lady Lyubytska?" she inquired of Mykyta when they came to the street on which the lady lived.

"Yes, let's go," Mykyta agreed.

"But . . . how can I go now, without any gloves?" she seemed to be asking herself this question, but her voice had such an unpleasant ring to it that Mykyta once again shuddered.

"I won't go to visit the lady," he said quietly.

"What do you mean, you won't go?" Dunya asked in surprise.

"I won't go, and that's the end of the matter," Mykyta replied severely.

"But she's prepared a gift for me," Dunya observed.

"To blazes with it—you'll get along without that gift!" Mykyta said.

"Are you going to get me some material for a dress, or what? That will be the day! It was just a pair of gloves—and even those you had to steal!"

Mykyta did not wait to hear anymore. He veered sharply in the opposite direction, turned off into a narrow lane, and, in a short time, arrived in his own home. He hung up his cap, took off his coat, and began to pace the room; however, he tired quickly and sat down at the table.

What was he like when he left this house, and what was he like when he returned to it? Where was the contentment, the happiness, the confidence in his own abilities that he had felt until so recently? This house, where he had know such happiness, no longer brought him any joy; the portrait of Dunya that he used to wear on his chest no longer touched his heart. What had he done? What had been done to him, and what had changed him so greatly? Could it have been the gloves? Yes, it was the gloves. They had done this to him.

He had not wanted to steal them; he had not stolen them. He had wanted to buy them, but he did not have any money—only seventeen *kopiyky* to see them through the next two weeks—and so, instead, he had paid for them with his good name.

He had given Dunya his heart, his soul, and his money long ago. And today he had given her his last valued possession—the good reputation that he had worked so hard to attain. He had given her the respect he had worked for so many years to win from people, and she was still unhappy with him.

What else could he give her? What would she say to him if the merchant kicked him out? And there could be no doubt that he would do this, because he did not tolerate thieves. And even if he did not kick him out, he would no longer entrust him with the key. He would no longer have confidence in him, and would watch him closely.

Mykyta was not accustomed to being treated like this; he would leave the merchant of his own accord. He would leave. But where would he go? Where would he find refuge for his head that was now covered with eternal shame? Where would he be able to hide himself from Dunya's harsh words? There was no place he could hide—he was surrounded by Dunya's tears and reproaches, by the smile on the merchant's face, by the gloves . . .

Unless, perhaps, beneath the ground? Yes, that was it—beneath the ground. It was only there that he would not see anything, or hear anything; nothing could reach him there. But what about Dunya? Dunya had been the first to call him a "thief"; she had told him to his face that he had "stolen" the gloves—what need could she have of him, a thief!

Three days later, Mykyta's body was carried out of a special chapel designated for those who died in hospital after attempting suicide. The merchant had not skimped on money for the funeral. Neither he, nor Halyna, nor their guests, so much as hinted at the unfortunate incident with the gloves, and if it had not been for the young widow who, copiously shedding tears, told all her neighbours about her grief as she followed the coffin in her black mourning clothes, no one would have ever known why Mykyta had been driven to commit such a great sin—to cut short his life by taking poison.

"It would be understandable if something like this had happened in the winter, when the cold in your fingers is bad enough to make you cry, but it's spring—it's like God's paradise. It's warm now—of what use were those gloves?" an elderly townswoman wondered as she hurried after the coffin.

And the sun—as if to provide proof that the old woman was speaking the truth, that one did not need gloves, that it was shining warmly as it should be, that it was not to blame for what had happened—shone still more warmly, shimmering luminously on the cupola of the church in the cemetery past which they carried Mykyta's coffin.

Mykyta was carried past the church, past the cemetery that was green with periwinkle, past the burial grounds. And, without a priest, without cantors, and without prayers, he was cast into a hole that had been dug in a meadow that stood apart, almost outside the city limits. There already were a few little mounds there, but there were no crosses, and there were no trees . . .

Horpyna's Oath
(1905)

Horpyna married off her son before the harvest and, on Thursday of their wedding week, sent the young couple out to hill the potatoes. Left all by herself in the house, she began to feel lonely and dejected.

"Oh God, my God," she thought, "how short a person's life is— before you know it, before you're fully aware of what is happening, death is looking over your shoulder. It wasn't so long ago that I was young myself, but now I have a daughter-in-law. Life has flashed by like the summer night before the Feast of Saints Peter and Paul; it's rushed by like the spring runoff, and what's left of it could fit on a mosquito's nose—I won't even have time to do penance for my sins."

She started to worry and ruminate about how she should live out the remainder of her life without falling into sin, how to save her soul from temptation. And so she took an oath not to love her husband anymore—to leave the conjugal bed.

Nykin walked into the house. She glanced up at him, looked at his grey beard, and became even more terrified when she realized how long she had lived on this earth without repenting, without doing penance.

"Oh, my husband and my spouse! How much of our life we've already lived, and how grey you've become!" she struck her hands together in despair. "The summer of our life has passed, the years of our youth are long gone, and the time has come for us to prepare ourselves for our final journey to the other world, but we haven't even thought about it.

"Let's forget, Nykin, how we used to love one another, cared for one another, how young we were when we married, and how our love led to misunderstandings throughout our life together. We'll live out the rest of our lives, Nykin, without arguing, without quarrelling, and without any problems; if you do something that isn't quite right—I won't say anything, and if I'm the one who does something not quite so—don't you be angry.

"I'll go on a pilgrimage to Kyiv, pray to God, and then I'll begin to live like a grandmother. I've piled up as many sins as there is sand on the shore, but maybe my grandchildren will be able to intercede on behalf of my sinful soul. You do as you see fit, but as for me, I've taken an oath to care only about my soul . . ."

"It has nothing to do with the upcoming harvest, does it?" Nykin laughed.

"Don't laugh, Nykin, don't lead me into sin. I don't want to argue. Maybe fate has granted you a long life, so go ahead and live as you think best, but I've already taken an oath, and I won't go back on my word," Horpyna said quietly.

"I'm not arguing with you; if you want to live like a grandmother, so be it—it doesn't hurt to have an extra *palyanytsya [flatbread]* in the house," Nykin laughed once again.

"You're always joking, but I'm talking seriously. When I stop to think how many sins I've committed because of you, I'm overcome with sorrow . . . But now I'm no longer going to be jealous of you, and I'm not going to spy on you. Live as you know best; love whomever you want to—it makes no difference to me, and I'll stop nagging and avoid sin."

"Fine!" Nykin quickly said, grabbing his cap.

"Where are you hurrying off to? Can't we carry on a pleasant conversation any longer?"

"Let's do that when the weather's bad," Nykin flung over his shoulder as he disappeared behind the door.

Horpyna started to rush after her husband, to turn him back, but then she thought better of it.

"God be with you," she thought. "It's your sin and no one else's if you don't respect your wife. If you don't want to listen, then don't—so long as I've confessed to you."

She sat down by the table, sighed softly, leaned her head on her hand, closed her eyes, and sat motionless.

The young couple returned from the field. The daughter-in-law—a dark, short, lively, and competent young woman—carried in the milk pail, strained the milk, brought a load of firewood into the house, and peeled some potatoes; the son came into the house twice—first for a rope to tie the cattle to the manger, and then for a hempen sack.

Horpyna did not see or hear anything. Her soul felt joyous and at peace. The entire world with its troubles, its worries, and its daily grind vanished from her mind and concealed itself from her eyes. Enchanting dreams, wonderful hopes, and righteous thoughts flitted through her head like butterflies in the spring air; the church bells for the divine liturgy enveloped her, the smoky, aromatic fumes from the censor wafted past her, and her soul, cleansed by her oath, was fainting in a sweet drowsiness.

She saw herself in Kyiv on a pilgrimage, imagined herself in conversation with righteous monks and pious beggars, heard the words that she would speak to the young women as she instructed them how to live on this earth without sin.

The straw blazed in the stove; the windows, reflecting the flames, gleamed cheerfully, and the cottage was suffused with a rosy glow. Only the icon corner, where Horpyna sat, appeared to be shrouded in a fog, and her pensive, immobile figure almost disappeared in the darkness.

"Mother! Why are you so dejected? Or are you dozing perhaps?" her son approached her. "Tell my young wife what to fix for supper; she's been looking at you, but doesn't have the nerve to ask, because you're not saying anything."

"Prepare whatever you know how to cook, whatever you want to cook, my daughter, because I will no longer be eating anything except for radishes, horseradish, and holy bread," Horpyna replied with a sigh.

"If it's all the same to mother, cook some buckwheat *halushky [dumplings]*," Dmytro suggested to his wife.

"Eat in good health, my children, but food is no longer important to me. You'll bake a few wheaten *palyanytsi* and toast some rusks for me, Stepanyda, because I'm setting out for Kyiv on Sunday," Horpyna stated solemnly.

"But what about the harvest?" her astonished son asked her.

"You'll have to gather the grain slowly with father, my children, but without me—for I probably won't return in time for the harvest," Horpyna replied, and she sighed once again.

Nykin came home, and they had their supper. Horpyna grated some horseradish, ate it with a stale chunk of *palyanytsya* from the cupboard, drank some water, and lay down to sleep on the bare wooden bench, with only her fist under her head.

"Mother, lie down on the *peech [a large clay oven with a sleepiong area on top]*, or at least let me make you up a bed here," her daughter-in-law said.

"The Holy Saints suffered more torments than this," Horpyna replied, refusing to accept either a blanket or a pillow.

After working hard all day, everyone fell asleep quickly. But Horpyna could not sleep. The confounded boards dug into her sides, and the hand under her head was growing more numb by the minute.

Remembering that a partially sewn apron was lying on the window, she stretched out her hand, felt around for it, and placed it under her sides—it did not help. She groped the wall for Dmytro's jacket, took it off the hook, and tucked one end of it under herself—the boards still dug into her. At that point, she folded the jacket in four, placed a bundle of bran siftings under her head, removed everything from the bench to make more room for her feet, covered her face with a cloth so that the full moon would not peer into her eyes—and, before she knew it, she was fast asleep . . .

II

The millet was ripe when Horpyna returned from her pilgrimage. Nykin, together with his son and daughter-in-law had gathered the rest of the grain, ploughed the fields for the winter rye, and even prepared the threshing floor for the cut grain. Horpyna came home after all the work was done, but no one reproached her or condemned her. She visited all her relatives, gave them the crosses and icons she had brought from Kyiv, and then went on to visit even people who were not related to her, telling them all that she had seen and heard.

The young women surrounded Horpyna like bees drawn to a sweet-smelling flower. They listened to her without stirring and found her truly amazing. She floated over the ground when she walked, and spoke softly, like a child; she greeted everyone, humbled herself before everyone, and tried to please everyone.

And it became strangely quiet in Horpyna's house, as well. The animated Stepanyda fell silent, and there were no more songs. Dmytro stopped smoking cigarettes in the house, and Nykin, even though he did not cease his bantering, began to visit the neighbours more frequently to regale them with his jokes.

When the villagers went out into the fields, Nykin also went to work with his son and daughter-in-law. Horpyna, left alone in the house, would remove her apron and sash, light some Cherubimic incense in the lid of a pot, place it in the icon corner, and begin intoning first the morning matins, and then the noonday mass up to the transubstantiation of the Holy Gifts, when the Holy Spirit is invoked to sanctify the bread and wine; and she would sing everything—the priest's part, the cantor's, and the reader's. And it was the Lord who had chosen her for such a righteous life!

"Wherever I go," she told the young women, "wherever I am, holy angels and dear nuns appear before me, and I can hear their voices; they sing with such high, clear voices: 'Lord, have mercy! Lo-o-o-ord, have mercy!' And I hear them when I bow to the ground, and when I look up at the stars, and even in the house. I'll soon consecrate myself to the service of God."

"You won't consecrate yourself while you're dozing, but the wind is shaking the seeds out of the millet as we speak; come out, at least today, to do some raking," Nykin said to her one day.

"God be with it—that blessed millet. I'm not meant to live much longer on this earth, and I don't want to preoccupy myself with worldly matters. You gather up your portion, and let the wind shake out my share of the seeds if it so desires," Horpyna responded.

Nykin stood and scratched the nape of his neck. In this very busy season, he would gladly have dragged her off to the field by force, but he had to abandon this tempting notion. The year before last, Horpyna had made him sign a document in the district office that stated he was not to beat her—and she carried this paper around with her in the bosom of her shirt.

The harvest ended, and only the odd sheaf of buckwheat was still ripening in a few of the farmers' fields. Stepanyda baked and cooked, tended the cow, looked after the boar, and stripped the hemp—and Horpyna did absolutely nothing. She just prayed and instructed young women how to live on this earth without sinning.

The Feast of St. Mary the Protectress arrived. Stepanyda rose before dawn, lit the stove, and asked if she could go to church. Hopryna, who was staying at home, gave her daughter-in-law permission to go, and even lent her a brand new calico shirt that she herself had never worn.

The young woman came home from church very happy, chattering and joking. Horpyna listened to her, but did not stop her, because the Lord gave people holidays so that they could pray and, after their prayers, enjoy themselves.

After finishing their family dinner, they sat around the table, sliced up a watermelon and began eating it. Horpyna joined them and reached for a slice as well. Just then, Stepanyda glanced at her father-in-law and burst out in gales of laughter, almost choking on the watermelon.

"Why are you laughing so hard, my daughter?" Horpyna asked her. "It's only servants who are permitted to bare their teeth continually; it's not fitting that you should laugh like this, especially in front of your father-in-law and your husband."

"But it seems so funny to me," Stepanyda replied, blushing furiously.

"What is it that seems so funny to you?" Horpyna asked somewhat testily, because it occurred to her that the young woman might be laughing at her.

"It's father," Stepanyda replied, scarcely able to restrain herself from laughing again, "He threw a piece of peel, and it fell right in the bosom of my shirt."

"It's not seeming for an older man to joke like that," Horpyna blinked at Nykin, and her slice of watermelon with its wonderful, flaming red, fleshy comb, dropped unexpectedly, as of its own accord, out of her hand. She stared fixedly at her husband and did not seem to recognise him.

And Nykin, who in honour of the holiday was cleanly shaved, neatly combed, and attired in a new vest and a white embroidered shirt, truly did look at least ten years younger.

"I was aiming for the slop pail, and I hit the young woman," he said, picking the seeds out of a slice of watermelon. "And perhaps I'll strike a widow as well," he added, winking at Horpyna.

Stepanyda choked with laughter and fled like a madwoman out of the house. Dmytro smirked, grabbed a dipper, gulped down some water and, clamping his teeth together, rushed out blindly, as if to flee as far as possible from sin.

Only Nykin remained beside Hopryna, but that was exactly what she wanted.

"Why were they laughing like that? Why were they laughing?" she asked Nykin. "What kind of a widow am I, you old dog? Why are you laughing? I went to Kyiv to pray and, in the meantime, you got together with your daughter-in-law?"

"That's enough! Watch out—don't go too far, or I'll thank you so properly for such words that you'll grit your teeth," Nykin said.

"You're lying, you old dog; even though you used to beat me, you won't beat me now," Horpyna leapt to her feet and pulled out the paper from her bosom.

"Then don't babble such nonsense, because if you exasperate me even a paper won't help you . . . Satan!"

"Satan doesn't hear the holy angels, and nuns don't appear before his eyes. It's you who are Satan, may his name not be mentioned in the house; it's you who are the sinful father who has fallen into the temptation of taking away his son's wife," Horpyna did not stop talking.

"Shut up, or I'll beat you!" Nykin thundered.

"Even though you have beaten me, you won't beat me now! You won't!" Horpyna shouted, shoving her paper into Nykin's face.

Nykin jumped up from the bench, grabbed the paper, threw it in the slop pail, swung his arm, and knocked off Horpyna's head-dress. Her dishevelled hair tumbled down her back and covered her face and eyes—but she did not stop to adjust her hair. She dashed swiftly to the slop pail where her paper was floating. Crying and cursing, she retrieved it, carefully spread it out, and placed it on the chimney to dry.

They argued and quarrelled, and it might have ended with that. But Horpyna had not remembered to have her daughter-in-law take off the shirt she had lent her and, within a day—as any fortune teller could have told her—Stepanyda had worn out all the beauty that her mother-in-law had ever possessed.

And so, the next day when Horpyna glanced at herself in the mirror, she flung her arms out in despair. Her face was sallow, wasted, and twisted to one side; her eyebrows were sparse and tangled; her cheeks were sunken, and her nose was like the beak of a stork. At that moment, she recalled how Nykin looked; she compared herself to him and began wailing, weeping, and cursing her sorceress-daughter-in-law.

And the nuns disappeared in a flash.

Horpyna went outdoors that night, pressed her ear to the ground, peered down the road, and spoke to a star—but she could not hear the nuns' voices anywhere; their singing was nowhere to be heard. And it seemed to her that a snake had coiled itself under her heart, and as soon as she closed her eyes, something—it could only be the evil spirit!—sang softly to her: "Nykin loves Stepanyda . . . Nykin loves Stepanyda . . ."

She tossed and turned on the floor, lit a light, prayed to God and, at dawn, ran to Solokha for advice.

"Save me, dear sister, save me in any way you can! Turn away Stepanyda's charms from Nykin, because I took an oath not to be jealous."

"Wash some cuffs and collars, rub down the mouth of the oven with the water, and everything will happen as you want it to," Solokha advised.

Horpyna washed all the cuffs and collars she could find and used the water to rub down, not only the mouth of the oven, but the entire oven. It is true that after she did this, Nykin no longer yelled or quarrelled with her, but he still glared at her like a wolf.

Solokha gave her more advice: "Boil up some gentian plants, wash his blanket and the ticks from his feather pillows in the water, make a comfortable bed for him, place some fragrant mint and basilisk in it, and he'll forget all about Stepanyda."

And Horpyna did as she was told. As soon as Nykin decided it was time to go to sleep, she came up to him and said: "Lie down on this bed, my dear old man. I made the feather pillows and wove the blanket for you, so that your weary bones would have a place to rest well."

Nykin glanced at Horpyna, looked at the clean bed, spit, and crawled up to the *peech* strewn with rye straw.

Horpyna went to Solokha for more advice.

"Heat up some pokers in the fire, scrape off the burnt parts, steep them in whiskey, and then have him drink the whiskey," Solokha advised her the third time.

Horpyna ran to town, bought a small bottle of whiskey, heated up her pokers, scraped them, steeped the scrapings in the whiskey, washed herself with fresh flowers and lovage, and three times treated her husband to a drink—but the whiskey did not have the least effect on him.

At that point, Horpyna became really worried and truly anxious. She went to see all the sorcerers that she knew; she did whatever she was told to do, but it was all in vain—nothing helped, no one could turn her daughter-in-law's charms away from Nykin. And the unclean spirit began to sing out loudly now: "Nykin loves Stepanyda . . . Nykin loves Stepanyda."

She suffered, and when she could no longer endure the pain, went to see Solokha once again.

"I don't know, my darling, what you can do now, how you can turn around your misfortune and protect yourself from your daughter-in-law. Maybe you should rip open your feather pillows—you might find something there to help you," Solokha said.

Horpyna rushed home, grabbed a feather pillow, and ripped it open. Sewn into one of the corners, she found the dried out head of a tiny kitten. That was when Hopryna began to make life miserable for Stepanyda. She kept after her until she finally succeeded in chasing her out of her home. After throwing all of her daughter-in-law's grain out in the snow, she forbid her to come near their yard ever again.

III

One evening Horpyna fell asleep while Nykin was still mending his jacket; when she awoke during the night—her husband was gone. She jumped up, girded herself and, clad only in her long shirt and apronlike skirt, hurried to her daughter-in-law's home at the other end of the village. She stepped up to the window and called out to Dmytro—but he did not hear her and did not respond; she then called out to Stepanyda—but the latter also did not answer.

Horpyna dashed swiftly to the cattle enclosure, untied a cow, and drove it into the cabbages in the garden.

This small act of revenge appeased her a bit. The cabbage was of top quality, and Horpyna, happily counting up the losses that the cow would cause Stepanyda in a single night, turned around to go home.

At that very moment, a figure jumped out from behind the stable, and strong claws grabbed her around the waist.

"Help! Save me!" Horpyna tried to jerk herself free.

"We'll save you, all right! Sydir, Semen, Ivan, Trokhy! Come, come quickly—I've caught a witch!" shouted a voice that was Horpyna knew very well—her daughter-in-law's brother.

"Mykhaylo, my dearest son, let me go—it's me," Horpyna pleaded softly.

"I know, I know that it's you. No wonder my mother is troubled that the cow is hexed. Quickly lads, the witch is trying to get away."

"Let me go, Mykhaylo dear—it's me! I swear to God it's me—Horpyna."

"Even if you're Horpyna, you're still a witch—I won't let you go. Why are you wandering around in other peoples' gardens at night?"

"I was looking for my Nykin at Stepanyda's place. May the Lord strike me down if I'm lying. Let me go, sonny, release me," Horpyna asked for a third time.

In the meantime, the boys ran up and stood with canes and flails, ready to punish the witch.

"Have mercy on me, my doves," Horpyna flung herself at them. "I've never had anything to do with witchcraft since the day I was born, and I've never in my life wandered about in other people's gardens—I was just looking for my Nykin."

"Ha-ha-ha!" the boys roared with laughter. "So that's what this is all about! But you're not on the right track at all—Uncle Nykin went to the cobbler's to get the heels on his boots fixed. Go home with God and lie down on the *peech* before you come down with the ague."

Furious and humiliated, Horpyna ran home. She dashed into the cottage, latched both the porch door and the door to the house, crawled up to the *peech*, and covered herself with a blanket.

Then Nykin began shouting.

"Open up!"

"Holy, holy, holy! Perish, unclean spirit! I'm chasing you into the reeds and the swamps, into the bushes and the marshes from where you've dragged yourself to come here," Horpyna answered from her bed.

"Open up! Are you crazy, or what? It's me—Nykin," Nykin once again rattled the door.

"Go away, evil one, in the name of the Father, and the Son, and the Holy Spirit. Nykin is sleeping on the *peech*," Horpyna replied.

"Open up, I tell you! Why the devil are you keeping me out here in the rain?"

"The Lord will rise from the dead and His wounds will be cleansed," Horpyna intoned loudly.

Nykin knocked and thumped, but he finally had to ask a neighbour to put him up for the night. After that night, however, Horpyna heart felt much lighter.

When her husband came home in the morning, she fluttered up to him like turtledove: "Why are you so unhappy? Why are you walking around all gloomy? Are you hungry, perhaps? Are you not well? Has some misfortune befallen you? Don't conceal it, my dearest spouse, don't hide it from me."

"Get away! Leave me alone, viper!" Nykin thundered at her and gave her such a look that Horpyna turned cold.

"I'm done for now, I'm done for—he really hates me! Take me to you, O God! Let me die! End my suffering! Or at least send an illness down on me so that he'll feel sorry for me, or lure someone to my home so that he'll be jealous!" she prayed to God in despair, and instantly she groaned, moaned, and grabbed at her stomach.

"Help! Save me, my husband! Oh my God, I'm dying. Save me, my dear husband! Do whatever you have to—but save me!"

"Am I a doctor or a sorcerer? Just leave me alone," Nykin hissed through his teeth.

"At least call a righteous person to palpate my stomach. Oh my God! The pain is so sharp, so acute; I can't stand, I can't lie down," Horpyna tossed about on the ground.

"As if I needed the trouble! It'll hurt for a while, and then it'll stop," Nykin growled, picking up his cap.

"Trouble or not," Horpyna thought, "but he still went to fetch the sorceress. Glory to You, O Merciful One, for making him feel sorry for me." Horpyna crossed herself and ran to the threshold to see where it was her husband had gone.

But Nykin did not have the slightest notion of going to fetch a sorceress; he was pleasantly whiling away his time fussing with his wagon.

Horpyna flew out into the street in a rage. Swearing loudly that she would get even with that damned infidel, she ran through the village in search of help.

On an earthen embankment by his cottage, warming his old bones in the sun, sat old Opanas, a widower and sorcerer.

Horpyna fell at his feet.

"Granddad, father! Don't let a Christian soul perish. Come to my home, granddad, and palpate my stomach, because I'm dying."

The old man rose to his feet, took his cane, and tottered after Horpyna. The latter felt that the world had grown brighter. Her feet barely touched the ground as she ran along, praising the All-Merciful One for making everything turn out so well.

"Yes, yes! Now the devil's son will see how it feels to be jealous! It may seem to him that I'm uglier than all the other women, but if someone is attracted to me, then never fear, it'll stab him right in the heart, and he'll forget about his goggle-eyed Stepanyda," Horpyna rejoiced as she urged the old man to hurry along.

As soon as they entered the cottage, Horpyna went to the oven to get some bread, while Opanas stood in front of the icons in prayer.

Horpyna took the bread out of the oven, chose the smallest *palyanytsya*, lay down on the floor, moaned, groaned, removed her sash, placed the hot *palyanytsya* on one side of her stomach and told the old man to palpate her.

The old man sat down on one side, whispered something in his beard, sighed, crossed himself, and began palpating Horpyna.

Quite a bit of time went by. The old man grew tired; his hands were turning numb, his back ached, and he was sweating profusely.

But Horpyna, looking out the window and seeing that Nykin was still fixing his wagon, begged time and again: "Keep on palpating, granddad; it's getting a little better . . . maybe I won't die."

Finally, Nykin finished with the wagon and entered the house.

Horpyna at once began speaking sweetly and lovingly to the old man: "Oh, my dear Opanas, why haven't you come to see me before now? I was longing to see you, I was grieving for you—just as you were grieving for me. You're all alone, and I'm even lonelier; you're unfortunate, and my eyes are always filled with tears . . .

"Come to visit me, my dear Opanas, come in the morning, in the evening, whenever you want to, if I'm so pleasing to you . . . Come to see me, my dear neighbour, my dearest; I'll even buy some whiskey just for you . . ."

"Why, sure, I'll come!" the old man agreed, happy that the fortunate moment had finally arrived when he could rest.

"Come to comfort me tonight. My cottage is big, and I'm all alone in it, like the moon in the sky," Horpyna pleaded once more, looking obliquely at Nykin and nudging the old man.

"Why, sure!" the old man agreed for the second time.

Nykin listened for a while, looked at the two of them, smirked, and walked away laughing. But the old man truly did begin to visit Horpyna's cottage—as soon as dusk fell, he would hobble over there.

More than one *karbovanets [dollar]* flew out of Horpyna's wallet, and she went hoarse from shouting to the deaf old man. The other older women began to sing songs about her, but Nykin was totally indifferent to the situation. He got up in the morning, washed, said his prayers and, not caring whether he had breakfast or not—oh, unfortunate hour!—wandered off after Stepanyda. And it did not bother him at all whether Opanas was in the cottage or not.

Horpyna once again began to grieve; she grieved so hard that her face turned black from sorrow. She suffered and agonized over her fate, and then she came to her senses.

"Are they having a joke at my expense? My husband, the villain, is sapping my blood, while that deaf scarecrow is sipping my whiskey. The holy earth is not completely without justice. If Nykin didn't feel sorry for me when I was ill, and if his unfeeling heart is not capable of jealousy, let the district office teach him how to respect his wife . . . I'll go and lay a complaint."

The moment she thought of this, she was on her way.

Outdoors, a cold wind was blowing, bending the trees and making it difficult to breathe; and snow was falling thickly, making it impossible to see. The light padded cotton coat that Horpyna was wearing would not have kept a young body warm, even in a sheltered spot, but the old woman was too hot in it out in the open steppe. She undid her Circassian kerchief, unbuttoned the collar of her coat, and headed straight for the district office, oblivious of the wind, the snow, and the icy road.

At long last, the church glimmered into view and, a little while later, the district office with its clean clay walls and its hedge of trees could be seen. Horpyna crossed herself and walked more quickly.

On the steps leading to the porch of the office sat a few men; there were also some people in the porch. Horpyna just nodded to everyone and, red-faced and out of breath, bolted, as if she had been shot out of a canon, into the expansive main room where a man was being sued for damage his cattle had done on someone else's field.

"Merciful judges, compassionate judges," Horpyna threw herself at the feet of the presiding judge. "Don't allow me, such an unfortunate person, to perish! I don't have a life—I can't live with my husband; he treats me worse than a dog. Our daughter-in-law has enchanted him—and I'm ruined!"

"Just a minute, old woman, wait for the court to be adjourned," the presiding judge stopped her.

"Take pity on me, and the Lord will not forget you. Call my husband here to answer for his actions—why is he abusing me like this? I'm not an evil woman; I'm a mother, I'm a wife, I'm a proper mistress of my home . . . ask any of my neighbours," Horpyna wailed.

"We'll judge your case this Sunday, and now, go with God," the judge replied.

"Oh, my God! I won't live until Sunday! Have mercy on me, have pity on me; send him a summons right away, so that the trial can be held tomorrow."

"Well, fine," the presiding judge laughed. "It there's such a hurry, let the secretary send him a summons; just don't interfere with what we're doing."

Horpyna took the summons, gulped down a mouthful of water in the porch and, without stopping anywhere for a rest, rushed home. By the time she arrived, it was turning dark. Nykin was whittling a stick for a rake. Horpyna threw the summons down on the bench beside him and, fearing for her safety, went to Solokha's home for the night.

But she did not sleep very well. She kept opening the door all night to wish upon a star and to see if Stepanyda had lit a lamp to welcome Nykin.

As soon as dawn broke, she set out for the district office. Quite a few people had already gathered there. Horpyna spotted a group of reputable men, bowed to them in the customary manner, and drew nearer to tell them about her bitter and hopeless life.

"Good-day! May you be healthy on this Monday!" Nykin's voice rang out unexpectedly right behind her as he greeted the men.

Horpyna turned around, glanced at her husband, and almost struck her hands together in shock. The devil's son had dressed as if he were going to a wedding—he had put on a new overcoat, girded himself with a green belt, and donned Dmytro's grey hat.

"Are you going to court?" the men asked.

"Yes, indeed," he smiled cheerfully and sat down with them.

Horpyna hurried over to another group of people.

Finally the judges came, and the trial began.

"What is your complaint against your husband?" the judge addressed Hopryna. "Does he beat you? Is he a thief? Or doesn't he feed you?"

"I'm complaining about everything," Horpyna stated loudly and clearly. "He doesn't beat me, because he signed a paper that he wouldn't; as for clothing me—yes, he clothes me, because I can't walk around naked; and as for feeding me—yes, he does, because I'm the mistress and I can cook whatever I want to. But I can't live with him. As soon as morning comes, he wanders off from home, and when he comes back he doesn't look at me, or talk to me—as if I weren't his wife, and he wasn't my husband . . ."

"Why do you treat your wife so badly, old man?" the judge asked, with deliberate severity.

"She took an oath," Nykin replied.

"Whether I took an oath or didn't, it's my sin, and I'll have to answer for it, but you shouldn't chase after your daughter-in-law," Horpyna flew into a rage.

"Who should I chase after? You're old . . ."

"I'm old? What do you mean, I'm old? Have you forgotten what a beard you already had when you courted me?" Horpyna became even more infuriated.

"Well, I'm not forcing you to look at me. Opanas comes daily to palpate your stomach, but I'm not complaining."

The men roared with laughter.

"Quiet!" the judge stopped them. "What did you see that made you think Nykin loves his daughter-in-law?" the judge turned to Horpyna.

"What did I see? He's talked for a long time about how he likes dark women, and he often reproached me for being fair, and Stepanyda is like a gypsy, like a devil, all black on the outside— just the way he likes them!"

"Is that it? That's all you saw and that's all you know?" the judge asked in astonishment.

"But what the devil else—may the Lord forgive me—did I need to see?" Horpyna became angry. "I didn't eavesdrop on them—I have the voices of angels to listen to. I didn't spy on them, because I have enough to look at—the holy icons and God's temple . . . And I don't look at such unworthy men as this infidel," she pointed at her husband, "and I don't fall into sin. I'm not like others. Everyone knows me. Praise God, I'm . . ."

"That's enough, auntie, that's enough; we can see that your case is as righteous as the sun," the judge, losing patience, interrupted her self-serving monologue.

"And what about you, my good man, what have you to say for yourself?" the judge turned to Nykin. "You leave your wife in the shade during the entire harvest, while you sow, and plough, and mow, and thresh with your daughter-in-law! Well, if you don't begin to respect your wife as you should and take her out in the field with you, we'll have to put you in jail for a whole week! Do you hear?"

"Yes, I hear you," Nykin replied. "Well, wife, what's to be done? The authorities are giving orders—we have to obey them. Get ready at once to lug sacks to the train station, so that we wouldn't be separated any more . . ."

The courtroom erupted in laughter that drowned Nykin's last few words. The presiding judge was holding his sides, and the secretary was turning livid.

Horpyna stood still for a few moments as if she had been scalded, seemingly incapable of protecting herself from the unexpected humiliation she had been subjected to by the judge, and powerless to stop the general laughter of the people. But she soon regained her senses.

"May you, you devil's son," she attacked Nykin, "perish with your wicked court! And as for you," she approached the bench, "may you turn to stone, you damned, accursed judges! I'll take the entire district office to the regional office!"

"Policeman!" the judge shouted. "Throw the old woman in jail."

The cruel people did not show any mercy or pity—they eagerly assisted the policeman.

And no matter how Horpyna resisted and fought back, she had to spend the whole day in jail.

The Forester
(1905)

I

Harasym took great pride in his small oak forest in Berdykivshchyna, and it truly was something to be proud of. All the other groves in the vicinity had been decimated long ago, and only rotten stumps remained to remind people that centuries-old giants had once stood there; but the young oak trees that had been entrusted during the time of serfdom to the care of Harasym's father, and later to Harasym himself, extended their branches ever more and more luxuriantly and stretched their curly heads ever higher and higher, giving the people a great deal of pleasure. And it gave them no more that pleasure—not once had anyone dared to jump across the deep ditches dug by Harasym, crawl through the barb wire enclosures, and either strike one of the oak trees with an axe or take advantage of the old man's pasture in the raked and swept clearings in the forest. The old man knew what magic words to utter to protect the forest both from being felled and from being damaged.

"I'll kill you if I catch up with you in the forest, so don't go crawling into it," he said earlier on, when he was still young, and people did not know his character all that well.

"I'll kill you, so don't go crawling into it," he said later.

And still later he just said: "I'll kill you."

And finally, he did not have to say anything to scare anyone off, because the people, having learned to fear the old man's words when they were children, did not seek out paths to the forest when they became adults.

All of Harasym's life was spent in that forest, all his strength went into looking after it, and all his thoughts were devoted to its care. And it truly seemed that the roots of those oak trees were intertwined in his heart—he found it so painful to struggle through the dry years, and so rewarding to look at succulent leaves watered well by the rains and to drink in the damp air of the forest.

One time, on a minor spring holiday, some men gathered in the village common to talk. Harasym, who had nothing to do in the forest just then, joined them.

"Are you bored by the woodland sprites, granddad, that you're cuddling up to people now?" the men greeted him.

"You're always laughing and making fun of me. But tell me, do any of you have anything to be proud of in the same way that I can be proud of my forest?" Harasym asked.

"But you know, granddad, it isn't really yours," Okhrim reminded him.

"What do you mean, it isn't mine? It's been mine since I was born, and it will remain mine as long as I live," Harasym replied.

"So you've bought it, have you?" the men broke into gales of laughter.

"A child's mother is not the one who bears it, but the one who rears it. And this old adage can be applied to me. It doesn't matter that it's a lord's forest, that it's entered in the records as belonging to Mykhaylo Mykhaylovych Stokratenko—I'm the one who nurtured it, so I'm it's father, and I'm its master.

"And there's no point in laughing at me, because you've lived as long as I have, but when you die, you won't leave a single trace behind. You've fathered a lot of children, but what's the good of that? They, like you, will suffer in this world and then vanish from the face of the earth; you'll have grandchildren, and they also will die, but my forest will still be standing and thanking me— Harasym."

"So you're saying that it's charmed, that it will stand until the Final Judgement?"

"It will stand as long as it's meant to stand, and when its time comes, it will be felled, because every tree grows for the benefit of people," Harasym said.

"There, you see, that's just the point! You yourself say that a tree grows for the benefit of people—but what benefit does anyone have from your forest?" Antin—a short, sallow, emaciated man— picked up on Harasym's words. "My house burned down and I have to build another one, but I have to go all the way to Sahaydak, some thirty-seven kilometres away, to get some oak wood, while your forest just stands there dumbly like a fool—neither a candle for God, nor a poker for the devil."

"It's the same kind of benefit that your father had from you when you chased around the village common without any pants on. Now you're a mower, and a ploughman, and a so-so carpenter, but back then all you did is eat well—that was the sum total of your usefulness," Harasym responded.

"Go ahead, talk all you want to," Antin gestured indifferently with his hand and, caught up in his own thoughts, turned away from the old man.

"Here, have a look at this staff. I chopped it down way back when I first began to guard the forest by myself, after the death of my father. And just compare it now to the trees that were planted at that time, and you'll see that I had good reason to spend countless nights tending the saplings, to quarrel with you, my neighbours, and to bring sins down on myself. I spent my entire lifetime taking care of this forest, and it may well be that my son will do the same, but my grandchildren may live to see a temple of God built out of these oak trees."

"Uh-huh, they sure will, granddad. You've seen yourself how they dragged twenty-four oak trees out of the forest," Nazar, a young man, spoke up.

"Yes, I saw it, I saw it . . . Well, what could be done? The lord was marrying off his son and must have wanted to build a separate home for him, so he sent men here for some lumber; they chopped down twenty-four oaks a little before their time had come. There were only twenty-four trees like that in the entire forest; they were growing before my time—they must have been left there at one time, as older trees among the younger ones. They were fine trees, very fine, and they would have grown for a long time yet, but they had to be chopped down . . .

"There was a need for them—you see, he had to build his son a house, or maybe a storage shed; in a word, they had to be felled, but if there had not been a need for them, the lord would not have chopped them down as long as he lived."

"Well, granddad, the time has come for you to build a new house. You'll be marrying off your son any day now, and it won't be possible to even lead the bride to the place of honour during the wedding."

"And the young bride won't have any place to walk; no matter where she steps, there are only wood shavings; and if she wants to look out the window, she'll have to either crawl under the bench, or climb up on the table, because one window is sinking into the ground, while the other is pushing upwards towards the main beam," Okhrim intruded into the conversation. "Hey, Sydir, where are you going to find a young bride who would agree to come to your hut?"

He turned to Harasym's son who, sitting a little apart and exchanging the odd word with his friend Ivan, was listening intently to the conversation; he became even more attentive when the conversation turned to the building of a house.

"There's no need to look for one; just let him succeed in getting to see the lord and in buying some oak trees from him, and I'll find him a better bride than he ever dreamed of; but if he doesn't, I'll forbid other matchmakers from going there as well, because old Maksym will give them a cuff in the neck," Mykyta spoke up.

"Really, Sydir, you should do what Mykyta is suggesting. The lord needed to chop down some oak trees, but your need is even greater—because of your hovel no one will give his daughter in marriage to you," Ohkrim supported Mykyta.

"That won't happen as long as I'm alive," Harasym said. "Even when the lord himself wanted some trees, I allowed them to chop down only twenty-four trees, and two wagons had to go back empty because, despite all the efforts of his foreman, I did not let them destroy any young trees."

"But you know, Father, we will have to build a house," Sydir said hesitantly.

"So build one if you have to; the forester in Sahaydak is shredding oaks and all sorts of trees, so go ahead and buy some wood, as much as your heart desires."

"But just stop to think where in God's name that Sahaydak is! Is it easy to haul, with someone else's nag, enough trees to build a house?" Sydir said, drawing nearer to his father.

"You should ask me, your father, if it was easy for him to tend those oaks that are so tempting now to your eyes, if it's easy for him now to have cramps in his back, his legs, and his arms, if it was easy for him to roam through the forest for forty years like a fierce beast, spying on his neighbours with a rifle, and if it's easy for him now to listen to his own son disparage his bloody toil?" Harasym asked, casting a glance at his son.

His face flaming, Sydir lowered his head.

"No matter what you think, young man, your father is speaking the truth," interjected Yevmen. "I saw the forest grow up before my eyes, and I saw your father grow old before my eyes . . . And don't you listen to people that egg you on—there are many of us who covet what's already there, but very few of us who know how to create something worthwhile. All of us are capable of destroying a few acres of forest in a day, but during our lifetimes we weren't capable of planting even so much as one tree."

"Who's egging him on?" the men muttered. "We said it as a joke, but granddad Yevmen is already passing judgement on us. Would that forest still be standing tall and green today if everyone didn't know that granddad Harasym gave his whole life to that forest, and that he would not begrudge his soul if it had to come to that."

"So, it's just as I said," granddad Yevmen smiled. "It isn't someone else's bloody toil, or the trees that you feel sorry for, it's the gun and the stick that you're afraid of! As for Harasym, you see, he wouldn't begrudge his soul for that forest."

"No I wouldn't, I sure wouldn't, and I wouldn't be afraid of committing a sin if I had to shoot a thief . . . Everyone knows how little benefit I have from that forest—I gather some dry wood for the winter, store up some hay for the cow, and plough up a bit of it, but it seems to me that I wouldn't exchange it for golden mountains—I care for it as I care for my own heart."

"And it gets you right in the heart," Antin mumbled in great disdain.

"Don't laugh, Antin, because I'm the first one to admit that if, this summer, I had come across the scoundrel who stole the fruit off the branch that I grafted, the matter probably wouldn't have ended without a sin being committed!" said Okhrim.

"Because you're a scoundrel yourself," Antin spit out his reply.

"Why am I a scoundrel? I grafted the pear tree myself, looked after it for four years, watered, it, pruned it, and then someone came and stripped it bare of its fruit! Isn't that maddening?"

"But you tended it for only four years, and only one tree at that, and I've worked hard for forty years and reared a thousand, one hundred and four trees—so how am I to let a thief escape alive from the forest?" Harasym asked Antin.

"And as for you my son, I'll tell you this," he turned to Sydir, "if I should ever become convinced that you're not capable of looking after the forest, I won't take pity on your poverty. I'll talk to the lord himself, bow at his feet, and beg him to appoint as forester the person I advise him to appoint. And I'll tell him not to permit you to go into it at all."

"May that forest be damned—all this talk about it is disgusting! The least you could do is not shame your son in public. Or are you saying that he does a poor job of looking after the forest?" Antin defended Sydir.

"If he looks after it well, then let him also love it, and not covet the oak lumber," Harasym retorted.

"It's no wonder he covets it—he doesn't have a house," Nazar laughed.

"Well, here's a riddle for you—not all those are smart who seem to be smart; my guests have houses with wooden floors, and the ones I distrust have rickety doors," Maskym who was standing behind Sydir spoke up in an exceptionally merry tone.

"Who's supposed to guess your riddle?" Nazar asked

"The one who's not saying anything," Maksym laughed and winked at Harasym.

Sydir lowered his head and walked away. An unspeakable sorrow seized his heart—Maksym's riddle truly was not solvable except, perhaps, by someone who was not saying anything. It was Maksym who had stated intentionally and publicly that he would not give his daughter in marriage to someone who lived in an old hovel; but, considering the impecunious state of Sydir's family, it was impossible to think about a new house, especially if you had to go all the way to Sahaydak's forest for the wood.

Sydir sat down with the young men, but as soon as the young women began gathering for an evening party, he set out for home—he did not want to see the girl who was fated not to be his; he did not want to allow his heart to be broken.

That evening, Harasym stayed out surprisingly late. He returned home in such a good mood that it seemed to Sydir that if he had even the slightest desire to talk with his father, the sun would peek through the cloud blown in by their conversation in the meadow.

But the youth was in no mood for joking; an even heavier sorrow enveloped his soul when he saw his father's happy face, and it pained him to think that his own bitter lot appeared to add to the merriment of his family. Refusing to reply to his father's attempts to engage him in conversation, and hissing curt answers through his teeth, he went to bed early.

He could not, however, fall asleep.

Spring songs were resounding in the air, and young men and women were making merry in the village common. He heard youths running past his house to carouse at the other end of the village; he saw an enamoured couple stroll by his window; the full moon peered into his eyes; the warm, fragrant air wafted in through the open window; and in the forest a nightingale trilled mournfully . . .

He lay silent for a long time. Finally, however, unable to restrain himself any longer, he sighed heavily.

"You aren't sleeping yet?" Harasym asked.

"No," Sydir sighed.

"Well, that's fine; if you don't feel like sleeping we'll go into the forest."

"All you think about is the forest," Sydir retorted reproachfully.

"Sometimes I think about the forest, but sometimes I think about other things . . . So, listen; I just mentioned the forest, and now I'll say something else. Send the matchmakers tomorrow if you intend to get married."

"To who? Is it a beggar that you want for a daughter-in-law?" Sydir smiled bitterly, barely restraining himself in his anger from flinging an offensive word at his father.

"It doesn't matter to me—let it be a beggar, or let it be Onyska, it's all the same to me," Harasym drawled as if he was truly indifferent to the whole matter.

"What about the house?" Sydir sprang to his feet. "Didn't you hear the riddle Maksym threw at us? Or do you think he'll agree to pack his child off into this hovel?"

"Nothing will happen to her if she lives for a couple of years in a hovel; you'll get married, live through the summer and the winter, and in the spring you'll hire yourself out and bring some money home; I'll sell the cow—and we'll have a new house."

"Do you suppose Maksym will agree to that?"

"If he wasn't going to agree, then I wouldn't be telling you to send match makers, you fool. We talked about it the entire evening and finally came to an agreement."

"Father, my dearest daddy . . . Thank you, thank you!" Joyfully squeezing his father's hand so hard that it cracked, he dashed out of the house.

"And you didn't tell me anything about it!" Motrya spoke up from the bed on the oven. "Glory to the All-Merciful that you talked things over with Maksym—it's made my heart feel easier, because whenever I looked at the two of them, I didn't have any peace of mind myself.

"It's terrible to see the change that has come over them this spring! May God have mercy, and may the Queen of Heaven prevent anyone from falling in love like that—he seems to have wrapped himself in a cloud, and she seems to be oblivious to everything around her. I don't know if they were bewitched, or if God sent them a love like that, but they probably wouldn't be able to endure being parted."

"Well, they won't be parted now. Let them love one another; it's a good thing that they're well-matched—they won't be reproaching each other with their poverty, and when they build a house, it'll shut Maksym up as well," Harasym responded, recalling how long and hard he had to convince Maksym to agree to let his daughter marry Sydir.

"The only bad thing is that Sydir will have to go find a job," Motrya sighed.

"So, go with him then; you can pick him up in your arms and carry him," Harasym instantly boiled over. "I know to which well you're beating a path, but you won't drink any water out of it! You've hinted that it would be cheaper to buy lumber from the lord, but you've no business meddling with the lord's oak trees. I won't destroy a single tree to save Sydir from working, and don't you try to make me."

"Why would I try? Do as you know best, think as you see fit— I only want him to get married, and put an end to our problems," Motrya hastened to placate her husband. And he calmed down at once and, before long, he was fast asleep.

II

In the meantime, the enamoured couple was billing and cooing in Maksym's orchard. This was the first evening, the first hour of their happiness—a happiness that was not clouded by either fear or grief. It was the first time this spring that they could press each other close to their hearts without looking around, without fearing either their parents, or other people; it was the first time they could look directly into each other's shining eyes—eyes that were not clouded with the heavy thought of parting; it was the first time that they knew the joy of loving one another openly, as their hearts desired.

"Lord! If only the marriage could take place as soon as possible! Then you'll see how I'll try to please your father. Fool that I am, I thought that he didn't want me as a daughter-in-law, and that was why he didn't do anything about the house; but, you see, he came to our place himself, and he had a hard time convincing my parents to let me marry you!" Onyska laughed joyfully.

"I also nearly lost my mind because of that house. I knew that they wouldn't let you get married and move into an old hovel, and my father didn't want to even talk about a new house—he pretended that my happiness wasn't worth a straw insole to him."

"Well, just look at how silly we were, both of us! We cried, worried, pined away, but it didn't occur to us that we could come up with the money for a house. Why, the house of my brother Antin burned to the ground, and he himself is ill and has a large family, but he still managed to earn the money and to put up the posts . . . this summer he'll finish it."

"But could I ever have dreamed that my father would permit me to hire myself out? If I even dared to mention day labour, he'd look daggers at me. I don't know what has come over him, or where my good fortune came from, that he decided to let me look for work."

"It's so you won't try to go after the lord's oak trees," Onyska laughed.

"God be with those trees! I vow not to ever mention them again. I'll take care of them, guard them, and protect that grove both day and night, in gratitude to my father for our happiness," Sydir said, pressing his sweetheart still closer to his heart.

"I'll look after it too. If he tells me to go there in the middle of the night—I'll go. I'll do everything to please him," Onyska stated fervently and, at that moment, at this happiest juncture in her life, she was truly ready to go even to the ends of the earth, to take upon her shoulders any kind of a load, to suffer torments—if this were desired by Harasym, the man who now was dearer to her than her own father.

"Hey there!" a voice shouted unexpectedly from behind the bush.

Onyska jumped up in alarm.

"What's the matter, silly?" Sydir took her by the hand. "I think it's Ivan . . . but even if it were someone else, we have nothing to hide now."

"And that's what I say too," Ivan said, coming out from behind the lilac bush. "If neither the mother nor the father are trying to eavesdrop on what their daughter is chirping away in the orchard, then it's no one else's business either."

"Why are you still roaming around?" Sydir inquired.

"I'm not roaming around, my brother; I'm taking a short cut."

"To Hapka's?" Onyska guessed.

"No matter when the evil hour takes me there, I'm still afraid that her father might be at home!"

"No, no! He isn't, I myself saw Antin heading towards the neighbouring hamlet, probably to his kinsman's home."

"Oh-ho-ho!" Ivan leaped for joy. "If that's the case, farewell! By the way, Sydir, someone's making himself at home in the lord's grove," he added as he vaulted over the stile.

"Where, exactly?" Sydir bounded to his feet.

"Down below. As I was walking by, I thought I heard someone sawing."

"You see! My father had a premonition that something was wrong—he wanted to go to the forest. It's I who will be to blame if someone really is sawing down a tree. Farewell, sweetheart; expect the matchmakers to come tomorrow.' Sydir embraced Onyska in parting and made a bee line for home.

Half an hour later, he was in the forest with his father. The moon had dimmed, and it was dark under the heavy tent of the oaks' curly caps; however, accustomed as they were to every tree, to every bush, the foresters ran through the woods as if they were racing down a beaten path in broad daylight; concealing themselves behind trees, they kept heading straight down.

Both were very concerned, boundlessly enraged, and had no pity for the unknown enemy who dared to commit such an unusual crime in Berdykivshchyna, and both were certain that they would not spare either their bullets, or their fists, if they found the thief. However, for a long time, they could not hear or see the thief. There seemed to be a lot of noise in the forest; indistinct sounds echoed here and there, and something seemed to be falling, rustling, and sighing, but Harasym could not discern any hint of either an axe or a saw among the forest sounds.

"That Ivan—he must have imagined it," Sydir finally said, coming to a halt.

"Shh! . . . A horse neighed somewhere!" Harasym stopped him with his hand and rushed off as fast as he could down to the lower boundary.

Sydir glanced after his father and instantly saw what had given such strength to the old man's legs—why his father was racing to the boundary. Directly in front of his eyes, down below, where the young oak trees grew the thickest, the sky had cleared, and two stars peered into the forest. He tore off his jacket and dashed to the spot. As he passed his father, he could hear how heavily the old man was breathing, and how his chest rattled—and he made him stop.

"Don't let him go! Don't let him go!" Harasym croaked in answer to his son and, gasping for air, leaned against a tree to catch his breath.

Sydir, in the meantime, reached the bottom. By the very boundary lay a toppled oak tree, and a man was heaping earth over the stump. Sydir dashed out from behind a tree, pounced on him like a tiger leaps on his prey, and crushed him to the ground.

"Hold him! Hold him!" Harasym shouted insanely.

"Don't worry; I won't let him go," Sydir replied.

"Brother, my dearest . . . my own . . . Let me go!" the thief whispered.

Sydir jumped back as if someone had bitten him.

The thief slipped out of his hands and dove over a ditch.

Harasym fired his rifle once, and then he fired again, but both bullets lodged in trees, and the thief vanished in a neighbouring grove.

"You let him go? You let him go? What have you done?" the father attacked the son the way a hawk swoops down on a chicken.

"It was Antin, father . . . Onyska's brother," Sydir said quietly.

"Onyska's brother? So he's dearer to you than your father, dearer than the forest?" Harasym thundered, and without realising what he was doing, raised his rifle to teach his son a lesson.

Sydir plunged into the woods and hid in the deepest thickets. There he sat down on the ground, seized his head in his hands, and fell deep into thought.

What was he to do now? How was he to begin? Should he plead with his father, or bow low to Maksym?

But his father would never forgive Antin as long as he lived, and Maksym would never let his daughter get married and move into an enemy's house . . .

Nevertheless, he could not sit here with folded arms—he had to do something to save himself; he had to seek some way out. People were often forced to cross deep oceans and tall mountains to attain their happiness; was he to abandon his fate because of a single oak tree?

"I'll go to kinsman Maksym, and I'll beg him to go and talk with my father," he finally decided, and as soon as dawn began to break, he set out for Maksym's house.

Maksym stood with his hands on his hips as he listened to Sydir's worries.

"You're a fool, a fool three times over! You shouldn't be thinking about getting married—you should still be sitting by the hearth, eating gruel like a baby. Aren't you your father's son, and would he trade your fate for a little oak? He wouldn't have come to see me, he wouldn't have asked about Onyska, he wouldn't have pleaded with me and my old woman to let you marry our daughter if he truly was indifferent to the fate of his son . . .

"Antin has to have the fear of the Lord knocked into him—I'll be the first to teach him a lesson, but don't even think that your father will have him put in jail. Don't worry about that—he won't want any trouble, if not for Antin's sake, then for mine," Maksym said, setting out confidently to talk to Harasym.

"Well, now, kinsman Harasym, have you got over your anger? That damned Antin has to be taught a lesson," Maksym tried to placate Harasym.

"He won't get out of it so easily—let him not rejoice that he's found himself a new relative—that relative better be careful that he doesn't fly out of the house himself," Harasym replied, adjusting his belt.

"You're really determined, kinsman!" Maksym laughed. "You'd better put in a good word for us at least, my dear kinswoman," he turned to Motrya who was carrying a sack and two large *palyanytsi [flatbreads]* out of the hovel. "We've come to our kinsman with great reverence, but he's breathing fire on us."

"There's no way in the world that I can persuade him or plead with him either, my dove. He's made up his mind: 'I'm going to go see the lord about this and lay a complaint,' and he won't budge from that position," Motrya replied, and it was only then that Maksym noticed his kinswoman's eyes, swollen and full of tears.

"Oh, so it's no jesting matter for you either, is it my kinswoman? My dear kinsman, my dearest kinsman, what is it that you've decided to do? To cause everybody so much grief because of a little oak tree? May it be damned, that lord's grove! Maybe you have something against me as well—if so, tell me right now, and I'll weep along with my kinswoman Motrya."

"I didn't see you in the forest, and you've done me no harm, but don't plead for your son the thief, and don't threaten me, because I won't spare him. The trunk alone was fifteen yards in height; it was three quarters grown . . .

"You could shower me with gold, but I won't forgive him. I'll go to see the lord—let him punish your son," Harasym said, pulling on new boots.

"You don't mean it, do you? You're really not going to show him any mercy? You're going to have the lord put him in jail?" Maksym asked, still in a jocular tone.

"I'll have him jailed, the damned villain—he'll sit there for a while, and then he'll forbid his children to go near the grove. And as for this villain . . ." Harasym jabbed his finger at his son who, white as chalk, was standing by the door post, "he's also in for it."

"Perhaps we should hold the wedding first, and then, when we're all hung over, we can tend to the villains as a group . . ." Maksym joked.

"Don't try to jab me in the eyes with that wedding! If you want to you can have your daughter marry my son, and if you don't want to, you don't have to; but even if we become kinsmen through marriage you won't live to see the day that I'll let Antin out of my claws," Harasym retorted.

"In that case you won't live to see the day that I'd allow my daughter to marry your son! I came to you as to a person who had some sense, as to a kinsman. I wanted to talk things over in a good way, and to part amicably, but if you're really so inhuman that you would trade your own son for a little oak, then may you be damned . . . go to hell itself to complain if you want to," he spit, and moved away from Harasym.

"Oh Lord! He'll be angry for the rest of his life now. He won't let Onyska marry our son as long as he's alive! Have the fear of God in your heart, have some pity for your son," Motrya was awash with tears.

"Daddy! That oak, after all, doesn't cost that much," Sydir spoke up hesitantly.

"And did you rear it, take care of it, that you now know its value? Get out of my sight!" Harasym stamped his feet.

"What are you doing? Come to your senses! Are you in your right mind? Look at your son, what he looks like now. And what will he be like if you really do make all that trouble with Antin?" Motrya spoke up.

"Give me a kerchief!" Harasym ordered.

Motyra passed him one.

Harasym wound a chunk of fat and a wheaten *palyanytsya* in the kerchief, threw it into a bag along with some salt, placed a barley *palyanytsya* in it as well, and, without saying another word, stamped out of the house.

"Oh my son, my dearest, don't take it so hard," Motrya flung herself at her son, who had collapsed on the bench like a mown sheaf. "Don't pay any attention to your father, don't curse your fate! The world is wide—you'll come across some kindness in strangers, even if you couldn't please your own father."

"Oh, mother, my dear mother! How unlucky I am, how unfortunate!" Sydir wept.

"Father, father dearest," Onyska ran into the house as if she were hardly conscious.

"Harasym isn't here—he's on his way to see the lord," Motrya said through her tears.

"O God, O my God! Save us! Save us!" the girl wailed as she fled to catch up with Harasym.

Sydir quickly jumped up from the bench, and Motrya dried her tears—hope once again fluttered in her heart. They both tore out of the house and raced down the street where Onyska had flown.

But two or three minutes went by—and their last spark of hope faded. Onyska was running back home, crying inconsolably.

III

The trip to the lord's home was long and difficult. In the course of it, Harasym had to trek more than fifty *versts [kilometres]* and go over four steep hills. Those hills and valleys were perhaps the best protectors of the Berdykivshchyna oak grove from the fierce axe of the lord's foreman, but this did not even occur to Harasym, and he was as irritated with those hills as he was with his own legs—those traitors that were slowing him down.

On the third day, towards evening, he finally reached the lord's manor yard. Innumerable dogs of both sexes and of various colours roamed the yard, but none of them approached Harasym, and he could look things over at his leisure.

Directly across from the gate stood a long, one-storey blue building, with lilac bushes and roses planted all around it; in front of it spread a colourful carpet of flowers and herbs. To the left, almost at the very edge of the yard, glimmered a green-roofed red house that was even longer than the first one. Alongside it there were two smaller houses surrounded by a hedge of acacia shrubs. To the right stretched a long row of various barracks and outbuildings, and farther on, there was another yard built up with barns, sheds, pens, enclosures and huts.

Harasym looked all this over with an attentive eye, but he did not spot the oaks from Berdykivshchyna anywhere, nor any new house. "They must have built it on a new plot," he thought and, fully satisfied with his guess, set out for the barn, where he could see the red shirts of the coachmen.

After greeting them, he addressed an exceptionally fat, bearded, and unkempt man in a red silk shirt: "If you would be so kind, please tell me how to get to see the lord."

"I'm not one of the local men—I'm Volodymyr Nykandrovych's coachman," the man in the red shirt boomed—as if he were speaking out of the top of his head.

"Perhaps you could take me there?" Harasym turned to a second man.

"I'm also not from here," spat out a stocky old man in a green shirt, his face red and shiny.

"I'm not a local man either," a third one, sitting by the ladder leading to the hayloft, volunteered.

"And why do you need to see the lord?" a fourth man inquired, as he led a wonderful horse, black as a raven and as high-spirited as fire, out of the barn.

"I have a matter to discuss with him," Harasym replied. "Take me to him, please."

"The lord won't let you approach him," the stocky old man observed.

"Yes, he will. You only have to tell him that the forester has come from Berdykivshchyna with a very important matter, and he'll see me right away," Harasym said confidently.

"What kind of a matter?"

"An urgent one—I must see the lord as quickly as possible to tell him about it."

"Your matter won't burn up, and it won't drown, and the lord can't be disturbed now," said the stocky old man.

"You should go to the foreman and not trouble the lord," boomed the illustrious lord's coachman.

"Oh, no. The foreman can't help me with my matter—I have to see the master himself . . . Take me to him, please, or at least tell me where I can find him," Harasym asked once again.

"I don't have time to take you there, but the lord is on that porch over there," the man who was leading the horse pointed his finger at the blue building.

Harasym hurried off, but after taking about ten steps, he slackened his pace, then stopped completely. On the huge porch, tightly sealed off from the yard with hangings, a sharp conversation was taking place, or, perhaps, even a quarrel. Five or six strong male voices were trying to shout one another down, and above all this noise rose a piercing youthful voice that overpowered all the others and seemed to be demanding special attention for itself.

"Some kind of trouble has arisen," Harasym said to himself, scurrying off to one side, so they would not think he was listening in.

"It's Mashka, I tell you!" the reedy voice rang out on the porch and echoed through the entire yard.

"No, it's not Mashka!!" some shouted angrily.

"Mashka!" "No, it's not Mashka!" "Follow Mashka!" "On Mashka!" the gentleman on the porch argued.

"They're quarrelling over some Mashka! Back home it's over Onyska, and at the lord's place there's a problem because of Mashka!" Harasym sighed.

"Oh, now they're fighting!" he crossed himself in alarm. He could hear chairs toppling over and falling in all directions, and a terrible stamping of feet.

"Don't argue! Don't quarrel! I'll prove it to you right away! I'll show you right away!" the piercing voice once again rose above the others, and everything instantly calmed down and fell silent on the porch, as if there never had been an argument.

"They've settled down, praise God; now I can approach the lord," Harasym started abruptly and walked quickly to the porch, in order not to let the opportune moment slip by. He approached carefully and peeked in through a crack.

Down the entire length of the porch stood a table covered with a white cloth and set with bottles, glasses, and plates; all around on the floor lay overturned chairs. One dignified grey-headed lord sat sideways from Harasym, while the other lords were huddled by a wall, attentively watching the hand of a blond, rather small lordling, who was drawing some patterns with chalk on the blue wall.

"That must be Mykhaylo Mykhaylovych sitting over there," Harasym thought, stepping onto the porch.

"It's not like that, it's not at all like that!" the grey-headed man sprang to his feet. "Give me the chalk!" he yelled and, shoving his way through the group of men, stepped up to the wall.

"What's not like that? It seems to me that I remember better!" the young lord fumed.

"Well, it turns out that I know better! You say that Mashka jumped over here, but I say that it was more to the left—over here," the old lord argued, drawing a horse on the wall.

"More to the left! To the left!" the lords all cried out in unison. "There, where there's a mound."

"That's not true," the lordling shouted. "I'm telling you that it was here; she stopped by this bush and jumped here."

"She couldn't have jumped in that spot—there's a dip in front of that fence."

"She couldn't? Did you see her take the prize last year?"

"Yes, I did. There was a lower barrier there, but she can't jump over a fence like that."

"She can't?" the lordling flared up. "Let's take a bet! A thousand *karbovantsi [dollars]*. Karpo! Tell them to saddle up Mashka and bring her here!" he ordered his servant.

"And why are you here?" he attacked Harasym.

"I came to see my lord, Mykhaylo Mykhaylovych," Harasym bowed deeply and placed the wheaten *palyanytsya* and the chunk of fat before the grey-headed lord.

"It's not me, it's not me who's your master," the grey-headed man roared with laughter and shoved the treat to the young lord who had drawn the steppe, the mound, the valley, and the fence on the wall.

"I've come to see you, my lord. Are you the son of Mykhaylo Myklhaylovych?" Harasym bowed a second time.

"Who are you? What do you want?"

"I'm the forester from Berdykivshchyna."

"What Berdykivshchyna? I don't know anything about any Berdykivshchyna!" the young lord flared up.

"Your grove is there."

"So what do you want?"

"I've come to see you! A certain damned villain has harmed us. He dared to . . ." Harasym began.

"Karpo, where were you? Why weren't you watching? I've asked you time and again not to allow anyone in here without my permission!" the lord thundered at his lackey.

"Why are you here? This isn't the place for you! You'll come when you're called," Karpo shoved the old man by the shoulder and sent him packing from the porch.

Stunned, Harasym groped his way down the steps. A boy of thirteen or fourteen, with an armful of firewood in his hands, was running and hopping across the yard.

"Show me the way, my boy," Harasym asked.

"Where to? Unless we go to Uncle Fedohon's," the boy replied, running on up ahead.

Harasym walked into a spacious room with high ceilings. Notwithstanding the open windows and doors, it was very hot and stuffy. A thin, tall middle-aged man, wearing a white apron and a white cap, was skilfully mixing something in a big bowl on a stove in which the fire had gone out.

Harasym found an icon, blessed himself, and greeted the man.

"Good health to you, granddad, good health to you," replied the cook, always ready to talk, and always happy to meet a stranger. "Sit down and rest; I'll serve the dinner, and then I'll find something for you as well."

"I don't want anything; I only want to see the old lord, Mykhaylo Mykhaylovych," Harasym said.

"Mykhaylo Mykhaylovych is no longer on this earth, granddad; they held the fortieth day remembrance service yesterday."

"Oh, dear, dear, dear! May the Kingdom of Heaven be his! So he's died without ever seeing my forest, and I was always expecting him to come . . . I'll have to tell at least the young master to come and see it; I know that he won't find fault with it."

"Is it a nice forest?"

"Oh! It's such a fine forest! It's the best in our county now, and in another thirty years or so there won't be a better one in the entire district. I guarded it for ten years with my father, and now, for forty years, I've looked after it myself, just as I look after the fingers on my hands. Everything was fine until the day before yesterday when a damned thief, a villainous neighbour, brought down trouble on us—and so I had to come and see the lord."

"You won't get to see the lord, granddad! All sorts of guests have arrived; they go hunting every day—looking for woodcocks. You'd be better taking your concerns to the foreman."

"To Yosyp Ivanovych? No, I didn't end up singing his praises when he came last winter for some oak lumber—he almost destroyed two of my trees. It would probably be better if I spent the night here and talked to the master tomorrow. I'll tell him about the forest—how many oak trees I have now, and what they're like—tell him about the theft, and find out what punishment will be meted out to the thief. And, while I'm here, I'd like to make a case for my son before the master."

"To hire him in his manor yard, or what?"

"To hire him? No, the master probably doesn't have much of a taste for servants like my son," Harasym replied sadly, sighing heavily.

"Here's a bowl of borshch for you; eat it in good health," the cook said, placing the food in front of the old man.

Harasym moved closer to the table and began slurping the fragrant, meaty borshch with great gusto.

"Where am I to put this wood, Uncle Fedohon?" the boy who had led Harasym to the kitchen asked the cook, as he dextrously swept some trash into the stove.

"Why the devil did you bring it here? Throw it in the stove to let it dry out a little.

"Fedohon! Quickly, in a flash, in an instant—boil the visiting lord some cream for his coffee."

"Ah! May the devil boil him in the abyss with his whims! What lord drinks coffee with cream after dinner? Where will I boil that cream now, the devil take it—the stove's gone out already?"

"But uncle, I've just filled the stove up with wood," the boy said.

"You filled it up! If only you, at least, wouldn't irritate me! As if you don't know what kind of wood that is! Put some kerosene on it."

The boy grabbed a tin container and splashed some kerosene in the stove. The wood blazed for a moment and then died down.

"May they all burn up on their own stumps! I've had to use a lot of different firewood in my lifetime, but, since the day I was born I've never seen wood like this—it's like iron," Fedohon raged.

"It must be very raw," Harasym observed.

"The devil only knows where it grew and from where they hauled it to bring me grief! Pour more kerosene on it, because they're going to be shouting right away for the cream," the cook ordered.

The boy splashed the wood a second time.

"It's really sizzling," Harasym commented.

"Well, you yourself can see what it's like. Before you can get it to burn—this damned firewood—you'll curse your own soul. I've been burning it as fast as I can, but there's still a full shed of it."

"It would be good firewood if it were dry. They must have brought it from the crown lands, because there are oak trees like that there," Harasym said.

"No, it was brought from their own forest, from some place called Berdykivshchyna, or something like that," the boy volunteered.

"From Berdy . . ." Harasym started to say, and the spoon dropped from his hands.

"Yes, from Berdykivshchyna," the cook said. "The forests closer in have all been destroyed, so the old lord sent some wagons all the way there."

The fire in the stove was now roaring . . . The oak wood, splashed with kerosene, was no longer able to fight the voracious force of the heat, and one log after another was engulfed in flames.

Harasym sat opposite the flames and watched his oak wood blaze; he watched the life-giving juices that nurtured and clad his trees in green leaves fall in cloudy drops on the red-hot iron, where they were heated up until, hissing in vexation, they turned into steam and vanished into thin air . . .

He could not quite comprehend if all this was an illusion, or a terrible dream. It was so painful for him to believe his own eyes, so galling to accept the fact that his bloody sweat—his biggest oak trees, the crowning glory of Berdykivshchyna—was being consumed in the stove.

Had he nurtured those trees for this? Had he struggled so hard all his life, and reduced his family to such grief and tears, just so the lord could have something on which to heat a pot of milk?

"Eat some meat, granddad," the boy reminded him.

"Thank you," the old man said, rising from the bench as if he had awakened from a dream.

"Where are you going?" Fedohon asked him.

"Home."

"What about your matter with the lord?"

"I no longer have anything to say to him, Tell the lord this: the forester from Berdykivshchyna was here to see him about a certain matter, but he realised that he had spent forty years on this earth as the greatest of fools, and so he returned home . . .

"And tell Yosyp, the foreman, that he had better appoint a new forester, because neither Harasym nor his son, nor his grandchildren, are going to look after his forest any longer."

"But you can't do that, granddad—you've tended the forest and guarded it for forty years, and you're going to leave it all at once, so unexpectedly," Fedohon laughed.

"So you'd want me to spend another forty years raising oak trees to put in your damned stove? You won't live to see the day, you villains!" His whole body shaking, Harasym slammed the door with all his might.

"Just look at that! Ha-ha-ha!" the boy roared with laughter.

"The devil only knows—maybe he's been insane from the day he was born. Here, the milk's come to a boil, take it to them," the cook ordered, happy beyond measure that he had finished his duties and could now leave the stove, which was blazing white-hot, fuelled by the oak firewood from Berdykivshchyna.

IV

It was late in the evening, but Motrya still had not lain down to sleep. She had done everything that was within her power to comfort her son, but all her efforts had been in vain. Maksym did not even want to hear about his daughter marrying the son of his enemy, and the youth was waning like a wax candle before her eyes.

Her heart was deluged in blood, and her eyes could not stop crying; excruciatingly miserable even now, she foresaw the greater grief that was still awaiting her and, straining her withered breast, she was already lamenting over her dead son.

"He won't be able to cope with his grief; he won't be able to. He'll bring about his own death," she grieved. And every time she saw Onyska pass by their hut on her way to the well, she ran out to her and invited her into the house to find out what her son intended to do.

But Onyska did not enter their house and did not engage in any conversations with her. She listened to Motrya in a semi-conscious state, and then, placing the yoke with the buckets on her shoulders, silently walked home.

"They've thought of something; they're conspiring to do away with themselves," Motrya grieved even more intensely. Cursing the oak trees, Antin, and the doomed love of the young couple, she ran out into the fields to see if her husband was returning. But he was nowhere in sight.

A week went by. Rumours ran rampant in the village. Some said that Harasym was in the hospital; others said that the lord was not at home; still others said that Harasym had gone to see a judge.

Motrya was enveloped in an ever-deepening grief and, by the eighth day, she was no longer capable of either work or tears. And, having sat for the better part of the day like a stone on the floor, she came to her senses only at night when big drops of rain rattled on the windowpanes. She recalled that Sydir had not come home in the evening for warmer clothing.

"O merciful God! O Queen of Heaven! Where can he be?" she sprang to her feet and looked out the window. Outside, it was dark, as in a tomb, and as gloomy as her heart.

She fell down on her knees and, flooded with hot tears, raised her gnarled hands to the icons.

At that very moment, the door opened, and Harasym walked in.

"Where have you been so long? You've certainly taken your time, haven't you? I didn't know what to think already . . . Did you, by any chance, see Sydir as you came through the forest?"

"Give me a shirt!" Harasym cut off his wife without looking at her.

Motrya took a shirt out of the trunk and passed it to him.

"Were you at the lord's?" she asked after a little pause.

"Hang up my coat to dry," Harasym ordered.

"I'm asking you, were you at the lord's?" Motrya asked for a second time.

Harasym crawled up on the *peech [a large clay oven with a sleeping area on top]* without replying.

"Maybe you want to eat?" Motrya asked. "I'll give you some *pyrohy [turnovers]*.

Harasym remained silent this time as well.

"What a downpour, and Sydir is somewhere in the forest," Motrya sighed. "You're annoyed with him but he, poor thing, hasn't eaten dinner for an entire week; he's always looking after the forest. I'm just sick with worry—how will he manage in such a rainstorm, just in his shirt? If I knew where he was on guard right now, I'd take a coat to him myself. I know that last year you kept watch far away from the road, but now, it's probably on Ivantsa's boundary, is it?" she asked Harasym.

"Are you sleeping, or have you become dumb?" she flared up, terribly vexed and disquieted by her husband's silence. "I'm asking you, where are you standing guard in the forest now? I'm not asking you because I want to dance at his wedding—I'm asking you so that I can save our son. I can see that even after a week your anger has not abated, that you still think badly of him, but I don't care what you think—I'm a mother. If you don't tell me where to look for him, then I'll go and wander through the forest myself, all night long."

Motrya, fully expecting that Harasym would stop her, jumped to her feet and crawled up to the oven bed to get a kerchief.

But Harasym did not even glance at her.

"May the power of God strike you down! How long are you going to wound my heart? Tell me, what have you decided to do? What news are you bringing from the lord? I know, and I can see, that you've cursed our son, cursed him forever, so tell me at least about Antin—what will happen to him, and when will his trial be?"

"Mother, open up," Sydir knocked on the door.

Motrya wiped her tears with her hands and jumped down from the oven bed.

"Your father's come back," she told him as soon as she opened the door.

Sydir glanced anxiously into his mother's eyes and instantly perceived the bitter truth.

"Give me a wool coat," he sighed, taking off his wet shirt.

"Don't go into the forest," Harasym said.

"People are chopping willows at Ivantsa's, so it could be that they . . ."

"Don't go, I said!" Harasym thundered.

Sydir lowered his head, leaned against the door post, and appeared to turn to stone.

Motrya burst into tears again. Even the slightest hope that Harasym would be merciful vanished when she heard Harasym thunder at their son: "Don't go!" He had done everything as he said he would; he had done everything that he had wanted to do—he had removed Sydir from the forest, packed Antin off to jail, ruined his son's life forever. She wept bitterly, without even daring to look at the corner where Sydir, chalk-white, was standing.

"Turn off the light," Harasym said.

"Make up your bed, son, and go to sleep . . . don't worry that your father is acting hatefully to you . . . the world is wide, you're still a young person—you'll find some kindness among strangers," Motrya said, and her wailing filled the room.

"Why are you crying, mother?" Sydir asked. "It's father's will—if he wants to remove me or if he doesn't . . . But I can't help being bitter that he's exchanged my fate, my happiness, for the lord's oak grove." At the outset, Sydir appeared to be speaking calmly, but as he finished what he was saying, he also was crying.

Motrya turned out the light. It was almost dawn, but it seemed to her that this short time span would never end—it dragged on like a hungry summer.

In three different corners of the room lay three people who were close to one another, and all of them were equally miserable, equally grieved—as if they were pressed down to the very ground with their sorrow; in three different corners, three hearts were breaking, crisscrossed in lacerations by the same grief, but it did not occur to any one of them to stretch out a hand to assist one another.

The mother had no word of comfort left for her son, the son had nothing with which he could calm his mother, and the father . . .

The father had his own affliction in his heart—the terrible memories of the life he had wasted for the sake of one person's whim, of his lost goal in life, and of his shattered dreams. He would sooner give over his body to suffer the torments of an executioner than share with anyone that affliction, that grief . . .

"Perhaps I should go and at least have a look at the forest now, father," Sydir got up the nerve to ask Harasym once again at dawn.

"You'll go to Maksym's," Harasym said.

"To bring Antin news about his trial? No, even if you whip me I won't bring him such a treat. Tell him yourself, if you've succeeded in doing what you set out to do . . . I've had enough!" Sydir boiled over.

"You'll go to Maksym's . . . you'll ask him if you can send matchmakers to Onyska," Harasym said seriously and quietly.

"Father! For the love of God! Don't torment me!"

"Just look at that!" Motrya exclaimed. "He's laughing! You should at least be fearful of bringing down sin on your soul in your old age . . . He's sending matchmakers to the daughter, and at the same time he wants to send the son to jail."

"I didn't lodge a complaint about Antin . . . And as for you and me, Sydir, we're no longer foresters . . . Let anyone who wants to take over now, let them manage the grove . . . I'm weary . . . I can no longer watch over it; but you're still young . . . you'll get married; I'll build you a house . . . and you'll be a master, even if it's on a stranger's field . . ."

"Father, daddy!" Sydir fell like a thunderbolt at his father's feet. Thank you, daddy, thank you, my own, my dearest. I was at the point of taking my own life."

"Yes, yes . . . you see, I've grown old, my son . . . I can't guard it any longer . . . We'll live out our lives without the lord's forest . . . I've grown old, but you're still young . . ." Harasym hastened to say a second time to his son, so that neither his son, nor his wife, would guess the real reason and his heavy sorrow . . .

Two Days out of a Life
(1905)

From the moment that Hannah Mykhaylivna's heartfelt sigh first echoed through the house, Mykola Pavlovych had no peace. Instead of answering his troubled question: "Why are you sighing?" she had fallen deeper into thought.

Fom his childhood, as a son of wide, open spaces, of an unclouded sky, and of the bright, sunny days of the southern steppe, he was an enemy of clouds, mountains, forests—of everything that obscures the landscape from view. He despised lowered eyelashes and sighing, and did not permit any misunderstanding or confusion to arise in his relationships with people. He harboured no thought which he could not utter at any moment, no feeling he would have to hide. And so, his wife's heavy, unexpected sigh—completely incomprehensible to him—evoked, instead of sympathy, a sharp anger.

He loved his wife; he loved her immeasurably, more than anything in the world, but he loved her as she had been when he had first come to know her. He had fallen in love with her when she was a happy, active young woman contented with everything, and grateful for everything, and he had married her when she had the uncomplicated psychological make-up of an obedient wife. He loved her for her generous heart and her sunny glance; he believed every word she spoke; and he lived for his Hannusya, but only as long as he could see into her soul, as long as she did not lower her eyelashes before his penetrating gaze, and as long as he did not have the occasion to ask: "Why are you sighing?" As long as she belonged wholly only to him—both in body and in soul.

From the time when he first noticed that she was hiding something from him, that some small niche of her soul was now closed to him, it was as if something shattered in his heart. His thoughts became clouded. His dear beloved Hannusya, hitherto so transparent to him, began to puzzle him, like a sphinx or a riddle.

He began to observe her closely, follow her every movement, and listen carefully to every word. And, before long, he convinced himself that she truly was concealing something from him. But what? Obviously, it was something offensive, something terrible, for only wicked intentions and evil thoughts are nursed in the soul in secretive solitude.

"She hates me," Mykola Pavlovych finally concluded. The pensive face of his wife became odious to him. Every word now seemed false, every glance—evil, every deed—hostile.

The house also appeared to have grown cold, sad, and unwelcoming. When he came home from the field, it seemed to him that the rooms lacked light, that every corner of the household was spun over with cobwebs, and that everything, beginning with their daughter and ending in the smallest trifles, reflected the neglect of a mother, a housewife, a woman.

At such times he became furious. He fell into a violent rage, called together all the servants, summoned Hannah Mykhaylivna, reproached her for the disorder, and reprimanded her sharply. But Hannah Mykhaylivna, lost in a deep reverie, absorbed in her own thoughts, only cast an occasional surprised look at her husband and, confident that farming problems and fatigue were affecting his mood, listened in silence to his intemperate words without attaching any significance to them.

The summer dragged by in this manner, and autumn approached. In previous years, this season had been the best, filled as it was not only with countless problems and concerns, but also with many happy moments. Mykola Pavlovych was extremely busy with matters concerning the ploughmen, the threshing machine, and the tobacco fields. Hannah Mykhaylivna was equally occupied with the storage cellar and the fruits. The energy of one sustained the other; the pressing, urgent work was taken care of joyfully, in a spirit of congeniality; and free time was celebrated as a reward that had been truly earned.

On feast days they almost always harnessed the horses, packed some food, and drove out into the meadow for the entire day. There, the autumn sun with its golden rays continuously provided new subjects for Hannah Mykhaylivna's sketches and drawings of autumn, her favourite painting theme. In the meantime, Mykola Pavlovych walked around the meadow with their little daughter, looked for mushrooms, and talked with the forester and the occasional fisherman. He generously praised every drawing executed by his beloved little wife and was especially pleased when her shining eyes passionately imbibed all the shadows, all the colours, of the multihued meadow, bushes, and trees.

This autumn, the easel was not carried out of the house, and the meadow was not even alluded to. It was as if Hannah Mykhaylivna had taken an aversion to those places where they had experienced such happy times, as if her favourite pastime no longer brought her comfort or joy. All of this served as further proof to Mykola Pavlovych that his wife no longer loved him.

And so, one cool and foggy evening, when Mykola Pavlovych felt as dispirited as if he were entombed, when the searing pain of his lost happiness was squeezing his heart like a pair of pliers, when even the eager chattering of little Olesya did not console him, and when Hannah Mykhaylivna seemed to be even sadder than usual, he resolutely decided to have a talk with her and, in this way, to bring some kind of closure to his suffering.

"You're bored," he addressed Hannah Mykhaylivna in a derisive tone.

"The way you stressed the word 'bored' makes me hesitate to speak with you. And I was just about to seek your advice," Hannah Mykhaylivna responded.

"Well?" Mykola Pavlovych asked, and he began to tremble.

"Olesya, darling. Go to sleep, my little dove. And nanny," Hannah Mykhaylivna addressed the elderly woman who took care of Olesya, "tell Domakha to remove the samovar."

"Yes, go to sleep, Olesya." Mykola Pavlovych quickly followed his wife's lead, as he hurriedly kissed his daughter goodnight. "And let Domakha take the samovar away later," he added. As soon as the old woman had crossed the threshold, he turned the key in the lock.

"Well?" he asked his wife for the second time. He felt the blood recede from his head, and his heart stopped beating.

"I've been wanting to confess something to you for a long time now, but I kept putting it off until you had finished the fall seeding and harvesting and had some free time. I won't deny what you've just said; I have been very sad these last few months," Hannah Mykhaylivna admitted.

"Well, of course you've been sad! Living in isolation in a village, without any entertainment, without any formal balls, without the theatre, and with a repugnant husband!"

"How could you say that? How could you get your tongue around words like that?" Hanna Mykhaylivna burst out in anger.

"No need for any superfluous or fancy words! You're bored. Anyone can see that, and I can see it too. But I don't know how to entertain you. Don't keep things to yourself, don't sigh, don't wander about in the orchard in the moonlight, don't pretend you're a romantic young girl with a broken heart, don't pine after knights, but tell me plainly and frankly what it is that you are lacking, what it is that you want from me, and then, perhaps, we will somehow be able to piece together the fragments of our happiness. That is, if you don't want . . ."

"Mykola, what in the world are you saying?" Hannah Mykhaylivna interrupted her husband in despair. "Have we destroyed our happiness? Have I ever so much as even hinted to you that I'm unhappy? Where is this coming from? Why are you making such statements?"

"Happy people do not sigh, wander about like lost souls, and conceal their thoughts—and they always gladly answer questions put to them by those closest to them," Mykola Pavlovych observed.

"But you must believe me, Mykola, I did not know how to answer your questions. Recently, I've felt as if my life has been split into two different halves—incompatible perhaps—but both of them equally dear to me, as two children with different dispositions are dear to a mother. In those moments when I lived according to the dictates of my mind, my responsibilities, my habits, I would gladly have replied to every question, gladly permitted everyone to explore the depths of my heart and read my every thought.

"At other times, I would have been more willing to have the earth swallow me whole than to admit to feelings that seemed powerful only as long as they were guarded at the very bottom of my heart—and which became trifling the moment I dared to give voice to them. Can you believe me? I could not find the words to admit them to you. Even now, when you are demanding that I do so, when I myself see that there's no point to concealing them any longer, I'm ashamed to ask for your assistance."

"Assistance in what?" Mykola Pavlovych, upset even more by his wife's obscure preamble, said testily.

"Let's go to Petersburg for the winter, Mykola."

"Let's abandon the house, the farm, or, more to the point, let's burn the house down, strangle the cattle . . . is this what you meant to say?"

"You have two trustworthy assistants, and other reliable people can be found. It's only for one winter, for five or six months."

"And what are we to do there—in Petersburg? After a month, the theatres, museums, and art galleries will lose their appeal, and then what will we do to amuse ourselves?"

"You have acquaintances there, and relatives. You can find some kind of work for yourself, or if you prefer, you can have a rest. You can relax after six years of unceasing labour."

"So, I will rest and relax. And what about you?"

"I want to try . . . I'm planning to enrol in the Academy."

"Wha-a-a-t?" Mykola Pavlovych roared with laughter. "You—in the Academy?"

"You see, Mykola, you find it amusing," Hannah Mykhaylivna reddened. "You're astonished at my boldness, and it's not so long ago that even I didn't dare to dream about the Academy."

"But now, having painted a dozen twisted willows, a couple dozen bedraggled bushes, and five hundred thousand reeds, you consider yourself to be talented? If that's the case, then I must remind you that in addition to those rags with which you have plastered our walls, you have a husband and a daughter for whose peace and happiness your conscience must give a full accounting, and that, no matter how great your talent might be, your obligation to the two people who have entrusted themselves to you is even greater."

"You're talking as if I had already bought a ticket for Petersburg and was sitting in a passenger coach, having abandoned both you and our daughter to a hungry death. I do remember my obligations. I understand very well that even hundreds of thousands of paintings are not worth the life or happiness of a single person. I do not want to deprive either you or Olesya of anything, or hurt you in the slightest—for any reason—and that is why I've been hesitating so long. Now I've had time to think things through, to take everything into consideration, and I can see that my desire to go to the Academy will not harm anyone or anything. This is why I believe I have the right to fulfil some responsibilities towards myself as well, especially since they are torturing me, oppressing me, and giving me no peace of mind.

"I would gladly forget all my own needs, gladly tear out of my heart everything that might disquiet you in the slightest. I would dearly love to live as others live, to rid myself of these useless fancies, and to be interested only in the present reality. But what am I to do, inasmuch as I am unable to conquer myself. I lack the power to suppress these foolish dreams, and I'm drawn to an enchanting vision, instead of to reality. I wish with all my heart, with all my soul, that I could be just a wife, a mother, and a housekeeper."

"And you can't be anything more than that," Mykola Pavlovych was speaking noticeably more calmly now. "Talent has no fear of constraints," he continued. "Talent is the force that makes it possible for a little blade of grass to force its way through a stone. It is a mighty power that is reflected in every trifle that the hand of a talented person touches. And, in conditions incomparably worse than yours, that power expands and flourishes.

"In the first place, you are the mistress of your own time and can work at your painting as much as you wish—whereas most talented people are reduced to counting on their fingers the moments they can devote to their beloved work. You have everything you need—something which, once again, only a small percentage of famous painters can claim. In such conditions, your works should have improved considerably by now, if you truly did have talent."

"You've forgotten that I'm lacking in what is most important—training. No one has ever taught me," Hannah Mykhaylivna observed quietly.

"It's too bad you haven't been taught, but there's no point in starting now. It's a little too late to sit down behind an easel at the age of twenty-four," Mykola Pavlovych responded.

"It's not too late to try, and all I want to do is test my creative powers."

"It isn't worth ruining the peace of our family, disrupting our whole life, and placing a great many problems on your own shoulders and on everyone else's, just for the sake of testing them. Probably only a genius has the right to demand such a sacrifice. Order yourself some books on the theory of painting, more texts of various kinds, examples from the past, a publication specialising in art, and paint more, and I'm convinced that you'll be satisfied with your work here in the country no less than if you had completed it in an academy."

"I will not paint anymore," Hannah Mykhaylivna sighed.

"Why not? You've painted for ten years. You were enthusiastic about it. You were happy with your work."

"I was never happy with my work. Every painting I did brought me only momentary happiness—and many years of the kind of anguish that only those mothers whose children are crippled because of their neglect can feel," Hannah Mykhaylivna responded sadly.

"Reconcile youself to the bitter truth that you will never be a Raphael, and you will no longer be attracted by Petersburg," Mykola Pavlovych advised her with a mocking smile on his face.

"You're mistaken, Mykola, if you think that I consider myself to be something better than I am. Until this year, I thought so little of my paintings that I did not even dare to try to understand the strange feelings that sometimes possessed me. Whenever they did start getting in the way of my responsibilities, I cast them out of my heart like some kind of unnecessary garbage. I most certainly would not even have dared to consider the Academy if . . . I'll give you two letters . . . I received them at the beginning of the summer."

"You received them at the beginning of the summer, and you haven't told me about them until now!"

"I didn't want to start today's discussion without thinking things through."

"Of course, it's easier to come up with all sorts of reasons in secret," Mykola Pavlovych burst out angrily once again, and he sounded as if he were severely wounded. "It would be interesting to know from whom you received those two letters."

"From Pavlo Hryhorovych."

"Aha!"

"I'll let you read them," Hannah Mykhaylivna hastened to calm Mykola Pavlovych, who had suddenly turned pale. And she scurried off to get the letters.

"There's no need for the letters, there's no need for lies!" Mykola Pavlovych wanted to shout after her, but his curiosity got the better of him, and he stopped himself for the moment.

It seemed to him that now he understood everything. The blinkers had fallen from his eyes, and the image of the famous landscape artist stood before him as if it were alive. He understood the "call of the muse" to which Hannah Mykhaylivna had responded all summer with heavy sighs, and the "demands of her talent," and "her responsibility to herself," "her vision," "her dreams," and her wandering through the orchard at night.

His memory, confused by jealousy, seized upon last year's summer and autumn, when the young lion was visiting with the neighbours. He recalled interesting anecdotes about young girls and women who placed their hearts at the feet of the famous landscape painter. He remembered the long, frequent, and quiet conversations that Hannah Mykhaylivna had with him, the studies they sketched together of a certain birch tree. It all became clear to Mykola Pavlovych—his wife had fallen in love with Pavlo Hryhorovych, and she was looking for a way to flee to him.

Hannah Mykhaylivna brought the letters. They were the letters of an older mentor to a younger student, filled with advice from beginning to end about the technique of painting, observations, and questions. To Mykola Pavlovych, however, the tone of the letters did not correspond at all to their content. Between the lines filled with ordinary words, he read a hidden sympathy. In every phrase praising Hannah Mykhaylivna's talent, he saw praise of her beauty. And the ending of the second letter, where it was written— "My sincere advice is to leave behind the mundane matters of a 'Martha' and to come to Petersburg as a 'Mariya',"—testified so clearly to love, that Mykola Pavlovych was surprised she had dared to show him this letter.

"What do you think?" Hannah Mykhaylivna asked when his eyes reached the signature.

"What do I think? I think that I no longer want to look at hypocrites like you. Go to your lover. He's calling you, and your place is with him," Mykola Pavlovych thundered in a violent rage, flinging the letter at his wife.

"Mykola! My God! What are you saying? You don't know me at all! How could you have loved me?" Hannah Mykhaylivna clapped her hands together in despair.

"I don't love you . . . I hate you! I've hated you for a long time now. I can see right through you. I always did expect all kinds of hideous deeds from you. Don't think—don't you dare think you've fooled me. All summer long I knew you were deceiving me."

Hannah Mykhaylivna grabbed the edge of the table to prevent herself from falling. It was as if an abyss, a chasm, had opened up in front of her, and the person who was dearest to her in the whole world suddenly ended up on the other side of it. The terrible, cruel words "I hate you" from the lips of her beloved husband were imprinted in bloody letters in her heart. "I hate you," "your lover," "traitor," "hypocrite,"—and not a drop of empathy, not a shred of understanding of what was making her soul ache.

Hannah Mykhaylivna just stood there. She felt helpless and both morally and physically weakened, incapable of either defending herself or protesting. She was trembling, and her heart was contracting with grief. Her feet and arms were turning to lead, her head was spinning, everything was going black before her eyes, and she began to sway.

"Domakha, help the lady out of the room!" Mykola Pavlovych shouted in a voice as strident as a bell. And this voice brought her back to reality. She regained her consciousness, overcame her weakness and, lifting her head up high, strode out of the room.

"Domakha," Mykola Pavlovych flung over her departing shoulder to the servant. "From now on you will come to me for all your instructions. The lady is leaving tomorrow for Petersburg. And bring Olesya's bed into my study immediately."

Hannah Mykhaylivna did not turn around or respond to this new insult. Every insult, every offence seemed trifling now in comparison with the terrible thought that her husband did not know her at all. He did not understand her.

She walked into her bedroom, turned on the light, threw the letters from Petersburg into her chest of drawers, and stood, as if turned to stone, in the middle of the room. The great misfortune that had fallen so unexpectedly upon her so far oppressed only her heart. She was not capable, as yet, of grasping it with her mind. She did not have the strength to understand either the consequences of her grief or its future significance, and only her broken heart foreboded that the last few minutes she had lived through would never be erased from her life.

"Perhaps it would be better to move Olesya to the master's study tomorrow?" Domakha asked quietly, as she came up to the child's bed.

"Move Olesya? I will not give up Olesya. I will not permit it. Tell the master that I will not permit it. Get out of here!" Hannah Mykhaylivna, gripping the bar of the bed tightly with both hands, thundered at Domakha.

"Mother, mummy!" Olesya called out in confusion in her sleep.

"Go to sleep. Go to sleep, my little daughter. I won't give you to anyone. I would never forsake you for anything." Hannah Mykhaylivna collapsed on the bed and clasped the child to her breast.

II

Ten years went by. On a railway platform in a foreign train station, Hannah Mykhaylivna, pale and completely exhausted, was sitting in the sun waiting for the express from Nice. Behind her reclining chair stood her daughter Olesya—now a young lady of sixteen with a dusky complexion, rosy cheeks, cheerful dark eyes, and exceptionally thick, straight hair that reached to her waist. Next to her stood Mykola Pavlovych, tired, but still fresh in appearance, energetic, and very sun-tanned.

The infinitely kind expression in his eyes when he addressed his wife, and his endless solicitations as to how to best protect her from the wind and keep her feet warm, caught the attention of the other passengers and evoked in them feelings of compassion for his great sorrow. For it was obvious to everyone that the lady was dying, that her days on this earth were numbered, and that the trip to Nice was but a straw that truly only the most loving of hearts could reach for.

To Mykola Pavlovych, this trip was like a sturdy lifeline that the benevolent hand of a doctor had cast into the sea of unspeakable grief in which he was drowning after he learned that his wife was ill with tuberculosis. He kept pulling out his pocket watch and checking the time on it against the clock in the train station. He rushed about, inquiring of others if the trains were ever late. And, all the while, he kept peering into the distance so impatiently that it seemed as if his whole life now depended on a few seconds.

Tuberculosis is a word charged with inescapable significance. A cold, weak lungs—and death is breathing over your shoulder—this is the certain, undeniable grief, made more terrible in this instance because it had come on so suddenly, so unexpectedly, and was progressing with such rapidity. From that memorable evening, when Mykola Pavlovych had cut short—as it seemed to him even now— the beginning of Hannah Mykhaylivna's love affair and extinguished the spark of her love for landscape painting, nothing more had troubled him. His life had long ago resumed the unruffled course of a contented person.

Hannah Mykhaylivna had never asked or pleaded for anything else. She had erased from her daily conversations any mention of Petersburg and the Academy, removed her paintings from the walls, given away her easel to a high school student, used up the paints sketching butterflies and flowers for her daughter, and hurled herself with indefatigable energy into her household affairs and the raising of her daughter. Her stubborn muse—broken in spirit, its hands and feet firmly bound by the incessant worries of unending housework—only moaned softly on occasion, not daring to speak up more loudly.

It is true that Hannah Mykhaylivna was wasting away and growing paler by the day, but she did not complain about anything, and when asked about it, she always replied: "I'm this way by nature." She said this so casually, that Mykola Pavlovych was able to continue sleeping peacefully.

He himself, being sturdily built, always in good health, and extremely impatient with even the slightest illness, was satisfied with this response. He never would have believed it if someone had told him that Hannah Mykhaylivna was neglecting her body on purpose, that having cursed the day when she was born, she was no longer interested in how her soul would expire, and was seeking oblivion in physical work. And so the dreaded word "tuberculosis" had resounded like a clap of thunder on a clear day.

That very same day, he put his most important affairs in order, entrusted his estate to a responsible person, sold his wheat, collected money from those who owed it to him and, within the week, set out for Nice. Hannah Mykhaylivna did not take any part in the preparations for the trip, nor did she show any interest in anything. It was only on the last day before the trip that she summoned tailors and seamstresses, and sent Mykola Pavlovych to the Institute to fetch their daughter.

Even though he was most reluctant to upset their daughter's school year by taking her with them, he brought her home the same day, as he did not want to oppose his wife. The will of his wife with her diseased lungs had become the law for him.

Three days later, they were already out of the country.

"Olesya!" Hannah Mykhaylivna tilted her head slightly over the back of the recliner to address her daughter. "Take a look at the sunset. I don't know what it's usually like here, but today the sky is more beautiful than it ever is during one of our sunsets back home. Look at how it's all aflame over there. Look at the western sky."

"The western sky?" Olesya inquired. She glanced away from an interesting group of four children who were dividing up oranges among themselves and raised her eyes to the sky. "To tell the truth, mummy, I don't see any big difference between this sky and ours back home. A sky is a sky."

"A sky is a sky!" Hannah Mykhaylivna repeated sarcastically after her daughter. "You never perceive any beauty anywhere!"

"Don't get all upset because of such trifles, sweetheart!" Mykola Pavlovych hastened to calm her down.

"Because of such trifles! It's no trifling matter to me that my daughter has a heart of stone!" Hannah Mykhaylivna responded in a low, drawn out voice.

"What can be done, mummy, when . . ." Olesya wanted to justify herself, but Mykola Pavlovych glanced at her so meaningfully that she immediately remembered her mother's "weak lungs" and abruptly stopped talking.

"A heart of stone, the same kind of stone heart your father has," Hannah Mykhaylivna sighed. "From the time you were a child, I've wanted you to respond with your soul to the magnificent beauty of nature, to observe it and understand it. It is for this very reason that I've taken you with me now. I'm still hopeful that these wonderful countries, where so many famous masters were nurtured, the countries of those great enchanters who knew how to bring marble to life, will speak more eloquently to your heart than my feeble words ever could. I believe that the rays of the southern sun will warm your soul more than the hot tears I shed over your cot when you were a child.

"We'll stay for a while in Nice, and then we'll travel to Italy. This time your father will not mind spending the money, nor will he mind the trouble, for tuberculosis is not an illusion, nor a whim, nor the suffering of a soul. Tuberculosis means ruined, rotten lungs, and your father will agree to everything because he can see my 'pain' with his own eyes. We'll travel through all of Italy. You'll see many beautiful things, and you'll examine everything carefully.

"I'm placing much hope on this trip. But your father shattered so many hopes once before, and you, perhaps, will shatter these. You're so much like your father."

Olesya glanced at Mykola Pavlovych with a look full of sympathy and sorrow. Her mother's severe judgement of the very person who had given her his heart and his soul, who so patiently tolerated her undeserved reproaches, who catered to her every whim, made an even stronger impression on her because it was partially aimed at her, a completely innocent person who was always generous and obedient.

"Mother wasn't able to come up with a worse reproach than to compare me to my father?" the girl asked herself. "A heart of stone! On the contrary, isn't it my mother's heart that has turned to stone during her illness, if she couldn't find it within herself to thank my father for his sincere kindness, for his pampering, and his concern?" She decided she would come to the defence of the unfortunate man as soon as the opportunity arose. She would plead with her mother to show at least some pity for him.

"You've uncovered your feet. You'll catch a cold," Mykola Pavlovych said in a worried tone, and he moved forward to adjust the plaid throw.

"Oh, for God's sake, stop being a nuisance!" Hannah Mykhaylivna shoved him away.

"Just let me . . ." Mykola Pavlovych pleaded.

"Don't be a nuisance!" Hannah Mykhaylivna thundered angrily. "If you want to help, fetch me some water."

Mykola Pavlovych suppressed a sigh and went to fetch the water.

"Mummy! Why do you attack daddy and yell at him like that?" Olesya spoke up as soon as Mykola Pavlovych disappeared into the train station. "He loves you so dearly."

"You're out of your mind! A blind, unfeeling stone! You still can't see that he hates me?" Hannah Mykhaylivna flared up.

"You're mistaken, mother. I can clearly see that he truly respects you, truly feels sorry for you, and truly loves you."

"'He 'respects,' 'feels sorry for,' and 'loves' only my physical body. You should understand this about your father, my daughter—only my physical body. As for me, he has never understood me, he could never understand me, and I don't want a love that doesn't belong to me."

"Hannah, my darling! Not so loud—you'll harm yourself," Mykola Pavlovych came running up.

"Do you feel sorry for my rotten lungs, my throat, my body? Is this what you wish to say? How worried you are about this body!" Hannah Mykhaylivna smiled bitterly. "But don't you know—have you forgotten to whom this body belongs? To that traitor who almost fled from you to her lover, to that hypocrite who was about to flee her responsibilities under the banner of her muse, to that woman whom you unthinkingly punished with your hatred when she got up the courage to bare her soul before you. Isn't it distasteful for you to fuss with the body of a traitor, a hypocrite?"

"What kind of a traitor, what kind of a hypocrite?" Mykola Pavlovych asked, completely taken aback by the extraordinarily angry expression in his wife's eyes.

"Have you forgotten already? Murderer! You've ruined my life, and sucked out my soul. For ten years you've toyed with this miserable body—and you don't even remember when you plunged a knife into my heart. I don't want to travel anywhere. I'm going home."

At that very moment, the train's departure was announced.

"Mother! Mummy!" Olesya pleaded with Hannah Mykhaylivna. "Don't be angry, mummy! Let's go!"

"I won't go!"

"Let's go, for my sake!" Olesya pleaded.

"I've given ten years of my life to you and your father as it is. You aren't worth any more. I'm not going!" Hannah Mykhaylivna retorted.

Mykola Pavlovych fell to his knees in front of her and began kissing her hands.

Two red spots appeared on the cheeks of the sick woman, her lips trembled, but she did not move from the recliner.

Some woman—a Ukrainian lady—shocked by this distressing scene, got up the nerve to approach her. "Madam, show some pity for your husband's grief, for your daughter's tears. Why are you punishing them so harshly? Don't destroy both them and yourself."

Hanna Mykhaylivna closed her eyes and turned away from the uninvited counsellor.

"My darling Hannah!"

"Mummy, dearest!"

The father and daughter continued begging her.

But Hannah Mykhaylivna's heart did not respond either to the boundless grief of her husband or to the tears of her daughter. She was breathing heavily and shaking her head angrily as a sign of her refusal. It was as if she did not see her daughter's tears, while the grief of her husband appeared just as hypocritical to her as, ten years ago, her desire for a spiritual life, for incorruptible beauty, for the enchanting muse, had seemed to him . . .

The bell rang for the second time. As she hurried to her coach, the Ukrainian lady once again attempted to remind the stubborn sick woman of her responsibilities to her family.

"Send a catalogue of tombstones to my husband. He's a person who knows his responsibilities. He will not begrudge buying even ten tombstones, and he'll erect only the best one over my body," Hannah Mykhaylivna flung at her in reply.

The bell rang for the last time. The train started to move.

Mykola Pavlovych collapsed on the back of the recliner and, for the first time in his life, began to cry.

"Hypocrite!" Hannah Mykhaylivna stamped her foot in anger.

"Daddy!" Olesya rushed up to her father. "Daddy, calm down!" she pleaded, covering his face, his head, and his neck with kisses.

Attendants swarmed out of the railway station. They were supposed to sweep the platform and tidy up. But not one of them dared to approach the strange passengers. They stood for a long time with brooms in their hands, watching the weeping "murderer" who had lost forever the life that was dearer to him than anything else in the world.

On Christmas Eve
A Christmas Story
(1906)

The lamp flickered gently in front of the icon, consuming the last droplets of oil bought by Oleksandra with her remaining *shahy [half-pennies]*. Those few drops would not last until the end of the evening, and the young woman, leaning her arm against the frame of a small window embroidered by frost, eyed with heavy sorrow the shallow, ever-receding dark circlet of oil in the lamp and the wick that was declining ever nearer to the water. Her soul was aching, her heart was troubled, and in her head various thoughts—all of them sad—buzzed like bees.

As far back as Oleksandra could remember, this was the first *Melanka [New Year's Eve]* that her table was graced with barley *pyrizhky [turnovers]* made with unbuttered potatoes instead of tall leavened wheaten breads and *varenyky [stuffed dumplings]*; it was the first *Melanka* when she did not have so much as a *shah* in her small chest to buy a candle; it was the first such destitute *shchedry vechir [bountiful New Year's eve]* in her lifetime.

What had happened? How could it have happened that her icon corner would remain dark on such an important holiday? How could she have let such a thing happen? Had there really not been the wherewithal to spend at least a *hryvenyk [dime]* for the holiday, or was it just that she was lazy and did not want to spend it?

The young woman reviewed in her mind the days since the Feast of the Transfiguration some four months earlier—days that had been filled with problems and with pressing, urgent work. She recalled the *kopiyky [pennies]* she had earned—they had all—to the very last one—been spent on bread and taxes. She questioned her conscience frankly, pitilessly, but she could not find any fault with what she had done. Even so, this self-examination did not calm her; the empty lamp was shimmering so reproachfully, and the holy faces on the icons looked so dark and sad in the corner, that she wondered whether God might not punish her, and her husband and children, for such a grievous sin.

Oh, why had she not borrowed at least a small glass of oil, or begged or cried for it? Why, fool that she was, had she not been smart enough to sell her green kerchief, the good green one with the long yellow tassels—the kerchief that had belonged to her departed mother? Yes, yes; she should have sold that kerchief, replaced it with a cheap one, and bought some oil.

Why hadn't she done so? Did it make any difference to her what kind of a kerchief she wore? Did her kerchief mean more to her than the salvation of her soul? Should she awaken her husband and have him take the kerchief to Motrya's right now? Motrya had eyed the kerchief once—let her exchange it now for a black one, or a checkered one, or any kind at all, and, in addition, let her give them a bottle of oil.

Motrya had oil; she had everything—a horse, and sheep, and suet, and milk, and . . . she had everything you could want. And she was not the only one. Other people also had so much wealth that even their grandchildren would not be able to use it all up. Motrya had a new house . . . a large garden . . . a full bottle of oil. She would send her husband to her; let him take the green kerchief . . . let him take it quickly . . . Here, take it . . . Exchange it for any kind of a kerchief. . . show her the tassels . . . how long they are . . .

The wick in the lamp crackled.

"Mother of God!" the young woman jumped with a start. "I must have dozed off—I saw something so strange. Of course, I must have fallen asleep . . . I'd better stay awake until the lamp burns down completely. The children are sleeping soundly, praise God. And Matviy is sleeping . . . Let him sleep; he need not see that our lamp is going out. Let him sleep; may he at least have a pleasant dream—they say that a dream on New Year's Eve is bound to come true.

"May he dream that our children are healthy, may he dream that our house has large, bright windows, may he see our fields covered with tall, dense rye and well-eared wheat. But no, let him not dream about wheat, because they say that wheat appears in dreams to someone who is dying . . . May he dream about the green steppe, lush grass, wide meadows carpeted with flowers . . . No, let him not dream about flowers, because flowers mean tears. May he dream about the sun, the moon, and the bright stars; may birds of all kinds sing for him. May the songs ring forth—for it means that there will be a welcome guest, good tidings . . .

"Tidings! Oh, my God! What kind of tidings can we expect this year? Should we wish for more of them? Should we want more of the same kind of tidings? Haven't we had enough? Haven't we had our fill of them? Isn't it the tidings that have muddled my head? Aren't they weighing like a heavy stone on my chest? Haven't they confounded my peace of mind? I didn't sew or weave as much as I should have—I seemed to be always waiting for the spring; and then the autumn and half the winter went by before I realized it, and I didn't prepare properly for the Holy Eve. Because of all those rumors, those tidings, I didn't eat enough, or sleep enough . . . Haven't I heard all the tidings by now?

"And as for a guest . . . What guest might we expect? Our parents have long been lying in the raw earth; our extended family will not want to make the effort to come to see us, and God's holy pilgrim will not want to stop in at our dark shack on this Holy Eve. In a moment, it will be completely dark in the house. The lamp is scarcely flickering . . . The flame is flaring and wavering more unsteadily—it won't last until midnight . . . If only it would burn a little longer . . . just a little . . . if only I had a tiny glass of oil . . ."

And she saw a most beautiful youth entering the house. He was wearing only a long shirt, but he was armed as if he were going into battle. His dark blond hair was swept back; his high, unfurrowed forehead was shining; his nose was slim, as if it had been honed; his pale, thin, closed lips were edged with a dark mustache. His large, bright blue eyes had a warm, tender look in them . . . He walked with the confident gait of a person who is bringing good tidings; he entered as quietly as a mother enters the room where her children are sleeping; he stepped as boldly as if he were walking into his own home.

In one hand he carried a large flask; in the other—a gleaming, crystal glass.

"I've brought you some oil," the handsome youth said kindly, lovingly, as if he were an angel from heaven.

"God will preserve you from danger, my good man," the young woman rejoiced. "Be so kind as to fill my lamp for me, so that there will be enough to last for the coming day."

"I give the same measure to everyone," the youth responded quietly.

"Give me as much as you can, as much as you want to. And may God bless you for not passing by my house."

A bitter grimace crossed the lips of the handsome youth, and an inexpressible sorrow was reflected in his eyes. He soulfully shook his head.

"Have I done something to annoy you?" the young woman asked in alarm. "Forgive me, my most welcome guest. Forgive me, don't be angry with me. Lift up your bright eyes, say something to me, be as pleasant as you were when you first approached me."

The youth sighed heavily.

"Will you forgive me? You're angry with me! But won't you at least tell me why? Allow me to do penance for my heavy sin against you."

"Why did you thank me, my inconsiderate sister?" the handsome youth said sadly and reproachfully. "Why did you offend me so grievously? You thanked me for not ignoring your house, but haven't you heard anything anywhere? Don't you know anything? Would it be possible for me to ignore any house? Haven't I worn chains all these years equally for every soul? Haven't I offered up my heart equally for all of you, all my blood-relatives?"

"My dear brother! My most unfortunate martyr!"

And the handsome youth tore open his threadbare shirt and bared his young breast and his heart.

All covered with lacerations, gashes, and wounds, his heart was scarcely beating; he was barely alive. The young woman pressed close to the deepest wound and, wonders of wonders—his heart began to beat rhythmically, and blood no longer dripped profusely from it.

"I'll return life to your heart, I'll heal all your wounds, my dearest brother!" said the young woman, overjoyed by such a miracle; and she grabbed her green kerchief—her wonderful green kerchief with the golden tassels—and was about to rip it in two to bind the youth's bloody breast.

"Don't! There's no need to do that!" the youth stayed her hand. "The word 'brother' that you uttered to me has more healing power than all the medicines of the earth's sorcerers. That word means more to me than freedom, than life itself. For that single word, I am prepared to wear chains on my hands once again, to suffer anew all my torments. Give me something, so that I can pour you some oil. I've tarried long in your home, and I must share the oil with everyone."

The young woman passed him the lamp. The youth lifted his large flask, raised his crystal glass, and began pouring the oil.

"Look, look—there's a dark drop floating at the bottom of the bottle," the young woman pointed at the flask, where a dark spot truly could be seen.

"It's blood," the youth responded.

"Blood? There's blood everywhere—only blood. Your innocent blood is everywhere, my martyr!"

The youth shook his head. "No, it isn't my blood. My blood is pale, light, and clear. This blood is dark; it is the blood of those who survive because of your bloody sweat, who feed their children with your work, and light candles in holy temples with your wax. It is their oil—it is yours. I took it from them to give to you, but I took it from the battlefield, and it contains a drop of their blood."

"Go away, get away from me! I don't want any of your oil!" the young woman shouted. "Go away! I see blood on your hands, I can smell the sickly sweet scent of blood coming from your glass."

"I came to give everyone some oil; I'll pour you some. . ."

"Don't! There's no need to. It will be better if my lamp goes out."

"You have not seen, nor do you know, how brightly my oil burns, but when I pour you some of it and light it . . ." the youth was persuading her earnestly.

"Don't! There's no need to!" the young woman interrupted the guest and, reaching out her hand, tried to prevent him from touching her lamp.

The face of the youth turned gloomy, a deep furrow lined his forehead, threatening sparks flashed in his eyes, and blood gushed from the wounds in his heart . . .

"You're insane! Have I allowed my heart to suffer torments so that you will be without light on this Holy Eve? Have I hurried to your side to abandon you in darkness? I will pour some oil for you by force," the youth said and, pushing aside the young woman, he filled the lamp to the brim.

It burst into flames, as if a hundred wicks had caught fire, and the entire house, to the most remote corner under the oven-stove, was illuminated like broad daylight.

"Put it out. Oh, put it out—it is blood that is burning before the holy icon!" the young woman fell to her knees in front of the handsome youth . . . and she woke up.

The lamp had gone out long ago. It was dark in the house.

Oleksandra, frightened to death, flung herself at her husband to tell him about her dream.

"Don't be afraid, silly. It's the evil spirit that is tempting us in our poverty. It's good you didn't give in to temptation. God willing, we'll get some oil without any blood in it," Matviy said, a tone of certainty in his voice.

And, making the sign of the cross over all the corners of his dark house, he added gently to his wife: "Lie down and sleep without any fear—I had a dream that the world's star has arisen."

In the Dark of the Night
(1906)

Ivan Arkhypovych Salenko dearly loved his little town where his mother, a shopkeeper, owned her own house, a large piece of land, and a dense plum-tree orchard. He respected the traditions of his people and considered the Orthodox Church to be the only one that was pleasing to God; he could play all the melodies from the operetta "Natalka Poltavka" on the fiddle, knew some of Shevchenko's poems, and read the Moscow monthly "Rodina." Because he was an electrical technician, he hated gas lamps and prophesied that a happier time was coming when the lamps of Swan, Fox, and Edison would be burning in every hut in the country.

He was neither a nobleman, nor a capitalist, nor any kind of a bourgeois—all of whom the revolution considered to be its enemies. He also was not a proletarian for whose rights the revolution had raised its banner, and he did not see any reason to link his name to this class or to any other, or to participate in even the slightest way in the political struggle.

The revolution did not cause him to fear anything, nor did it promise him anything. It could carry on as it best knew how—it could finish its reckoning in one day, or it could drag on for a month, a year, or ten years—turning either to the right or to the left, or ceasing for a while. It could proceed with the measured, deliberate pace of a fighter, or it could rage over his fatherland like a merciless blizzard and wipe both its defenders and its enemies off the face of the earth with its primordial strength.

No matter what happened, Ivan Arkhypovych was sure to remain on his plot of land with its plum-tree orchard, earning the secure salary of an electrical technician for whom there would never be a lack of work, regardless of political changes, and enjoying the kind of tranquillity that is experienced by a person who, during a blizzard, has found shelter in good time.

At least, this was what the newspapers seemed to be saying, the papers which he at first read daily, and then every second day, and on which he had now stopped spending his money, for he had quickly become convinced that neither the SDRP, nor the SRP, nor any other acronyms had anything at all to do with him, Ivan Arkhypovych, or his wife Mariya Trokhymivna, or his children— his five-year old son Yakiv and his three-month old daughter Ahafiya.

This was what Ivan Arkhypovych thought, and so he decided that it was not worth giving up even an hour of his rest and sleep in the interests of the revolution. And it was only when the manifesto about the constitution came down and the entire town was stirring, either in joy or in terror—when some of the citizens began kissing infants in swaddling clothes and greeting them as "free citizens," while others began hiding their children in the cellars and the attics from the anarchy of the free citizens—that something became muddled in Ivan Arkypovych's head, and fear for his son's fate painfully contracted his heart.

Both the Salenkos loved their little son dearly, and even though he was a somewhat difficult child, the hopes they placed on him knew no bounds. The manifesto, however, brought down a cascade of diverse questions and thoughts and, under this cascade, the golden dreams—the hopes of the parents—began to fade or change colour, like Mariya Trokymivna's shawl in the sunlight. All that day, Ivan Arkhypovych walked about as if he were not fully conscious and, in the evening, completely exhausted by new impressions and thoughts, he told his wife to read their fortune in the cards.

"Let the ace of diamonds stand for rule without a constitution, let the eight of diamonds be the constitution, and let our Yakiv be the king of clubs," Ivan Arkhymovych said to his wife. "Now, lay out the cards—under what kind of rule will our son have a better life?"

Mariya Trokhymivna laid out the cards once, and then a second time. It turned out that Yakiv would have a good fate under the constitution, and the same good fate without it.

From that time on, the existence of the Russian empire did not interest Ivan Arkhypovych in the least. It did not matter if everything went along its proper course, as when a gentle summer follows a snowy winter, or if this order was upset, as sometimes happens when the frost, through the will of God Himself, kills the flowers in the middle of summer. Ivan Arkhypovych was certain that, as predicted by the cards, the revolutionary storm would not touch so much as a hair on the head of the king of clubs.

And perhaps everything would have happened as he thought it would, and perhaps everything would have come to pass as foretold by the cards, if only and if . . . in a word, if everything had not, unfortunately, turned out completely differently.

On the twenty-fourth of December, the mailman handed Ivan Arkhypovych a short letter from the steward of the seminary in the city of N... where his mother used to deliver butter.

"All the wiring and the lights in our seminary have been destroyed by criminals," the steward wrote. "This is the second evening that we are sitting in the dark. The city workers are on strike. I remembered the address of your mother, and I'm inviting you to work for us under terms that you yourself will set. I am undertaking to supply you with enough work for no less than a month."

Ivan Arkypovych read this letter with great joy, his mother listened to it with greater joy, and his wife with still greater joy, for she had long dreamed of living in a big city.

There were a few words of advice, and then the young family started preparing for the trip. It is true that the railway strike was a bit of a hindrance, but it was not difficult to surmount this first obstacle associated with the revolution, because uncle Trokhym readily agreed to drive them to the city with his tired old nag. On the morning of the twenty-sixth, the Salenkos left home and, on the twenty-eighth, they were already in the courtyard of a Jewess they knew—the widow Surka.

"Oh, you did the right thing by coming here!" Surka greeted them. "You'll earn a sack full of gold. You hear about damage everywhere, and the workers are on strike, so there's no one to do anything—it's enough to make you cry."

"My workers aren't on strike," Ivan Arkhypovcyh replied cheerfully, holding up his tough, work-hardened hands.

"Bless the master, O God, for it is because of his leadership and good sense that his workers are not striking," Surka joked.

They went to choose a room. After inspecting all four rooms, they settled on a small, narrow room—the one that was the cheapest.

Mariya Trokhymivna unpacked in a flash, saw to it that her husband was dressed in clean clothes, and sent him off to see the steward. A little while later, after putting the children to sleep, she hurried to the market. When she got there, she immediately ran into some good luck. Right by the first store, she met up with the nephew of her son's godfather—Hnatyusha. They had last seen one another a full five years ago at Yakiv's christening. At that time, he had still been a young, whiskerless teenager, bashful like a girl, silent as a fish, and dressed in a short jacket and shiny narrow boots that squeaked. Now, he was a very robust, ruddy-faced man with whiskers, impressively dressed in a full-length, new, and still shiny policeman's uniform.

"Hnatyusha!"

"Mariya Trokhymivna!"

The compatriots, who had become relatives through the christening, exchanged kisses.

"How did you happen to come here? And how is my uncle's dear little wife? How is your dear mother? How is Ivan Arkhypovych getting along? What about Yakiv?" the delighted Hnatyusha peppered Mariya Trokhymivna with questions, but he did not wait for a reply—at that very moment, his sharp eye noticed a small group of workers at the other end of the street, and he rushed off to disperse them.

Although Mariya Trokhymivna was not fortunate enough to have a real talk with Hnatyusha, the chance meeting cheered her up greatly.

"It doesn't hurt anyone to have an acquaintance in a strange city, especially if he's a policeman; and for us, all alone among strangers, it's really a lucky break!" she thought, and she bought a lemon to go with the tea, just in case they had a guest.

Ivan Arkhypovych returned home happier than Mariya Trokhymivna. The steward had greeted him as a guest and taken him to meet the rector. Not only did the latter not bargain with him—he threw in some more money to close the deal, praised Ivan for his wisdom and strength of character, and promised to keep him busy for two months.

"If we're going to be here for two months, then Surka should lower our rent," Mariya Trokhymivna decided, and she ran off to see the landlady.

Surka bargained stubbornly and at length. From what she was saying, it would appear that all the newspapers, the government ministers, the workers, and the railways were united in a single desire to deprive her of her income, to punish her with a hungry death, to destroy her completely.

"What times we live in! May God have mercy on times like these! You don't know who to please, who to ask, who you can make a penny on. God forbid that such times continue!" Surka fretted and complained for a long time, but in the end she had to acquiesce to Mariya Trokhymivna's request, because the latter did not want to hear or listen to anything. Moreover, she did not believe a word the landlady was saying.

Surka lowered the rent, gave her tenants permission to boil water on her stove, provided enough heat for the room, and looked forward to a nice profit. The Salenkos began to enjoy such a good life that they might well have been living not in trying, revolutionary times, but in a blissful era of universal harmony and peace.

The days spun out one after the other like the even thread of a good spinner. Every morning Ivan Arkhypovych went to work; at noon he came home for dinner, and after dinner he returned to work; and as soon as the sun began to incline towards the horizon, he—without asking anyone's permission, without listening for any sirens, completely independent and not subordinate to anyone—hurried home; there, in addition to a good supper and a soft bed, awaited his biggest joy—his fiddle.

After greeting the children lovingly, he would hastily take off his work clothes and carefully wash his hands and face. Then he would take down his old yellow fiddle from the nail on which it was hanging. At the same moment, Mariya Trokhymivna would lift the baby out of the cradle and, holding it in her arms, sit down next to her husband. During this time, Yakiv was free to play with whatever he wanted to, with only one condition—he was not to shout or make any noise.

After a short melody in a minor mode, Ivan Arkhypovych would switch to a major key, and move his bow once, twice, and a third time across the fourth string. Mariya Trokhymivna had to listen carefully and, after her husband played the third sol, she picked up on this note and went up the scale in unison with the violin, singing: "This scale must be sung ra-pid-ly and quick-ly."

She did this willingly, using the full strength of her high, powerful chest. Her voice was rich and strong, but to the intense grief of Ivan Arkhypovych—it was very inaccurate in pitch. It was only rarely that the scale went up and came down again without any problems. Usually, things went along just fine until the middle of the scale, but when Mariya Trokhymivna reached the word "rapidly," she began to sing falsely, and by the last semitone she was surging ahead of the violin by two full tones.

"Ra-pid-ly, ra-pid-ly," Ivan Arkhypovych would turn red from exertion as he attempted to overpower his wife's loud singing with his faint tenor voice and the soft-sounding fiddle, and when he succeeded in doing this, he was overwhelmed with joy. "You see! You see!" he would say, "I will teach you to sing 'The Winds Are Blowing' after all. Come on, let's try it once more!"

Mariya would reposition her child on her other arm and begin once again: "This scale must be . . ."

She never managed to sing it correctly twice in a row, but the determined music lover was not easily discouraged. He would try it over and over again, more and more slowly, until finally he would completely lose his patience. Jumping up off the bed as if he had been scalded, he would hang up the fiddle, and turn on the light.

This was a terrifying moment for Yakiv; if he had damaged anything, and such a "trophy" happened to catch his father's eye, there was great grief in store for the boy. Ivan Arkhypovych would rush up to his son and, totally predictably, give him a cuff on the ear.

But this was an even more terrible moment for Ivan Arkhypovych. His son was quite a good politician, with clever tactics and his mother's voice. He knew the neighbours did not have the slightest desire to listen to him, and so he created such a racket after the first blow that all the other tenants came running to their door, and Ivan Arkhypovych did not know how to defend himself in the face of their reproaches.

One day, during one of these tragic moments, Yakiv was standing in the middle of the room with a red fez on his head and his mother's mantilla—which he had cut in two—on his back, and shrieking as if it were he who had just about been halved. His father, alarmed by Yakiv's screams, was shoving a gingerbread cookie into his hands and pleading with him not to disturb the neighbours.

Just then, the door opened, and a woman in black travelling clothes swooped into the room as if she had wings.

"Don't beat him! For God's sake, don't beat the child!" she threw herself at Ivan Arkhypovych. "Have pity at least for a child at such a time! There will be enough hangmen to take care of his fate; they'll have time to forge chains for his little hands, they'll manage to rip off his skin, tear out his heart, spill his blood . . ."

All the people who were in the corridor at the time crowded around Salenko's room to listen to the strange woman's strange words.

"My lady, you were asking my maid about renting a room? Come, I'll show it to you."

"I want one that's cheap!" the lady said.

"For a *karbovanets [dollar]*? For sixty *kopiyky [cents]*?"

"The cheapest!"

"For long?"

"Oh, how would I know? For a day, for two days, a week, a month. I don't know anything. Don't ask me anything!" the lady added impatiently.

Surka unlocked the room adjoining the Salenko's.

"Give me a room that's private!" the lady said. "Completely private. I have four children, and they're going to be singing, running around, dancing . . . I want my children to be happy."

"Well, so what? Let them! Let them be healthy and enjoy themselves. With all the grief and misfortune in this world, the laughter of children is the only comfort there is."

"Ah? So, that's what you think too? It's got to you as well? It's worn you out as well? So you, too, can't hear or see anything except . . ." the lady, without completing her sentence, turned around and set off down the corridor to collect her children from the coachman.

"She's crazy!" Surka's maid yelled out after her.

"She's probably met up with some misfortune. Oh dear, dear, dear!"

"Everyone has some misfortune now! Oh, woe is me!"

"Who's in their right mind now? Ohhhh . . . !" Surka's guests, the majority of whom were Jewesses, began to lament worriedly among themselves.

The Salenkos exchanged glances. They could barely refrain from laughing—they found it very strange that their neighbours were worrying and grieving over some eccentric lady.

The four children—dressed in black like their mother, and as anxious, weary, and agitated as she was—filed into the corridor and lined up in a row against the wall.

"Are you from far away, my dears?" Surka asked casually as she led the children to their assigned room.

The youngest one stammered something, but the three older ones just lowered their eyes.

"Oh, there's something strange here, something's not quite right—they want a completely separate room, and Surka tried speaking to the children—but they're like wild wolf cubs."

The lady entered soon afterwards, followed by Surka's maid and the coachman, laden down with parcels and baskets.

The lady wanted to pay the coachman, but her hands were shaking so hard that she could not undo her small purse.

"Here, for the love of God, open it yourself and take the money owing to you," the lady said, holding out her purse to the coachman.

He, however, did not dare to so much as touch it.

"What's the matter? What's going on here? No one wants to help me!" the lady suddenly flew into a rage and threw the purse to the floor. Surka picked it up and opened it; it was full of gold pieces. In order not create problems for herself by rearranging things in someone else's purse, Surka gingerly took out one large coin and gave it to the coachman. The latter dug into his pocket for the change.

"What kind of change? Go away! I don't need any kind of change!" the lady thundered, and she collapsed into an armchair as if she had been mown down.

"There's definitely something wrong here—she wanted the cheapest room, but now she's giving away her change to the coachman," Surka thought to herself. Then she said out loud: "My dear lady, you won't be annoyed if I ask you for your passport?"

"I'm tired, worn out—let me rest! At least an hour, at least ten minutes of rest!" the lady groaned.

"Forgive me, my dear lady, its the times we live in . . . may God have mercy on times like these . . . you know what it's like . . . the police . . ."

The lady grabbed her travelling bag, opened it, and spilled out its contents. Combs, thread, needles, and a whole pile of unhemmed handkerchiefs fell on the couch. Surka spotted the passport and shoved it in her pocket.

"Would you like to order up a samovar?" she asked as she walked out of the room.

"Yes, a samovar and something for the children to eat, only not any sausage, or chicken, or veal—nothing that's been slaughtered. Some cheese, milk, eggs, bread."

"Mother! Mummy! Daddy isn't here either, is he?" It was hard to tell if the eldest girl—who was about ten or eleven—was asking her mother or reproaching her, as she walked towards her.

"Daddy's here. You heard what they told me. We'll go to him, we'll see him very soon . . ." the mother replied, turning away to the window.

"Mother! You're crying again—daddy isn't here!" the girl wailed in despair.

"Daddy isn't here!" the younger girls seized upon her words tearfully.

"Daddy's here! He's here, I'm telling you!" the mother shouted at the children, and she tore her coat off with such force that two buttons flew to the other end of the room.

The eldest girl turned chalk white, moved away from her mother, and sat down in a corner.

"Don't sulk in corners! Don't sit like a corpse! You'll have plenty of time to sit yet—it may well be that you'll grow rigid while sitting, if you live long enough to . . . Don't sit! Take out your dolls, your books, your pictures! Sing, talk, play—you're children, not prisoners!"

The eldest child immediately rose to her feet and pulled out a basket full of little horses, cows, and pigs.

"Continue unpacking, go on. Take out the dishes, the treats . . . Children! Today I'm going to bring you a guest—a nice little boy."

"Bring him, bring him!" the joyful children began circling their mother.

"And I'll also bring a little dolly in swaddling clothes, and their mother, and their father; we'll have a lot of guests today! Today is a very important day for us—we've found out where our daddy is. He isn't far from us—just three streets away . . . And why are you sulking again?" she thundered at her eldest daughter.

The girl jumped as if she were awakening from a deep sleep, glanced anxiously at her mother, and rushed to pull out the remaining playthings from the basket.

"Marusya, you will go and invite the guests—our neighbours," the mother said to her after a short while. The girl lowered her eyes; her chest heaved. "Marusya! Do you hear me?"

"Mother . . . mummy . . . I won't go; we don't need any guests," the girl whispered.

The lady did not utter another word. She just looked at her daughter, but it seemed that a bottomless river of human grief, a sea of human tears was reflected in that look.

"Marusya doesn't want to go—mother will have to go herself," she said after a minute to the younger children, and she spoke happily, as if Marusya's answer had cheered her up.

It took quite a while to persuade the Salenkos—it was Yakiv who was the problem. The parents were afraid that he would break the toys and snatch all the treats, and so, for a long time, they tried to refuse the invitation. But, to the amazement of the parents, the boy did not attack the toys that were laid out behind the couch, nor the treats that were spread on the table—he gave all the children a questioning look and then ran straight for Marusya.

He could not have done a greater favour for the lady. She glanced at her daughter, saw how joyfully her eyes flashed, how happily she picked up the child in her arms, and how warmly she pressed him to her breast. Immeasurably grateful to the boy for dispelling the sorrow of her daughter, she greeted his parents as if they were close family.

They sat down at the table to drink tea. The lady tried various ways of carrying on a happy conversation—she recalled the happiest events in her own life, talked about her children, inquired about Yakiv, and—if one were observing the scene from the sidelines—it would seem that if one were to search the whole world, one would not find a happier woman, or one more contented with her fate, than the mother of these four children. They finished conversing about the past and began talking about the future.

"I have only one thought now, only one wish" Ivan Arkhypovych confessed, "to gather together enough money so that, in about ten years, I could buy Yakiv a little plot of land in my town."

"Ha-ha-ha!" the lady's laughter unexpectedly filled the entire room. "In ten years? You can plan ten years ahead? Ha-ha-ha! You're joking; I don't believe you. You can't count on anything now; you can't buy bread today for tomorrow's breakfast; you can't—you dare not—make your bed, undress, and lie down, certain that you will have a good night's sleep and wake up the next morning in your own bed . . ."

"All of us, of course, are in God's hands," Ivan Arkhypovych observed, surprised and somewhat offended by that laughter.

"In God's hands? In the hands of Satan, of Lucifer, but not in God's!" the lady attacked Ivan Arkhypovych as if he were her worst enemy, and sparks showered from her eyes. "Don't mention God now; don't blame God for all the grief, for all our tears; lightning from heaven strikes individually, but they're sweeping all of us, like garbage, into one pile, they're casting their nets on us, they're crushing us, sifting us on their sieve, grinding us, baking us!"

"Mother of God protect us, where did you see such things?" Mariya Trokhymivna asked.

"Where did I see them? I saw how they grabbed him, bound him, took him away . . . buried him! Not among corpses—in the kingdom of peace and rest—but among living martyrs, amid groans and despair. A living human being! A decent person, young, and full of vigour, courage, and enthusiasm for work! A person who from his birth never trampled an insect on purpose, who never casually picked a stem of grass on the steppe, who all his life taught his students only with the words of love and brotherhood, a person who resurrected in dead souls a belief in justice— they took a person like this and, before my eyes and the eyes of my children, they drove him away. . . like a thief, a murderer, they took him away in the night . . .

"This is the second month that I've been travelling all over, asking everywhere, searching for him in the prisons; it's my second month with four children . . . Things can't continue like this any longer—those who are responsible for peace and justice ought to come to their senses, understand their mistake. And they probably have come to their senses . . . I've come straight from Moscow . . . I saw the barricades there, the ruins. All the cities, towns, and villages will become such ruins. If they don't come to their senses at once, the only wealth left in our native land will be these ruins! What terror! What terror! Ruins . . . barricades!"

"What are barricades?" Mariya Trokhymivna wanted to know.

"Barricades—they're simply all kinds of wood—telegraph poles, gates, sleighs, wagons . . . They use them to fence off the rebels, then they hide there, and shoot . . ." Ivan Arkhypovych began to describe in detail everything that he had ever heard or read about barricades.

"Barricades," the lady interrupted him, "are walls for which people do not begrudge either silver or gold; they are walls on which people lay down their heads when they can no longer believe, hope, live . . . It's a monument to the terrible anarchy of some people, and to the infinite misfortune of others. It's a monument to fratricide, to the ignominy of people, to their curses, their inability to understand, their tears, their agony . . . You don't know what barricades are? You have never thought about them before? You haven't heard? Oh! God forbid! But perhaps you will still see them! Who knows, perhaps not today—but tomorrow they will be here as well . . .

"I came here to be with my husband; they did me a favour and finally told me into which hole they had thrown him. I did not come alone; many others—just as unfortunate, destroyed without cause, exhausted people, children orphaned by their living fathers—travelled with me. Like me, they sold everything they had, put their bartered money into their wallets and—with despair in their souls, but hope in their hearts—they rushed forth to wait for a righteous judgement. And just wait and see what happens if they don't find it! If their hopes fade! Their despair will change into a terrible hatred, into a ferocious revenge . . .

"Don't listen, don't eavesdrop when older people are talking!" the lady suddenly broke off what she was saying and turned her whole body towards the corner where the children were playing quietly.

"But, mummy, I'm not . . . I'm not listening . . . I'm playing!" Marusya protested.

"Ah! You're not listening? Then go on and play, play! Forgive me, it seemed to me . . . I'm so frightened for the children; I'm so sorry for these innocent little birds," the lady said quietly. "But isn't it all in vain that I'm concealing things from them, keeping

314 | In the Dark of the Night

secrets from them? Will I be able to protect them, to guard them from . . .

"Any moment now, an even greater terror will come closer. It's already covering the entire horizon with its cloud; it's descending lower and lower. This colossal weight will choke and crush everything that is not able to hide itself under the ground, in hell itself. But, who knows, perhaps here, not too far away, fighters still believe in their strength, perhaps they're conferring, considering. Perhaps quite close by here, they're sharpening their daggers, casting bullets, getting wood ready for the barricades, and in the dark of the night we'll hear cannons, we'll see brothers slaughtering one another, bathing in their blood . . ."

"Yakiv, it's time to go home!" Mariya Trokhymivna leaped to her feet.

She was shaking as if she had a fever. This lady now seemed to her to be even more terrifying than a madwoman. Her dull, pinched voice resembled the voice of a prophet, and it seemed that her eyes, staring at the children, already saw the cannons, Sodom and Gomorra.

"Yakiv, it's time to go !" she called a second time.

Yakiv stamped his feet and shook his head angrily.

"Don't you hear what your mother's saying?" Ivan Arkhypovych thundered at him.

The little boy jumped up and ran as quickly as he could to the door. Mariya Trokhymivna caught a glimpse of something flashing in her son's hand.

"He's taken something, catch him and take it away!" she shouted at her husband.

"It's a revolver," Marusya said.

"Let him play with it; it's not loaded . . . it has no bullets. Don't take it away from him!" the lady pleaded.

Ivan Arkhypovych, however, felt that it was his duty to make his son put down the stolen item, and he grabbed him by the hand.

A bloodcurdling scream—in no way resembling a child's cry— rang through the building. Yakiv was wailing as if his father had twisted his arm off.

"Don't touch him! For God's sake, don't touch him! I simply can't . . . I can't stand it . . . I must flee from this screaming!" the lady groaned.

Ivan Arkhypivych had to let go of the child. Yakiv dashed to their room, jumped on the bed without wasting any time, hid under the quilt with his wonderful booty and, certain that his parents would not dare to come near him again, calmed down.

"Never in my life would I have gone there if I'd known that she'd be talking about such terrible things! She scared me so badly that I could hardly listen," Mariya Trokhymivna complained to her husband as she lowered their little daughter into the cradle.

"One woman frightened by another one," Ivan Arkhypovych laughed.

"You think it's funny, but I'm actually trembling all over. She couldn't have dreamed it all up in her head. She knows something, she's seen something terrible . . ."

"She saw what she had coming to her. What do you think? If her husband was so holy and saintly . . ."

"You didn't notice anything when you were visiting at the lady's, did you?" Surka interrupted what Ivan Arkhypovych was saying as she entered the room, shutting the door tightly behind her.

"She's a little strange, that one!" Mariya Trokhymivna said guardedly.

"I know she's strange . . . I'm asking if you, perhaps, noticed anything . . . if she said anything at all or gave you any kind of advice . . . if anyone was trying to look in through the window, or if she was trying to hide from the window?"

"We didn't notice anything at all like that. But why? Perhaps you saw something?" Mariya Trokhymivna inquired curiously.

"I didn't see anything, but in such unsettled times you can expect anything to fall on your head. You live as if it were the dark of the night, you can't see where you should be going, you don't know what to be on guard against. My maid said she thought a policeman walked by the windows twice. Maybe he was just walking by, maybe he had his own reason for doing so, but I'm all upset by it . . . Oh, how difficult it is to live in the world now! When you finish reading the newspapers it's impossible to fall asleep."

"So don't read the newspapers!" Ivan Arkhypovych advised her.

"Surka has scared me even more," Mariya Trokhymivna confessed when the landlady left the room.

"Why should you be afraid? Leave the crying for those who are getting married. As for us—let's undress our son, pray to God, and go to sleep, because I have to work tomorrow. The times may be bad for some people—but they're not too bad for us. Today I was called in to the theatre, and now I've begun working there. Oh, just look how rosy our little lad is! He looks just like the king of clubs! And look how tightly he's holding the pistol—he's hanging on to it with both hands—there's no way you're going to take it from him."

"Well, leave him be!" Mariya Trokhymivna advised.

"We can't do that—he might kill himself in his sleep."

Ivan Arkhypovych carefully removed the revolver from his son's hands and put it on the table; then he prayed to God, undressed, lay down, and—as far removed from all the troubles of his compatriots as a snowy mountain peak from the turbulent waves that break at its feet—he instantly fell into a deep sleep.

Mariya Trokhymivna also did not tarry too long. The terror she had felt was dispelled by the words of Ivan Arkhypovych as smoke is blown away by a puff of wind; she felt as light-hearted and at peace as if the crazy lady and the troubled Surka did not exist.

She slept well almost the entire night, but two hours before dawn, the baby woke up; she changed her, fed her, lulled her to sleep and, as she was getting back into bed again, glanced out the window into the street. She looked out and was struck dumb— out there, beyond the window, something unusual and terrible was happening.

The whole street was heaped with something, blocked with something. Something long like a telegraph pole was lying across the street and, next to this wood, people were milling around. In a small store directly across from their window—one that Ivan Arkhypovych and Mariya Trokhymivna had vowed not to patronize ever since they had come upon a whole group of striking workers there—the doors were wide open. From it, a shaft of red light was falling on the street and, in the area lit by that light, two male figures were clearly outlined. They were bending down and then raising their bodies as if they were chopping something with an axe.

Mariya Trokhymivna instantly recalled everything that her neighbour had said. Her obscure allusions, prophesies, and warnings became real images in the middle of the night; they took on the bodies of rapacious animals, flooded with the blood of striking workers.

"Ivan, it's the barricades!" she shouted to her husband.

"Where? What?"

"The barricades!" Mariya Trokhymivna shouted more loudly.

"Where? What kind of barricades?" Ivan Arkhypovych leaped to his feet.

Mariya Trokhymivna was already pounding on Surka's door. Surka, frightened out of her wits, rushed out the back door to the next street. Ivan Arkhypovych had not had time to finish putting on his clothes and shoes when she returned with a policeman in tow.

"Hnatyusha!" Mariya Trokhymivna rushed up to him. "Hnatyusha, my dove, save us! Tell us, what are we to do?" she dragged him as quickly as possible into their room.

"Oh, my God!" Hnatyusha uttered unexpectedly, and he stopped in the doorway as if he had been struck by lightning.

"Come to the window, Hnatyusha, to the window . . . Look at what's going on outside the window," Mariya Trokhymivna pulled him by the sleeve.

"Oh, my God!" Hnatyusha exclaimed again. "How could you do this? Is this your room?"

"Yes," replied Ivan Arkhypovych.

"How could you do this?"

Hnatyusha ran up to the table and pointed at the revolver.

"Why did you do this? What for? This is a disaster! This is terrible!"

"The devil take it! Don't look at the pistol, but over here, through the window—look!" Mariya Trokhymivna pushed the policeman to the window.

"There's nothing going on there—I was just there myself, but this thing here is terrible—for this thing you can get a three thousand dollar fine or three months in jail . . ."

"Hnatyusha! For God's sake! Is this the time for making jokes?" Mariya Trokhymivna reproached him. "First, calm us down, tell us what's happening in the street, and then we'll joke around."

"This is no joke, Mariya Trokhymivna! You yourself know about the decree of the governor, and my duty . . . my job . . ."

The barricades were forgotten for a moment.

"Why are you trying to frighten us? To hell with your decree. We don't know anything, we have no knowledge of anything."

"And it's not our revolver," Ivan Arkhypovych observed, certain that his words would put an end to all the misunderstandings between Mariya Trokhymivna and the policeman.

"It's in your room, on your table," Hnatyusha began.

"It's not our room, it's not our table, it's not our revolver, and don't you go on about it if you don't want to get a tongue lashing from me," Mariya Trokhymivna said heatedly.

"Shhh . . ." her husband stopped her. "And as for you, Hnatyusha, don't accuse us about this pistol, and don't stare at us as if you've seen a wolf. No one can fine me or arrest me, because I've done nothing wrong . . ."

"And what about this?" Hnatyusha pointed at the revolver. "I'd be only too happy to free you from any misfortune, I'd be only too happy for your wife's sake. But I can't, because the decree of the governor, my oath, my job . . . I must arrest you."

"Help! Someone, help! Are you drunk, or have you gone mad? Lady, lady!" Mariya Trokhymivna banged on her neighbour's door. "Lady! Come here! Tell this madman, this insane one . . ."

"Mariya Trokhymivna!" Hnatyusha thundered at the incautious woman. "I'll have to write a statement, and when I'm on the job, I cannot allow such . . ."

Hnatyusha did not finish what he was saying, but his eyes bulged so terribly that Mariya Trokhymivna fell silent at once.

By this time, the lady was already in the room.

"Save us!" the Salenkos flung themselves at her. "Tell him it's your pistol."

"Yes, it's mine. It's my revolver. I bought it for myself—to end my life when I no longer have the energy to live. As yet, I don't have any bullets for it," the lady said.

"And he attacked us and wanted to arrest Ivan Arkhypovych," Mariya Trokhymivna complained to her.

"If you must arrest someone, then arrest me, because I'm telling you that it's my revolver. I gave it to the child to play with."

Hnatyusha was confused for a moment—the poor lackey found himself in a difficult position, and he did not know whom to arrest. It seemed likely that the lady was telling the truth, and it seemed even more likely that Ivan Arkhypovych would not go out and buy a revolver. In the final analysis, the personal sympathy that he had for the parents of his uncle's godson weighed the scales of Themis in favour of Ivan Arkhypovych. But, on the other hand—his oath, the "circular," the "decree," the promised reward for fulfilling one's obligations . . . He did not hesitate for long.

"There's nothing written on the revolver to state whose it is. I saw it in the room of Ivan Arkhypovych and, according to the decree, I'm arresting him," the policeman said abruptly.

"You have no right to do that—it's my revolver. Do you hear—it's mine!" the lady, her face pale and taut, approached him like person who is to serve an earned sentence.

"I beg you, Ivan Arkhypovych, come quietly . . ."

"Don't natter at me, don't annoy me! You're not deaf—you can hear what you're being told! I won't go with you, and don't you even try to arrest me!" Ivan Arkhypovych finally lost his temper and struck the table as hard as he could.

Hnatyusha did not hesitate another moment. He opened a pane in the window and whistled. Another whistle immediately responded, and before the Salenkos knew what was happening, there were two policemen in their room.

"Arrest him according to the decree of the governor 'for possession of firearms'," Hnatyusha said this as if he were reading it from a book, and he pointed his finger at Ivan Arkhypovych.

"Get dressed!" the older policeman ordered him curtly.

"It's my revolver—arrest me!" the lady said once again.

Hnatyusha removed Ivan Arkhypovych's hat and coat from a hook on the wall.

"Hnatyusha, have mercy, come to your senses!" Mariya Trokhymivna threw herself at him.

"It's our duty to keep order!" the older policeman replied, throwing Ivan Arkhypovych's coat on his back.

"My good people! I'm pleading with you, as I would plead before God—I'm not guilty . . . have mercy on me! I've started some jobs here, and no one will pay me if I don't complete them. Both my wife and I, and the lady, and the landlady will swear under oath!" Ivan Arkhypovych begged.

"At least wait until the morning. You're young people, and perhaps you've misread the decree—let your supervisor come and judge the matter!" Surka interposed a few words of her own.

Hnatyusha looked her over from head to foot, and Surka hastily stepped behind the door.

The older policeman took Ivan Arkhypovych by the arm and began leading him out of the house.

"Why?" Ivan Arkhypovych cried out again with infinite despair.

And this cry of woe, of suffering, of helpless despair by a victim of the law or of anarchy was a fresh blow of injustice that the lady's aching, exhausted head could not withstand.

Her entire body jerked convulsively as if from an electric current, and blood rushed to her head.

"To the barricades!" she shouted madly in an altered voice and, following the prisoner, she dashed out of the hotel.

"The barricades! The barricades!" Mariya Trokhymivna, overwhelmed by grief, echoed without understanding anything; and she rushed out after the lady.

Surka and her maid stopped her in the porch; she broke free of them, but a neighbour's yardkeeper and a worker caught hold of her again.

All the residents of the hotel streamed out into the street. Dawn was breaking. Directly opposite the hotel stood four carts with boxes and barrels that had been delivered to the store.

"That's what was taken for the barricades!" Surka said to her guests, pointing at the carts.

But no one heard her or listened to her. On the porch, Mariya Trokhymivna was beating her head against the wall, damning the whole world, and swearing by her children to take revenge on everyone.

"To the barricades! To the barricades!" the madwoman's voice continued ringing through the streets.

And it was followed closely by shouts: "Catch her, hold her!"

The Anniversary
(1906)

It is a frosty day, bright as happiness itself. The Sun, like a tipsy old man, is joking, laughing, frolicking, and flinging handfuls of pearls, crystal, silver, and gold from his treasure-chest. The roofs of the buildings shine and gleam like gems of the purest water, and every droplet of frozen dew, every little nail, every fragment of glass on the earth glitters, flashes, and overflows with all the colors of the rainbow.

Grandfather Frost has been standing on guard since before sunrise, but today the Sun wants to tease the old man, to test his strength. Oh, Grandfather Frost! Be most wary of your enemy; he will defeat you with his kindness, not with his strength. Just look! He flashes a smile—and old Grandmother Winter begins to glow like a bride seated at the wedding table. He casts a glance at her from behind a cloud—and your icy pearls come tumbling down from her attire; he comes one step closer to her—and tears begin to glitter in her eyes.

Be wary, Grandfather Frost. Your frozen icicles, twinkling suspiciously, are changing the intricate contours of your vignettes. Pull your cap down more tightly over your eyes, for your merry enemy is filling them with silver sand. Compact more vigorously and firmly the powdery headdress that Grandmother Winter has given to you for safekeeping.

Be wary! Just look! The Sun has taken aim, dispatched his hot rays, and the rabble is laughing in your face; impoverished cripples and beggars in mended cloaks are crawling out of their squalid dens and lairs, while the destitute are discovering new hope, glittering illusions, and a new enthusiasm for life in the bottom of their hearts.

Be wary! The Sun is in his zenith, at the height of his powers! And just look how your powerful, benevolent, and genuine enemy is lavishing its gifts on everyone, for the enjoyment of everyone.

At this very moment, he tosses a handful of silver through a crack into a tumble-down shack, and now his sunbeam is playing with an infant in a cradle. Farther on, he casts a golden ray on an elegant building, scatters a shower of fire on the mirrors, the velvet and the bronze of the hotel, and greets a woman with his fervent caress—and suddenly, she raises her deeply lowered head.

Ah! Rejoice now, Grandfather Frost! The pranks of your foe have abruptly ceased; he has begun to flash angrily and to scowl. All the people have greeted him affectionately, and it is only this woman who does not even smile at him. And he is angry.

"Can it be that my power is insignificant? I overcame the strength of the frost. I am turning to naught all of the winter's work. What kind of cloud has enveloped the heart of this woman—enveloped it so tightly—that even I am not able to dispel it?"

"Thank you, oh bright sun," the woman spoke with infinite sadness. "Thank you, my old friend, if it is me that you are greeting. Thank you for your kindness, but . . . I would prefer it if you were not present today. It would be better if the people were to salute me in darkness! It would be better if they did not see my wrinkles—these seamed witnesses of my thoughts, if they did not gaze into my eyes, if they did not see the tears concealed in the deepest recesses of my heart. Let them continue thinking today as they have always thought—let them assume that glory has brought me happiness."

Glory! The poetess, casting her quizzical glance over the expanse of bright sky that could be seen from the hotel, dropped wearily into an armchair. Glory! Had that glory brought her even the tiniest bit of happiness? Had it satisfied her heart for even a moment? Had the glory truly been earned by her? Did glory—the precious gratitude that one heart brings to another one as a sign of empathy—truly exist?

"So many honourable people have gathered here from various countries. They did not begrudge either the money or the effort, but do they know who it is they have come to greet? Dozens of written greetings in elegant envelopes, speeches, poems—these are all gifts from sincere hearts, they are all signs of true respect, but . . . oh, my bright sun, I know that I am alone, and neither glory nor you can lessen my grief a single iota.

"I am alone!

"This word, like an infernal curse, soars incessantly and vociferously over my head. I am alone—and this thought, like a termite, has gnawed away my inspiration. Alone! All my life—alone. The people are preparing for a great celebration—but is it truly a celebration for my soul? Does my heart desire this, want this, or rejoice because of it? No, no. Today, more than ever, I feel my loneliness. I will never have my own celebration; that celebration—a celebration of my soul is impossible. I lost hope for it long ago; nothing presages it.

"At one time, I dreamed of it, looked forward to it, but now life has shown me all its cards, and I have lost all desire to speculate, to think about it—to continue to drag myself along, like all other mundane souls. Amidst luxury, gold, affection, and respect, I am doomed to live out my life as a starving beggar—to write mountains of paper, to cast to the public an amazing number of beautiful thoughts, to smoulder on the flames of burning questions, to utter so many of the most beautiful words, and yet to be gasping for air, knowing the kind of suffering that perhaps only a mute experiences in his last agony. Always in the public eye, always among people, surrounded by the affection and the respect of close friends and distant ones—I shall die alone, like a leper, alienated and remote from both kith and kin, and from strangers.

"Such is the fate of a poet . . ."

This is what the poetess was thinking at the very moment when the most renowned sons of her native land were sinking under the weight of the problems associated with celebrating her twenty-fifth anniversary as grandly as possible; this is what the wife was thinking as her faithful spouse was running from one goldsmith to another, searching for exquisite goblets with which to toast her on this, the day of the great celebration; this is what the mother was thinking while her beautiful daughter, in the company of other, unknown young ladies, was arranging bouquets to adorn the room of her illustrious parent.

Alone! Oh damned word! How many times had she, in infinite sorrow, whispered this word in the middle of the night when she returned from a boisterous wedding at which everyone had greeted her so gladly. "I'm alone!" How many times had she said this, wringing her hands in despair amid the applause with which her poems were greeted? How many times had she said to herself in unutterable torment: "I'm alone," as she gazed into the eyes of her closest friends.

And often, this thought terrified her. "Am I insane?" she whispered to herself. "What more do I need? What am I striving for? What right do I have to complain about my fate? My name is covered with glory, my word is carried all over the world; my thoughts are known even to little children . . . What more in the way of empathy is my insatiable soul demanding?"

And at times, weighed down by her self-reproaches, she was seized with a new and greater desire to work. Her scattered thoughts and images swarmed together once again to do her bidding; the hope of saying something that was interesting, understandable, and clear to everyone, awoke once again in her heart, and she would sit down to write—and the verses came so easily to her, line by line—and new poems, ballads, stanzas, and songs flew out into the world from her home.

And once again she was enveloped by an insane desire to race after them—after her children—to see how they were greeted and understood by the people. Somewhere her verses were being read. She hastened there. They were reading them—they had already finished reading them. Applause! Glory to her! The colour of delight flooded her face. She was grateful, grateful beyond measure: oh, this time she had not written in vain; this time everyone had understood her.

But then a critic let loose his first word. It was not a word—it was a hymn. How many pearls, precious pearls he had gathered from the lines she had written! She had not known, she had never thought, that there were so many. Someone else added a wise word. Some extolled the first part; some liked the ending best. An impressionable youthful poet plucked five lines from the middle and recited them so charmingly that even the poetess listened to them with pleasure. A young lady, a musician, was seeking permission to set the sixth verse to music. It seemed that no greater respect, no greater glory was needed; nevertheless, the aching heart of the poetess was screaming for something.

"Is this all?" she asked herself sadly. "But what about the poem as a whole? Its main thought? Its essence? The engrossing idea that compelled me to sit down to write that evening? Where is it really? In which part? As I recall, I was obsessed by this idea the entire

time that I was writing . . . Where is it? Alas! What have I done?
I should have stated it better somehow . . . more powerfully, more
clearly."

And all the colour gradually faded from her face, and her heart
grew still, as if it had fallen and cracked. She felt cold, ashamed.
It was not her work; it was not at all what she had wanted to say.

She hid herself in a dark corner and looked with large, widely
opened eyes at all the people to whom she herself had brought
her confession, and it seemed that they were not those people, and
she did not recognize them. It was as if a wall had arisen between
her and them. It was as if they could not see her clearly. Their
voices also came to her as if they were an echo. They were all
still under the impression of her creation, but it seemed to her that
they were honouring only her body, or her shadow.

All the people here were her friends, acquaintances, sincere
admirers. They pressed ever so closely to her, but it seemed to her
that she was alone, lost in the middle of a forest, and, in infinite
despair, she gazed over the sea of peoples' heads and searched in
vain for . . . For whom? For what? For some kind of shadow, some
kind of dream, for something indistinct, some image that was
obscured by fog, some sorceress, something akin to a spirit,
something that could enter her heart, that could merge with her
soul, understand her thought without words, and read that which
could not be said in words, that which remained white on the paper,
between the lines she had written.

And, as time went on, she continued losing faith in her talent;
she began to lose her enthusiasm for her work. At last, five years
ago, she had said: "Enough!" In the whole wide world, one has
only one most precious pearl—one's own soul, and when there is
no light in which to display it, then it is not worth taking it out of
one's treasure-chest. She herself extinguished her lamp and poured
water over its wick, so that it would not emit any fumes.

And there was no regret in her heart. A word more or a word
less—was it not all the same, both for the world and for her? One,
two, three, or ten books—were they not all identical sparks of the
same flame, streamlets from one spring?

People said that for twenty-five years they had been entranced
by those sparks, yet no one had even once drawn closer to the
flame, and no one had added a log to the fire when it was dying

out; people said that for twenty-five years they had drunk from those healing streamlets, but no one had ever approached the lake, least of all when its banks had caved in. So let the flame die out, let the lake, dried by the wind and the sun, become an arid wasteland—they were not needed by anyone; they were superfluous.

"Mother! Mummy!" her beautiful daughter ran swiftly into the room and broke into her train of thought. "Dress more quickly! The horses are ready, and no one wants to travel ahead of you. If you could only see how many people have come, how many people have assembled for your anniversary. Even granddad Hanko has come; they've just carried him here from the train."

"Do hurry, sweetheart. Everyone is waiting for you in the corridors. People are standing by your door—everyone wants to see you from close up." It was her husband who was speaking, and he was just as happy and joyful as their daughter.

And where did the melancholy of the poetess disappear? A festive mood enveloped her heart. She was ashamed of her feelings, and thoughts. "I'm being ungrateful! Why was I so tired of the world just a moment ago? So many people have gathered here because of me, and still my heart is wailing that it's all alone."

She donned her cape and hastened to leave. Her acquaintances greeted her; others moved aside to make way for her. Like a queen, she swept down the corridor ahead of everyone. She was followed by a pleiad of writers, correspondents, sincere admirers of her talent, and then by people who were simply curious: the old, the young, men, and women.

Behind everyone else pattered a small man, neither blond nor gray, with a pockmarked complexion and bright blue, childlike eyes. An old gray coat, buttoned all the way up to his neck, did not warm his knees; the sleeves just covered his elbows, and his yellow suit jacket stuck out from under them. His hands were red, as if they were frostbitten, but his long, supple fingers and the unusually proportioned shape of his palms captured one's attention. From one pocket of his coat peeped the corner of a woolen scarf, and from the other—a well-worn copy of the book containing the latest verses of the poetess. He constantly felt for the book with his hand, reaching for his pocket whenever a careless neighbor poked him with an elbow.

No one knew this man; no one had seen him before; nevertheless, if anyone had asked any of those present what they thought about him, the majority would most certainly have said that he was one of those who are neither overly wise, nor insane, one whom schoolboys regard with fascination while pelting them with lumps of earth; one of those who wander through the world, but do not appear to know that they are living on this earth; one of those who are never invited anywhere to any weddings, yet are expected to help everyone at any time; one of those strange people who do not have anything and do not wish to have anything. No one knows where they were born, or where they die, and although they seem superfluous on this earth, not needed by anyone, they are, nevertheless, a joy to have around, just as a star that unexpectedly shoots through the night sky is a joy to behold—even though no one knows where it disappears.

He walked at some distance from the woman who was being feted, but he took note of her every movement. He did not take his clear eyes off her, and it seemed that he saw no one but her.

The poetess was beginning to descend the stairs, and the first flight ended in about twenty steps. At that point, there was a round expansive landing with a large Venetian window. The poetess crossed the landing and was just about to begin going down the second flight, when something struck the window full force. She stopped and looked back.

"Someone threw a sparrow at the window," a gentleman in a navy coat said as he moved away from the window.

The poetess turned back and walked up to the window. The small man with the blue eyes appeared next to her and stood shoulder to shoulder with her.

On a wide ledge directly under the window of the second floor, a sparrow, wrapped with grey thread, was fluttering and beating against the brick with its wounded wing.

The poetess pressed her face against the pane and stared in horror at the suffering of the unfortunate bird. An unspeakable grief clouded her face . . . Sighing heavily, she turned around. The man who had been standing next to her immediately vanished from view.

"How sad, that it is not possible to retrieve the unfortunate bird through the window," she said to her husband.

"Children today have no conscience," a lady observed.

"The school is to blame that children are growing up like this," a clean-shaven gentleman in a high white collar stated and, turning to the poetess, he hastened to add: "I'm Nilinytsky, a journalist with 'Nyva,' and I'm a slave of every word you write."

"How might it be possible to save this sparrow?" the poetess asked him.

"This is the second floor, my honoured lady," one of the main organizers of the anniversary, a curly-headed young gentleman, straight and tall as a poplar, entered into the conversation.

"How can it be that this sparrow is still alive? It struck the window full force and then slammed into the brick . . ."

Hearing this voice, the poetess turned around.

The man greeted her, saying: "I'm Orest Tsyhanenko. I had the pleasure of talking to you on a former occasion. Now I have come over two thousand kilometres with a tribute from a group of your ardent admirers."

"Perhaps, somehow . . ." she pleaded as she shook his hand.

"Unfortunately . . . it's most unfortunate," he contorted his face sorrowfully and gestured hopelessly.

"No one can climb up there without a ladder," the most important critic of the poetess' works interjected impatiently.

"And in order to get a ladder from the fire department, you'd have to set fire to the hotel!" a bald gentleman with a military decoration on his lapel and a green cap decorated with gold in his hand laughed into his thick long beard.

"So is the bird to be left out in the frost like this?" the poetess asked.

"It's ten minutes to three," the correspondent reminded her.

"It's three o'clock, sweetheart—and we were told to assemble at two," her husband supported the correspondent.

"First we have to save the bird. Just look how it's struggling, poor thing."

"The poor little sparrow," the daughter supported her mother.

"Such a terrible death! In the freezing weather! It will turn numb, grow stiff during the next few hours—and why? What has this sparrow done to anyone?"

The man with the medal on his chest cleared his throat. The critic impatiently shuffled his briefcase from one hand to the other. The husband of the poetess drew nearer to his wife. He felt uncomfortable, embarrassed for her: to display such a childish sorrow for a sparrow at the age of forty-five, and at a time when dozens of eyes were following her every movement, when the pencils of the correspondents were poised to write down every word she uttered.

"There isn't enough time, sweetheart—everyone is expecting you," he whispered in her ear.

"Is it truly an impossible task to save the sparrow?" the poetess asked out loud as she turned to face all the distinguished gentlemen.

"It's impossible, because there is no ladder," an elderly lyrical poet replied for everyone present, in a tone of voice that is usually reserved to admonish children engaged in capricious behavior.

"How long are we going to stand here? So many people are perishing in chains on the icefields of Siberia, and here we are in a warm building—fainting over a sparrow!" a stout young poet with long black hair hanging down his back, cried out.

His voice rang out like a shot from a rifle, and he ran—he flew—down the stairs, jumping three or four steps at a time, as if shame incarnate were pursuing him.

He was gone, but his words, like the pitch pipe of a bandmaster, set the tone of the mood for the those who remained: "A sparrow—and prisoners shackled in iron chains."

No, the poetess was making too much of this sparrow.

The people began to move slowly to the door.

The poetess was left surrounded mainly by those who were not taking part in the anniversary celebrations, who were not interested in when the dinner would be over, and at what time the literary evening would begin.

"Mother, let's go! Everyone is leaving."

"Let's go. We're wasting our time for nothing; the sparrow was fated to die, so let it bow to it's fate," the husband said in a somewhat jocular tone.

"But I can't leave like this. Someone has to . . . somehow . . ."

"Mother, let's go," the daughter interrupted what her mother was saying. "Everyone's looking at us. They'll think: what a comedy!" she added quietly, almost in tears.

A comedy! A familiar, terrible word. How many sacrificial offerings had she made in its name! How many of her dearest, finest pages had she cast into the fire, how many times had she curbed the wings of her most precious thoughts in order not to hear it. She shuddered, as if someone had turned a knife in her heart, and instinctively wrapped herself more tightly in her cape, as if hiding her loneliness, concealing it from people's eyes.

The carriage was waiting in front of the lobby. She stepped into it with her family, and the horses carried the famous guest of honour over the wide streets flooded with sunlight to the very best hotel in the city—the hotel which today was to be her personal shrine, and where the priests of her altar were waiting.

The hotel was far off, on the other side of town. It took a good fifteen minutes to reach it, but the poetess thought that the minutes were flying by as in a fairy tale, that she would not have time to calm her heart, that she would not be able to dispel the impressions made on her by the people, the bird, and the carelessly flung words of her daughter.

"You know, sweetheart, for some reason you do not much look like the heroine of the day," her husband observed.

"I feel sad for some reason . . . out of sorts . . . my heart is heavy. More than likely, all the people who have assembled here to honour me have at least one of my books of poetry, and probably a tenth of them know some of the poems by heart, but nevertheless none of them can understand, none of them can relate to the suffering of the sparrow . . ."

"That's enough enmity, quite enough, sweetheart! That sparrow has truly become an obsession," the husband cut short the musings of his wife.

And then they were there, in the hall of the hotel. The tables were set with silver and crystal. The poetess was seated in the place of honour. To her left and right were positioned the most distinguished guests. Wine bubbled in glasses. There was noise and feasting, and there were wise, witty words. She was encircled by a colorful wreath of the most famous flowers of her country. Speeches, extemporaneous salutations, orations, addresses—all the pearls of human wisdom and genius, were being cast at her feet.

The eyes of everyone were burning. Everyone was agitated. "The anniversary" was on everyone's lips, and only she, the poetess, was behaving strangely, as if she did not belong there.

She did not say a word, she did not look at anyone—she was sitting there, pale and wasted looking, as if she were very ill . . .

The wine was being poured. The speeches became increasingly impassioned . . . the improvised poetical tributes were becoming wittier . . . the noise continued increasing in intensity. One toast followed another, and they all spoke of her fame and wished her good health. It was not possible to stay silent any longer. All eyes were turned on her. Everyone was expecting to hear her say something—she had to speak.

And so the poetess rose to her feet. Immediately, the hall became silent. She raised her glass. The guests held their breath. But she was in no hurry . . . She drew her hand over her eyes, and a deep furrow settled across her forehead. Her chest was heaving rapidly. One could see the glass tremble in her hand. It was quiet in the hall; everyone waited expectantly. . .

But the poetess stood without speaking. She was straining her will power in vain: she could not think of anything to say, her heart was silent, as if it had turned to stone.

"I'm all alone." The thought beat in her heart like raindrops against a window pane in the autumn. "I'm all alone." The thought tore out of her soul like a sigh, like a moan. "I'm all alone." She wanted to shout this thought so loudly that the window panes would shatter, and her grief would be carried over all the earth.

Her eyes misted over . . . she grew still more pale. Her hand could not hold the glass, and the wine poured out of it on to the white tablecloth. If only she could say one word! Just one word!

Confusion and bewilderment enveloped everyone . . . Her daughter began to blush. Her husband gazed upon her in terror. Some guests covered their faces in embarrassment. Some began to smirk. Some gazed at her with sincere sympathy and counted the streaks of gray in her hair. Those sitting next to one another began to whisper; chairs began to scrape on the floor. Someone coughed.

She did not see all this, but she felt it acutely. The feelings of everyone in the room resonated in every nerve in her body. Suffering, infernal suffering, was breaking her heart, but the desired word did not cross her lips.

Finally, it seemed that the aging poetess managed to gather her strength, and she raised her head. A sudden silence descended on the hall.

She raised her glass once again: "Ladies and gentlemen! I thank you."

And she took her place again.

Universal laughter would certainly have rocked the hall if the people had not felt so sorry for the woman if they had not known that the muse had long since forsaken her, if it had not been clear to everyone that old age had vanquished the powers of the poetess, and that the two words of thanks were all that remained in her heart.

Once again there were speeches! Once again there were pompous toasts! The guest of honour had said her word—now everyone felt happier, easier, freer. The orators flitted from theme to theme, like butterflies among the flowers. Little by little they forgot about the poetess, and she was glad that they did.

The sun was declining in the west. Red and angry, it hurried to hide behind a cloud, so that the next day it could vent its anger and vexation on the earth with wind, rain, or even a storm.

The poetess gazed at it and thought: "The sun will set, and the sparrow will die. How many people there are here! If they put all their gold together, they could build a palace that would most certainly amaze the entire world. If they put all their wisdom together—they could fly up into the heavens; if they combined all their physical strength—they could demolish this hotel, brick by brick. Can it be that there is so little good will that there is not enough to save a single little bird?

No, there's something wrong here, something is not quite right . . . I was born in God's world as a cripple, and that is why there is no sympathy for me anywhere. But why did I write, for whom did I write? Who will give me back the sleepless nights, the days that I spent in unceasing work."

"A gentleman has brought this and asked that it be given to you without fail," a footman addressed the guest of honour as he handed her a white terra-cotta vase tied securely with a grey thread.

The poetess placed the little vase on her knees under the table. The guests, caught up in an interesting theme, did not pay any attention to her. Her daughter had risen from the table some time ago and, surrounded by a group of young people, was chattering away at the other end of the hall. The man sitting to her right was slightly deaf in one ear and had turned his back to her as he listened intently to the speech of an orator, in order to seize upon his words and respond with a hastily composed speech.

And only the person sitting to her left—the gentleman with the medal—was looking askance at the poetess, wondering how she could accept a broken piece of pottery from an unknown person during her anniversary celebrations.

She finally untied the thread and lifted the cover. Suddenly, her eyes blazed with passion. Her frown disappeared. Her back straightened—it was as if some unknown power had helped her to shed at least ten years.

"Ladies and gentlemen!" the poetess unexpectedly rose to her feet. "I want to say a few words to you . . ."

And, at that moment, her voice, now loud and clear, cut through the hall like tempered steel . . .

And words that had long been secreted in her heart flowed forth in a brilliant stream. One thought followed another, and a sequence of images, embellished with striking metaphors, adorned in beautiful rhymes, tied to one another with an inspiration that was as pure as the sails on the sun, were weaving themselves together into an elegant garland, a delightful wreath.

On the Horizon
(In Front of a Monument)
A New Year's Story
(1906)

"Sir! It's ten o'clock!"

My eyes flew open.

On the veranda, some children were mercilessly screeching a modern New Year's carol. In front of me stood Serhiy, my diminutive valet; my festive clothing draped the chair by my bed.

I leaped out of bed, threw Serhiy a few *midyaky [copper coins]* for the children, and rushed off to the bathroom.

At eleven o'clock sharp, I was standing in front of the mirror; smoothly shaved, my hair freshly trimmed, doused with expensive perfume from head to foot, wearing gloves, hat in hand, I was inspecting, from all angles, my dashing appearance and rather handsome face.

I looked a trifle paler than usual, but this fact did not concern me in the slightest; all people grow more pale when they're agitated, and I was terribly agitated; I had firmly resolved to ask Lesya to marry me this evening.

"The coachman's here!" Serhiy informed me.

"My coat, my galoshes!" I shouted at him, while I, in the meantime, drew nearer to the mirror to adjust, for the last time, the damned cowlick over my left temple.

As a matter of fact, this cowlick had caused me no end of grief in my lifetime. It was not a tuft of ordinary hair; it was an entire riot of whips with which I had been lashed all my life, almost from the time I was in diapers. There probably was not a single soul in my family, or among my friends, who had not taken note of this damned cowlick and who, in one way or another, had not reproached me because of my swirly whirlwind.

"Your hair!" my father thundered at me a dozen times a day.

"Smooth down your bushy hair, Petro dear," my mother begged me.

"Come here, I'll comb it for you," said my sister.

"Grab him by his thatch!" my friends shouted.

Even Lesya—yes, even she—had advised me to do something about my unruly head of hair.

I'd tried everything I could think of to subdue this stubborn tuft of hair, but it burst out from under both comb and scissors; it was impossible to grease it or slick it down, and once when I had attempted to glue it down while I was still in high school, it made all of its neighbouring hair stand on end, bringing down punishment on more than half the class.

Of course, I did not expect to appease my cowlick this time either, but an idea—one that had never occurred to me before—flashed into my mind. "*Divide et impera [Divide and conquer]*," I recalled.

I placed my hat on the table, took off my gloves, sat down in front of the mirror, pulled the candles closer, and, almost hair by single hair, began spreading my cowlick in all directions. But I did not remain at this task for very long—the damned cowlick took its revenge on me. I had not quite managed to finish separating it all when it stabbed me—as if with spears—right in my eyes, with a dozen shiny hairs that were grey all the way down to their roots. Stung to the quick, I leaped up from my chair as if I had been scalded; then I sat down, peered into the mirror and, once again, jumped up and spun around the room like a mouse caught in a trap.

Grey hair! The first harbinger of old age! I was growing old. I was no longer in full bloom! I had already begun to wither! Me? But when had I bloomed? When had I ever been in full bloom? That time had not yet arrived. It—that time—was still supposed to come. It could not be, it simply could not be that my sun was already declining, moving to the west; I had not yet seen it at its zenith; I had not revelled in its hot rays.

My soul was replete with feelings I had not yet experienced; my heart yearned for ideals I had not yet even come close to attaining; the curtain had not, as yet, been lifted before my mind—

I still did not know all that was most important, most interesting; as yet, my mental maturity had not reached a level from which I could view the entire field of battle, the field of human endeavour; I had not yet selected my niche where I could build my little nest and discharge my duty to nature by bringing tender young shoots into the world . . .

I was only beginning to live . . . I had the right to think so, because I was full of faith in my strength, full of hope. Why was I being cheated? For whose benefit? O, abominable nature! You are the greatest betrayer of all, the greatest deceiver!

And it felt as if a whole flock of rooks was swooping past my head, as if a dozen screech owls were shrieking shrilly over my home. Grief—a boundless, infinite, hopeless, and inexpressible grief—seized me. It sank its teeth into me, dug into me with its claws, ripped my heart into shreds, pulled out my soul, and wound it up on its skein. It seemed to devour the air around me, to fill every corner of my room with its filthy being.

There was no air left for me to breathe—I was choking. I did not have the strength to defend myself; I did not have the strength to seek relief from it. Firmly bound by its soft swaddling-bands and shackled by its chains, I lost all my strength, my will power, my mind.

There was, of course, no point to even thinking about the club. I no longer dared to dream about Lesya. I compared myself to a withered rose, while she was a nubile bud that was just beginning to bloom—and I no longer dared to hope for happiness.

I lay down on the couch and ordered that the candles be extinguished . . .

And I found myself in a strange country. It was an endless, deserted field, flooded with the light of a full moon and countless bright stars. As far as the eye could see, there was neither a shrub nor a blade of grass. The ground stretched greyly, monotonously, in all directions, as if it were covered with ashes, and it was only far off in the distance, at the very edge of the field, on the very horizon, that something shimmered darkly like a cloud, like a dense forest. I ran towards it.

What had seemed like a cloud to me turned out to be a host, a great multitude, of people—quite possibly all the people of the earth. It was obvious that all these people were doing something. They were engaged in something that was, without doubt, very important, pressing, and vital. I could smell from afar the odour of their bloody sweat; I could hear their heaving chests, their panting and wheezing, their groaning and moaning.

Overwhelmed with a desire to assist them, to join them in their labour, I picked up my pace and, a moment later, was at their side. But, it was in vain that I flung myself in all directions, that I pushed, begged, pleaded, and cursed—the people, engrossed in some strange task, stuck tightly together as if bonded by cement. The wall of people did not give way anywhere; it would not let me through.

I mustered all my strength, leaped upwards, flew the distance of hundreds of thousands, or, perhaps, millions of fields, and then descended. I could not remain standing—beauty's mighty power swept me off my feet and, before I knew what was happening, I found myself kneeling in front of a monument that probably had no equal anywhere on earth. It was a statue of a woman of exceptional, ideal beauty. Made entirely of pale opalescent marble, she had a tall, slim figure and a small crown on her head; confident in her power, in her beauty, majestic and proudly composed, she stood silently, flooded by the silver moonlight . . .

I put my hands together as if in prayer, and my lips were parting to sing her praises, but, at that very moment, a huge rock flew over my head and struck the monument full force. The rosy beauty shuddered on her tall pedestal, and her hand, broken off at the elbow, tumbled to the ground. Astonished and offended to the depths of my soul, I leaped to my feet, ready to pursue the vandal and punish him—put him to death.

"Ha-ha-ha," someone close by burst out laughing resonantly and merrily. I glanced around. Immediately behind the monument, protected by the wide folds of the beauty's elegant gown, an old man, holding on to his sides, was laughing uncontrollably.

His white beard quivered with laughter, and tears rolled down like peas from his deeply sunken, small grey eyes . . .

"Did you see that? Did you see?" he turned to me, wiping his tears with one hand, and pointing at the people with the other. "Did you see how . . . Look! Ha-ha-ha . . ."

Another rock flew by me . . . It slammed into the beauty's breast and rebounded; it was followed by a third one that sliced off her shoulder; a fourth one knocked off her leg . . . Stones flew like hail, and not one of them missed their mark. A terrible din spread over the field. The beautiful woman trembled on her pedestal; her transluscent body was crumbling before my eyes. Her exquisite arms, legs, classical lips, nose, and ears tumbled down, vanishing under heaps of grey rubble. Half of her head and her twelve-point crown fell near my feet . . .

I felt feverish; I did not understand anything, I could not comprehend what was happening, I did not know where to take shelter.

"Ha-ha-ha . . . You're afraid? Don't be—we're not subject to their will; not a single stone will strike us," the greybeard spoke up cheerfully and amiably.

"But, what are they doing, granddad?"

"Ha-ha-ha . . . Look, just look—this isn't the time for talking—look at that blond youth taking aim! Look at the anger, the diabolical anger flaming in his eyes! Ha-ha-ha-ha . . ."

A terrible racket muffled the old man's laughter. The pink woman completely disintegrated, destroyed by the youth's well-aimed rock.

A new hail of stones shattered the pedestal. The old man and I no longer had a place to hide—we found ourselves facing the enraged mob.

"Let's run! Let's run, granddad," I shouted frantically.

"Don't be afraid, don't be afraid of anything," the old man laughed. "You should praise God—for you are fortunate; you have arrived at a most fortuitous moment. I'm living the last few minutes of my life, and I'm submitting willingly to the eternal laws of the cosmos; but, to have such a good laugh as I'm having today, I'd be willing to be born a second time . . . Look, just look at those berserk people! My laughter has startled the birds and awoken the animals in the forest, but they . . . ha-ha-ha . . . they don't hear a thing . . ."

And truly, the people were not paying any attention to the old man. With the same laughter, the same taut nerves with which they had collected stones and pulverised the beauty, they now rooted through the piles of heaped rubble in an effort to dig out even the tiniest fragment of the monument's pink marble. Hastily, avidly, shoving and vying to get ahead of one another, bloodying their feet on the sharp stones, and ripping off their fingernails, they seized those fragments of marble, as if every shard contained succour from cholera or some other kind of catastrophe, and ran off somewhere beyond the horizon.

"Where are they running? Why?" I asked the greybeard.

"Ha-ha-ha! You don't know why? Where? You don't know that today is *Melanka [New Year's Eve],* that my son—the New Year—is to be born right away, and that over there, beyond the horizon, lies the beginning of his kingdom? You don't know? Ah! In that case, I'll tell you something very interesting while they're collecting their baubles in the field. You'll have entertaining recollections to the day you die.

"I was born exactly one year ago. At that time, this entire brightly lit field was as dark as it is over there now, beyond the horizon, and when I first opened my eyes, I could see only the monument. I didn't know what it meant, what it was called, who had raised it, and why it had been built. I didn't know, and it didn't interest me during my lifetime, and only today—just before my death—I found out that the monument is called "hope," and that it was raised in honour of . . . ha-ha-ha . . . in honour of me . . . Do you hear? In my honour . . .

"Who told them that I wanted such a monument? Who guaranteed them that I would be worthy of such a monument, that their work would please me, that I would thank them? Thousands, tens of thousands, millions of my forefathers died with stones heaped on them in this manner; every hair on my head will be cursed today; and amidst the same curses and rubble, my son—the one who will arrive shortly to replace me—will also perish; but—ha-ha-ha—look, just look how promptly, how rapidly the monument is being raised for him . . ."

I glanced up and gasped in astonishment . . .

On the green background of the misty curtain, on the very edge of the horizon, shimmered the rosy knees of a female figure being built up from the ground.

"You see, you see how they're hurrying? And they're in the dark —their backs are blocking the light shining from my field . . . They've forgotten about this light, and they're groping around and working in the dark so that later, in the light, they can destroy what they've built. And thus it repeats itself year after year, century after century, for tens of centuries—ha-ha-ha—isn't it a hilarious comedy? Isn't it a tragedy of the insane?"

The greybeard was laughing uncontrollably, and I, agreeing wholeheartedly with his words, laughed along with him.

"Ha-ha-ha! Look! Look! Take a look at that young couple . . . Look how exhausted he is! And she's barely dragging her feet. I swear to you—they lugged marble in the same manner for me. But did I ask them to do so? Did I promise to pay them for their backbreaking labour? Ha-ha-ha! Tell me, why did they build me a monument? Why did they shatter it? Why didn't they leave it for my son? Why undertake this new labour? Ha-ha-ha. Look over there! Look!"

The greybeard pointed at the monument and laughed so riotously that the waves must have risen in the sea. I looked, and this time, I, too, almost choked with laughter. What I saw was stranger than anything that I had ever seen in my life, or that I would ever see again.

The pink beauty—identical in the most minute detail to the former statue—was almost finished. One young gentleman was putting the final touches on her arms, and an oldster was fitting the last fragment of the marble into the heel of her shoe. Only her nose had to be affixed, and an old, musty, deaf and blind woman was attempting to do this. She had been lucky enough to find the nose while digging in the rubble, and no one had been able to overpower her and take it from her.

She was seated now on the right shoulder of the statue and, clutching the crown with the gnarled claws of her right hand and resting her feet on an elbow, she was blindly jabbing the beauty's forehead, eyes, lips, and chin with the nose . . . Her short, shaggy hair was blowing in the wind, her bony legs, bared to the knees, were buckling, her arms were trembling.

Millions of eyes were upon her, millions of hands stretched out to assist her; the people begged and cried out in terror and despair, but the deaf, blind old woman, not hearing or seeing anything, methodically slid the nose, in turn, from the eyes to the lips, to the chin, and then again to the eyes, the lips, and the chin . . .

This scene was ludicrous, like a cariacature; it resembled a coarse farce. . .

Anger began to seethe in my chest. A sharp, pitiless, sarcastic remark hovered on my lips—I could no longer remain where I was.

"Let's go," I said to the old man. "I have to pull the old woman off the pedestal, off the monument, and completely demolish it in front of everyone . . . I would sooner die than leave these berserk people their 'hope' . . . Let's go! I feel a great strength within me, the strength of a giant. Let's go!"

"Go! Go on!" the old man said gleefully, as he pulled back from me. "Go on alone. I'm not an assistant, either in the building of the monument, or in its destruction . . . I'm only a witness. Ha-ha-ha! Go!"

I was at the monument in a flash.

"Hey, you! Get away from there!" I yelled at the old woman. "Get away!" I called out again and, raising a rock the size of a head, took aim at the statue.

Warm, feminine arms unexpectedly wound themselves around my neck.

"Lesya!" I dropped my arm, but did not let go of the rock.

"Petro, darling! For God's sake! Have mercy!"

"Ah, so you're here as well?" I attacked her. "So you're no better than the rest of them? So you were in this herd the whole time? So you too carried stones and marble, and built the monument in order to destroy it later—to destroy it and then to build it anew?

"You're insane! For what kind of mercy are you pleading? Isn't last year's experience enough for you? Isn't the shame that you must have felt when the first stone was cast at what you had built enough for you? Don't you find it galling that the father did not want to have anything at all to do with your monument, did not deign to look at it even once? Yet here you are, raising a monument to his son, identical in every detail to the one you've destroyed."

Lesya clapped her hands: "Petro, darling! How could you say 'identical in every detail'?"

She seized me by the hand and pulled me to the monument.

The statue was completed—the arm was patched, the heel was affixed, and the classical nose was in its appointed spot; on the corner of the pedestal lay the old woman, stretched out in death. Blood was still dripping from her right temple, but there was no trace of her death agony on her face; her widely opened eyes were turned to the heavens as if she could see, through her cataracts, something enchanting, wonderful; her thin, tightly closed lips were frozen in a smile.

I did not deem the old woman worthy of attention. Lesya plucked a flower from her hair and threw it at her feet.

The people still encircled the monument in a tight wreath, but it seemed to me that these people were also completely different. Cheerful, happy, and contented, they joked, talked, and laughed. In their eyes flamed the fire of inspiration; in their figures one could sense vigour and strength.

"Thirteen! Thirteen points! Thirteen! Thirteen . . ." they shouted joyously, singing out the word in a chorus of voices and a multitude of tones.

"Thirteen! You see, my dearest Petro—thirteen! You see—there were only twelve before, and now there are thirteen points on the crown of our 'hope.' Thirteen! Do you understand?" Lesya was tugging at my arm, hugging me, and jumping for joy. "Do you understand?"

And suddenly, I truly did understand . . . The number thirteen assumed the form of a mighty enchantress; it became concrete, real, full of deep meaning, of great significance.

I let the rock slip from my hand.

"Ha-ha-ha!" the sharp laughter of the old man resounded even more sharply and merrily.

I flew into a rage, flung myself at him like a madman, grabbed his beard like a wild animal, and . . . woke up.

"A light! Bring a light right now!" I shouted at Serhiy.

As never before, I felt young, happy, fortunate, and strong . . .

Thirteen! Thirteen! Thirteen points on the crown of "hope."

Oh! I could ignore my grey hair now, I could scorn all of nature.

Thirteen . . . thirteen . . . thirteen!

That night, I proposed to Lesya . . .

Thirteen . . . thirteen . . . not ten, not eleven, not twelve, as there had been up to now, but thirteen . . . thirteen . . .

I no longer have any fears about my good fortune . . .

How They Hanged Her

(Granny Salomiya's Story)
(1908)

Dedicated to Yu. Yanovsky

Are we guilty? In what way are we guilty? There's no way we're guilty, my dear. After all, we weren't all going to be herded off to Siberia because of one poor soul. She wanted to die, but we, as yet, weren't tired of living; besides, it was almost harvest time, and who would have done my reaping for me if I'd been packed off to Siberia? Or, take Horpyna—her daughter-in-law abandoned her, and her daughter works as a servant . . . And then there's Melashka with her seven little children. Was she supposed to drag them with her to Siberia?

Well, there was no one, no matter who you think of, who could have gone to Siberia. Unless, perhaps, Sanka—it wouldn't have mattered to her; she's been left all alone, poor soul, with nowhere to turn, one could say, because when she got the falling sickness after her great fright, her neighbours no longer let her into their homes. That woman, perhaps, might be better off in Siberia. Let her follow her son and her husband there. But there was no way the rest of us could go, we just couldn't . . .

How did all this happen, how did it come about? Well, my dear, it all happened just as people told you—we really did hang her. You want me to start at the very beginning? But, my dear, do you suppose I know how this whole business really began? We'd been winding that ball of thread a long time—and we just knotted the end of it.

Up to then, I hadn't known this Mariya at all, but I had heard a lot—oh yes, an awful lot—about this ill-fated widow. She wasn't from our village, or from our district, but from the village of Bondarivshchyna—perhaps you've heard of it? It's said she lived quite grandly; her house was roomy, with as many as four windows in it; the benches were made of oak, and almost half a meter wide; and the floorboards, my good woman, were painted. In addition, there was a good-sized storehouse in the yard, two small sheds—one with a cow in it, and the other with a horse—a new mill, an orchard, a well-cultivated garden, and two sons. And for one of them she'd already found a good match. In a word, things were going very well for this Mariya—you couldn't have wished for anything better; however, as the saying goes, good fortune is here today and gone tomorrow.

It seems that her sons either hurt someone or went down the wrong path in life. Or, perhaps, their fate stumbled on something. Anyway, they were both taken away, bound, put in chains, and sent off to Siberia. A lot of people from all over our district were hauled away then—many more than were shipped off to fight the Japanese.

Our hamlet is right by the roadway, so we got our fill of watching them being carted away. There were bearded fellows, and shaved ones; and dark, skinny ones, and blond, round-faced ones. And there were also old men, and shepherds' helpers. And we saw two young women as well. In a word, there were all sorts of people of different colours and sizes, just like cattle in a herd. The district lost so many people—especially in Bondarivshchyna—that you would think there had been a cholera epidemic.

Well, the summer came, and there was no one—so they told us—to mow or to thresh, to feed the old people or to care for the little ones . . . the air reverberated with wailing and lamenting. And Mariya grieved most of all; the widow was losing her mind.

She ran around the village screaming: "Oh, they're not guilty! My sons—my darling falcons—aren't guilty! There's no justice in this world—it's no use expecting any."

And when she went home she stared out of all four windows and peered into all the outbuildings, lamenting loudly all the while: "Woe is me! I'll never see my children again as long as I live."

She sold whatever she could, threw her money to the wind and, in her grief, gave away everything she owned; she turned over all her household goods to her neighbours, but she did not hand over her sorrow, her unending grief, to anyone.

With every passing day, Mariya's possessions decreased, while her sorrow for her children increased; with every passing day, the widow's house and yard fell into greater ruin, while her grief for her dear ones thrived and sent down ever deeper roots.

And that grief of hers grew and grew, until it was too big for her house and her yard. She no longer tended her home; she neglected it completely.

The poor soul neither ate nor slept; her hair unkempt, and her clothes dishevelled, she wandered the whole day long over the steppes, unable to lull to sleep her forlorn and gloomy thoughts, unable to utter the charms that would make them disappear. And this was how she grieved, the poor dear, pining away the whole summer and the whole winter, until this spring.

When spring was just about here, some women folk began preparing to go on a pilgrimage to Kyiv. They came from the hamlets of Hryhorivka, Ivanivka, and Stepovy, and they formed a good-sized group. There were both old women and younger ones. Some had taken a vow to do this; some may have wanted to seek a better fate through prayer; while others, perhaps, wanted only to see the world.

I went with them, and Mariya tagged along with us as well.

We left right after Easter, and we found the trip to be neither hard, nor easy; we went neither quickly, nor slowly—we just walked along at a steady pace, and it was only Mariya who wasn't contented. She was always hurrying on ahead and urging us to go more quickly. It seemed to us that if she had wings, she would fly.

We arrived safely.

We arrived, and without wasting any time, immediately asked around to find out where, when, and in which church there was the best divine service. We found out everything, chatted for a while, talked things over, and agreed we would set out at once to the Church of St. Volodymyr. We stood through both the early service and the late one, and then we went to Sokhviyevsky's for supper. The next day, before the sun rose, we set out for the Lavra Monastery of the Caves.

We got there and found crowds and crowds of people . . . and they all looked as if they were waiting for the Last Judgement, or as if they had come from a country where there was no judgement at all. We looked at the people for a while, listened to them, and then went on to the Caves. We went through all of them, saying our devotions, and praying both in those that were close by and those that were farther away.

And Mariya went everywhere with us. We all prayed earnestly, but Mariya prostrated herself in prayer twice as much as we did; we gave money, without stinting, to have divine services said for our dear departed, but Mariya gave ten times as much. She paid for two litanies of supplication, and then she cried and prayed again. And it looked as if the Lord did help her, for she seemed to find comfort and peace and became a little happier.

We spent three more days at the Lavra Monastery, went to confession and communion, rested up, and started out for home. We left Kyiv behind. It had rained just before we set out, and so we found it pleasant to walk—it was neither dusty, nor hot. All around us the steppe was turning green, and throughout the forest the rooks, the cuckoos, and the nightingales sang without stopping. We walked along, chatted among ourselves, and didn't give a thought to Mariya . . .

We passed one hamlet, a second one, a third, and towards noon made our way to a large village. We had planned to spend the night there, but we took a look around, and the people appeared to be a suspicious lot; they seemed to look askance at us, and they didn't want to talk. We thought for quite a long time about what we should do; then we talked it over among ourselves and decided to keep on going.

So on we went. After walking for perhaps an hour or two, we came to a little river. Near the river there was a small grove, and beyond it stretched a village. We walked into the grove and found ourselves in a peaceful paradise; it was fragrant and green in there, the grass was soft, and the water was fresh, clear and cold. Should we keep on going? Or should we rest here? We got into a huddle, talked it over, deliberated. Then we filled our flasks with the pure water, found a comfortable spot, sat down on the grass, took out our rusks, and started eating our lunch.

Suddenly we looked around—Mariya wasn't with us!

We immediately became anxious. We asked one another about it, questioned each other, and then decided: why should we be worried? All of us had seen her walk into the grove. There was only one pathway through the grove, and the trees were not very thick, and the grass was not very tall. Even if she had strayed from the group or tarried by the river, she could not have wandered off too far. We discussed the matter for quite some time, and then we calmed down, rested, ate some lunch, tied up our bags, and rose to our feet. We got up, glanced up . . .

Oh, my poor heart! No more than half a dozen steps away from us, we saw Mariya swaying from a tree—the poor soul had hanged herself.

We rushed up to her, examined her, felt her from head to foot—and, praise God, she was still warm. We put our heads together, talked things over, untied her, hastily poured some fresh water into her mouth, and placed some wet kerchiefs on her head and her heart. We nudged her, cried, begged, and pleaded that she take pity on us and not bring down any trouble upon us—and then, lo and behold, we saw that she was slowly coming to. Her heart was reviving, and it seemed to us that she slowly moved her hand.

Overjoyed, we crowded around her and kept splashing her with fresh water.

And then we saw a woman passer-by slowly making her way down the trail. She had been trudging along the path, but now she turned and walked towards us.

She came up and exchanged greetings with us.

"And what is it that you, the servants of God, are doing?" she asked.

"It's like this," we told her, "we're saving a widow from an untimely death."

And she clapped her hands in dismay: "Oh, my God! Lord have mercy on you! May the Queen of Heaven protect you! You're all slated for Siberia—for hard labour, iron bars, iron chains! Who is permitted nowadays to take down a hanged person just like that, without any police, without any authorities being present?"

We all grew cold with fear and turned numb, and our hands dropped to our sides—it was Siberia for us! Without a doubt—it was Siberia! Were we any better or any worse than those who had been hauled away past our hamlet?

And we didn't stop to think, or mull things over, or seek each other's advice. We hastily threw Mariya's sash back on her neck, carried her to the very same tree, and found the very same branch.

Did we hang her?

Well really, my dear, we weren't all going to be herded off to Siberia because of one poor soul!

Grief
(1909)

I

Yivha came home from church, served her husband dinner, rinsed the bowls and spoons, and went to join the women in the village common.

Spring had not yet donned its delightful garments, but it had already washed itself in a warm rain, dried itself in the sun's rays, and was now greeting everyone with a vibrant "Good morning!"

It was sunny and dry in the village common. All the people poured out into the street.

The flower of the village men—the youngest property owners—gathered near the road at the very edge of the common; the more serious older men were conferring a little farther off, on logs near the mill; and the most elderly were smoking their pipes some distance away, in the field adjoining the pond by the village assembly hall.

The women folk were also divided into three categories. In their case, however, it was not so much their age and status that determined which group they joined, as similarities in their dispositions.

Close by sat a group of dignified women who had no interest in lies and no taste for whiskey. Dressed in dark jerkins and blouses embroidered in white, they wore fine black cords around their necks instead of coral beads, and almost all of them held infants on their laps. For the most part they sat silently, relaxing every nerve of their exhausted bodies and surrendering completely to the poetry and charms of spring that on ordinary working days go unnoticed by hardworking housewives.

Way out by the edge of the common, almost in the middle of the road, flashed the red and green kerchiefs of the village gossips. Brimming with youthful vim and vigour, and with hopes and desires deeply hidden in their hearts, they listened to the songs of the meadowlark and chattered animatedly.

A third group consisted of just three women neighbours.

Yivha walked out of her house, spotted the broad backside of her in-law—her daughter's mother-in-law—and made her way to this small group. She greeted everyone in her customary manner, and the others responded as usual; it was only her in-law, Odarka, who appeared not to take notice of her. Yivha, however, paid no attention to this and sat down beside her.

"So you're going to sit by me all the same, are you?" Odarka spoke as if she were joking, but her tone was rude.

"Yes indeed, I'm settling in close to you, so that it's easier to chat," Yivha replied. "I wanted to drop by your place yesterday, but I got all tied up with my cow; she has blisters, bigger than I've ever seen, all over her teats!"

"Well, just don't let your Katrya get near her next time," Odarka advised her.

"Why would you say that? My Katrya has been milking cows since she turned twelve."

"As if a daughter couldn't please a mother!" Odarka tossed out. "Just listen to how Ulyta praises her child, or that Bondarenko woman, or even Motrya . . . I don't want to criticise, but I'll tell you, my dear in-law, straight to your face—your daughter is not at all like you boasted she was."

"What did I boast about?" Yivha asked her in-law gently and calmly. "We didn't force our daughter on you. Your Havrylko took a liking to her, and he appealed to our daughter—and so they got married."

"You're being nasty beyond belief, Aunt Odarka! In what way is your Havrylo any better than Katrya?" Nastya flew into a rage.

"There, there now, Nastya, that's enough!" Yivha tapped her gently on the shoulder. "I don't mind when people criticise me. I have only one daughter, and I did the best that I could for her; I taught her as best I could, and I feel no guilt or regret if what I've done doesn't please someone. And as for the blisters, I've only myself to blame; I didn't dry off the teats well enough with a dry cloth before I chased the cow out into the spring wind."

"Oh sure, the 'spring wind'!" Odarka snickered. "The Lord punished my brother-in-law in exactly the same way—so many blisters appeared on his cow that eventually it died."

"Maybe he worked on a holy day?" Nastya asked.

"No, he didn't."

"Then God must have punished him for some other sin," Ustya said.

"He punished him because of me. He wronged me, and so I asked God to punish him."

"Go on! I'll never believe that!" Nastya said angrily.

"I don't believe it either," Yivha added.

"You don't have to believe it, but I've noticed more than once that as soon as I pray sincerely and ask nicely for something, then the Lord helps me. Why, not so long ago, my Havrylko was hauling some alcohol from the distillery with Ilko's horse, and something happened—one barrel broke loose, toppled to the ground, and started to leak. He rushed right over to it, but about twenty *karbovantsi [dollars]* worth of alcohol had already leaked out! He was so worried and distressed that he was almost in tears, but I didn't say anything.

"Well, he drove off, and I dropped to my knees: 'O merciful God! O most righteous God! Turn away the buyer's eyes, so he won't notice who brought the partially filled barrel.'

"When Havrylko came home, he was ever so happy. 'I was so lucky, mother,' he said. 'No one noticed anything!'"

"But I don't think that was the right thing to do," Yivha observed.

"It may not seem right to you, but the Lord can see more clearly what is right. He knows that the buyer's wallet is full, while I'm just a poor mother struggling to make ends meet, and so He protected me," Odarka replied with certainty.

The women laughed—they did not know how to respond to Odarka's boastful words. And even though Yivha knew what should be said, she also did not utter a word, because in her mind it was so obvious that it did not need to be said.

Everyone knew what kind of prayers there were; the holy Saints had composed them—the Lord's Prayer, the Creed, the prayer to the Mother of God, and the one about God's resurrection . . . There were also prayers you said to the stars when a child wouldn't sleep, to Saint Ilya when you suffered with cataracts, and to the Virgin Mary when you gathered herbs on the feast day of Semen Zylota. But no one would ever think of uttering a prayer that was like the one her in-law had just told them about. And even if someone did take it upon his or her conscience to recite such a prayer, God would not permit the buyer from the distillery to suffer in innocence and pay for Havrylo's loss out of his own pocket. This all seemed very clear to Yivha.

Moreover, she had other matters to discuss with her in-law. She had to find out what Odarka's thoughts were regarding the children. Did she want the young married couple to continue living with her in her damp old cottage, or would she be willing to have them settle in the new house that she, Yivha, and her husband owned?

"Sign everything over to Havrylo, and he'll go to live with you," Odarka replied to her question.

"Oh dear me! No matter how often I plead with you, my precious in-law, you always say the same thing. But you know, my dear, that we can't sign everything over while we're still alive. We could sign it over, and then he might become angry with us and chase us out of the house."

"My Havrylo would never do something like that as long as he lived! See here—I'm crossing myself and swearing that he would never do that."

"Don't swear, my dear in-law," Yivha interrupted Odarka. "Now he treats us as if he were our very own son, but no one can tell how things will turn out later."

"Don't sign anything over," Nastya joined the conversation. "Don't ever sign anything over. There are more cases than enough where parents are chased out of their homes by their own children. Don't sign. Let them move in with you, and let them live and praise the Lord as best they know how—but you must remain the masters in your own home."

"Uncle Ilko is so meek that he would cut short his own life if he signed over the house," Ustya added.

"The Lord will grant him a longer life for taking in an orphan."

"Are you saying that your Havrylo is an orphan?" Nastya burst out laughing.

"Shame on you!" Odarka cried in an offended tone. "Have you forgotten that he hasn't had a father since he was twelve? It's only through my prayers that I managed to keep our home. There was many a time when I had to abstain from eating meat, and I had to make many vows and say many prayers before I finally managed to pry loose my orphan's cottage from my son-in-law. Why, it cost me all of fifty *kopiyky [cents]* just to light candles in the monastery."

The women also recalled the two kegs of whiskey that Odarka had given the authorities and the witnesses on the day of the trial, but they did not dare to drop even a hint about the whiskey now.

"It's not the way you say it is, in-law," Yivha said after a pause. "It's not like that . . ."

"Then tell me, how is it?"

"Just listen to what I'm saying. My husband and I really want your son to come and live with us, but you want him to live with you . . ."

"And he will live with me!" Odarka snapped back at her.

"Don't say that, in-law. If it's God's will, then Havrylo will come to live with us, because you treat our daughter badly, but we care about your son—just as if he were our own child. And the children are more likely to be burdened by sins at your place because of all your problems and your penury."

"So you're saying that you're so very well off?" Odarka was offended. "All it would take is one match and a fistful of hemp— and that would be the end of all your wealth!"

"God be with you! What a terrible thing to say," Nastya exclaimed, jabbing her with her elbow.

Yivha's heart skipped a beat, but she consciously controlled herself. "Why would the Lord want to punish us so cruelly?" she asked. "We don't have any evil enemies or careless neighbours," she continued calmly. "I clean the chimney every Saturday, and my husband doesn't smoke a pipe . . ."

"That's enough talk about fires," Nastya said angrily, getting up and brushing off her skirt.

"Aunt Odarka is always like that—she's always trying to scare others with fire or the Last Judgement," Ustya blurted out reproachfully.

Yivha, even though she had not completed her conversation, also stood up. All things considered, there was no point in saying anything more. Why send your children to work in other peoples' fields if you have your own plot? Why live in an old and damp cottage, when you could live in a big, new dwelling that was bright and dry?

Everyone would think like that, but it was not at all clear what her in-law had in mind, and Yivha sighed heavily as she rose to her feet.

Odarka moved away even more reluctantly. She had joined this group on purpose today to have a talk with Yivha—and she had prepared for the conversation as for a decisive battle. Her thoughts were clear, and her desires were even clearer. No matter how much her in-laws protested, in the end they would have to sign over both the field and the house to Havrylo. That was when the young couple could start setting up their own home in earnest. Her son would care about his children, the old in-laws would look after running the household, and she could turn her attention to her daughter.

Her son had married well, but she still had a younger daughter to marry off. Where was she to get everything she needed in order to do that, if she did not succeed in snatching some of it from her in-law's household?

Odarka had everything planned to the very last detail; all that had to be done now was to put a lot of pressure on the old couple. As for asking them—well, she had already done that; and as for convincing them—she had tried that as well. But the old couple turned out to be so stubborn, that it had not been possible to wrangle even so much as a loan or an official piece of paper from them.

She had been determined to have a talk with her in-law today, so that the latter would no longer hope for some kind of compromise, so that she would understand that everything that happened in her, Odarka's, cottage, was done according to her wishes. But the conversation had become entangled, and more than an hour had been wasted talking about nothing.

"Damn it all anyway! I've wasted the whole day! Lord knows what dragged me out into the street today!" Odarka muttered wrathfully. "Maybe I should go to their place right now? No! Let them come and see me—it will be better that way. The old man hasn't seen his grandchildren for a long time now, and tomorrow's a holiday, so they're sure to come around," Odarka said, making her final observation.

II

And truly, the next day, after debating and discussing the matter at some length, the old couple set out to visit their in-law.

Yivha tucked a *palyanytsya [flatbread]* and a chunk of bacon fat in her jerkin, and Ilko took with him three lumps of sugar, half a quart of whiskey, and a *karbovanets [dollar]* "to cover the unexpected." During the night, they had come up with a good idea, a plan, as to what to say to their son-in-law. It could well be that Odarka had told him a bunch of lies, so now they would tell him everything in great detail—how they would live together, what small corner of the house they would occupy, how much of the household income they would require for their own needs.

Perhaps Havrylo thought that they intended to become rich and take their money with them into the next world, or start to live in luxury in this one—so they would tell him exactly how much they had to have for their livelihood. As it turned out, they required very little—the only major expense would be the cost of burying them and giving the monastery something for the requiem on the fortieth day after their death. They had already set aside the clothing, the linen cloths, and the candles for their death; moreover, if they chopped down their two poplars this fall, there would be enough boards for their coffins.

The entire family was at home when the old couple arrived at their in-law's cottage.

Katrya was delighted to see her parents—it was as if some great good fortune had befallen her. And the grandchildren flung themselves so happily at them that tears sprang to Ilko's eyes.

"Hey there, just look at the fine mower we have here! And here's someone to bind the sheaves," the old man said as he kissed the heads of the older grandchildren. "And this one is already turning his head to the light! See how clever he is. He doesn't turn it to where it's dark—he's staring at the bright window."

The old man's heart melted when he gazed at the smallest grandchild. He gladly would have taken this tightly wrapped little red bundle in his arms and pressed it close to his breast—but he was too embarrassed to do so, and so he turned his kind, grandfatherly attention to his dark-eyed four-year-old granddaughter.

Yivha also did not visit her daughter too frequently, because she did not find it at all pleasant to sit in the dark, sagging cottage. She did, however, come more often to see the grandchildren than Ilko. And so this time, when her head was filled with so many things she wanted to say, she greeted the children a bit less attentively and hastened to seat herself beside her son-in-law.

"Last night my husband and I decided to have a chat with you, my son. We're asking you to come and live in our house," she said without further ado.

Odarka glanced at Havrylo and stalked to the stove, certain that her son would not go against her will.

Katrya tucked the baby into the cradle and sat down on the floor to rock it.

Ilko, placing his grandson on one knee and his granddaughter on the other, moved in closer to the table where Havrylo was sitting.

"Do come, my dear son," he also said in a pleading tone. "Come and live with us. You'll be the master of the house, and like a son to us. The old woman and I don't need much room, but we're still capable of working for some time . . ."

"Sign things over to me, and I'll come to live with you," Havrylo retorted harshly.

Katrya blushed furiously and turned her face to the wall, so that no one would see the stinging tears welling up in her eyes. The old couple bowed their grey heads; stung to the quick by their son-in-law's insolent reply, their desire to engage in a heart-to-heart discussion abruptly vanished.

"We can't sign things over to you, my son; you can see that for yourself . . . " Ilko picked up the conversation after a pause.

"So who's forcing you to do so, my dear in-law?" Odarka spoke up, placing a frying pan with fried bacon on the table. "No one's forcing you, my dear in-law. Live under God's protection in your house, and we'll live in ours. Work on your own field, and we'll work wherever God gives us something to do. I've already agreed to reap a hectare of wheat and a hectare of barley for a percentage of the sheaves. Katrya and I will reap, and Havrylo will go away and hire himself out as a day labourer."

Katrya could endure no more; groaning as if a bullet had wounded her, she tore out of the cottage.

Odarka's eyes flashed joyfully. The happy thought of scaring the old couple by bringing up the subject of working as hired labourers had occurred to her quite suddenly and unexpectedly, but she immediately realised that this was her trump card. She noted with satisfaction that Katrya had rushed out of the cottage, and that the old man's face stiffened, while his hand, lying on the table, began to tremble.

"Havrylo will go away to work for a year or two, and when he comes home, he'll bring back some money and build a house . . . Of course, it might not be as large as yours . . ."

"Are you really planning to go away to work?" Ilko asked hollowly, as if he were speaking from a dungeon.

"Why wouldn't I go? The cottage is tumbling down, and there's nothing to be gained by staying at home," the son-in-law replied in an upbeat manner.

"Listen, son," Ilko said, and his face assumed a stern expression. "Do you remember what I said to you when you were courting Katrya?"

"I can't be expected to remember everything. You said a lot of things."

"I didn't say anything to you except what I'm saying now—I never intended to allow my only daughter to get married and live in someone else's home, and I let her marry you only because you agreed to move in with us."

"And I did live with you, for two whole years. I'm not refusing to do so even now . . . you see, I . . ." Havrylo started saying.

"No! Don't butt in—just hear me out. You know that a wealthy young man, Serhiy, was courting our daughter. Why didn't we let her marry him?"

"How should I know?"

"You do know. We didn't let her marry him because he was being called up into the army."

"But I'm not going to serve in the army."

"All the same—you're abandoning your wife; and what you're doing is even worse than what a soldier does. He abandons his wife because he's forced to do so, but you're going away of your own free will."

"My dear in-law," Odarka spoke up. "Such freedom is worse than slavery. How long are we to live in such a hovel? Are we to wait until it tumbles down on the children? It's not enough to sit around and feel sorry for ourselves; we have to come up with a plan, so that we don't perish from the cold. Havrylo is my son, but I'm not complaining about the will of God, and you have even less to be concerned about."

"Are you saying that he isn't dear to our hearts, as well?" Ilko asked.

"Perhaps he's even dearer to us than to his own mother," Yivha added.

"That's enough, my dear in-law, that's enough; don't say such a thing, don't even think it. If you truly thought of Havrylo as being your own son, you would have signed your house over to him long ago . . ."

"Oh no, my dear in-law, we wouldn't have signed it over."

"Yes, you would have."

"No, we wouldn't have signed it over, because a son of our own would not be asking us to do so; he would live in our house as if it were his own. You see, we're not signing anything over to Katrya, but she never so much as even mentions it to us."

"That's just the point," Odarka seized on his words. "Her husband is having such terrible problems, such worries, but she doesn't say a word. Now, you tell me—how is my Havrylo supposed to go and live with you when your own daughter doesn't want you to sign over the house?"

"Oh, my God!" Yivha exclaimed in consternation. "Did I ever say anything like that? Did I ever say, my dear in-law, that our Katrya . . ."

But her in-law understood that the time had come to do decisive battle. Like an evil fury, she dashed out of the cottage and, deliberately assuming a most severe expression, rushed about the yard in search of her daughter-in-law.

Katrya was standing by the pond at the lower end of the sloping yard; leaning against a willow, she was sobbing bitterly. It seemed to her that her father's pleas and her husband's harsh reply were echoing through the air.

For the very first time, the young woman became aware of the bottomless abyss that existed between her family and her mother-in-law, and it seemed to her that even in a lifetime she would not be able to fill this gulf with her tears.

She understood only too well her mother-in-law's clever, carefully planned approach; she was sure that Havrylo would not go away to find work, but how could she now live in a home where her parents were treated so rudely? As a genuinely truthful person, raised from infancy to respect the truth, she did not know how she could live through this first encounter with such a blatant lie. How could she keep quiet about it? How could she not come to the defence of her blood relatives, of the truth?

But at the same time, how could she position herself between the two hostile camps in such a way that she would not cause an even more serious rift and make matters worse? She believed in her husband, and it did not even cross her mind that he was capable of being untruthful of his own accord—but did he always have to submit to his conniving mother? Had he not defiled his soul and committed a sin by supporting such an evil mother?

"Kateryna! Katrya! Go to the cottage!"

The startled young woman shuddered. Her first impulse was to flee still farther down the hill, but it occurred to her that her baby might be crying, and so she went towards the cottage.

"Now it's time for the truth to come out! Now it's time to come clean and admit everything," Odarka said.

"What is it?" the young woman was stupefied.

"Go on, go into the cottage and you'll see for yourself," her mother-in-law alarmed her still more, flinging herself into the cottage and leaving the door wide open behind her.

Katrya followed her across the threshold. She was pale; her terrified eyes, encircled by blue shadows, seemed twice as large and dark as usual. She glanced quickly at the cradle, ran a piercing look over the entire room, and then fixed her eyes on her mother-in-law; she seemed to be expecting something malicious, predatory, and terrible from her—something she would no longer be able to tolerate quietly.

Yivha, realising immediately what was occurring in her daughter's heart, became alarmed.

"We've overstayed our visit!" she forced herself to say cheerfully, rising hurriedly to her feet. "It's time to go home. Let's go, old man. Good-bye, dear in-law! Good-bye, Havrylo!"

Odarka had not expected this turn of events, and she was at a loss for words to detain her guests. While she stood speechless, Yivha kissed the older grandchildren, blessed the infant in the cradle, and walked up to Katrya, who was standing petrified in the doorway.

"See! You're still wearing this coral necklace. It's strong, even though it's not made of glass; I don't regret searching everywhere in Kyiv for it," Yivha said to her daughter in an effort to rouse her, comfort her, and nudge her to utter at least a word or two.

And Katrya, hearing her mother's kind voice, did come to her senses. Seeing that her parents were preparing to leave, she threw a shawl over her shoulders, and the three of them walked out of the cottage together.

"Daughter, go back! You don't have to see us off. Your mother-in-law is angry, and she'll think you're complaining about her," Yivha advised Katrya.

"Let her walk with us at least through the yard! Why should she fear her mother-in-law? It's not as if she's stealing something from her, or criticising her, or bringing dishonour down upon her if she walks with her father and mother," Ilko said.

"But listen! It would be better if she turned back, so there woudn't be any trouble. Go on, my dear, go home," Yivha pleaded.

Kateryna obeyed her mother and walked her parents only as far as the gate; she stood there for a moment and then went back indoors. But, in the short time that she had been outside, something unpleasant had already transpired in the cottage; the children, subdued and apprehensive, were sitting quietly on the floor in a far corner, Havrylo was drumming his fingers angrily on the table, and Odarka, flinging around an oven-rake, was ramming whole armloads of straw into the stove.

"Let me take care of the stove, mother," Katrya said, hurriedly taking off her shawl.

"Aha! So you're being smart, are you? So it's because of you that I'm given so much respect by your parents? So it's you who doesn't want them to sign over the house? And today you even set your husband against me!" Odarka attacked her.

And she raked the hot embers out of the oven-stove so violently that an entire layer of straw tumbled out of the stove and landed on the fuel piled by the hearth.

The dry straw caught fire instantly. Katrya, already unstrung and stunned by the day's quarrelling, became even more confused and rushed to stamp out the fire with her bare feet. Her light skirt burst into flames. The fire raced up along her ribbons and wound itself like a snake on the coral beads around her neck.

She rushed outdoors like a madwoman. Havrylo finally caught up with her by the shed and, throwing a thick hempen cloth on her, pushed her to the ground.

III

For almost three weeks Katrya lay on the floor in her parents' new house. Her face was swollen, her entire neck, bandaged and tied securely, was wrapped in poultices prepared by an old woman healer. A cradle hung next to her, but she didn't touch it, because she found it too painful to move. Most of the time she lay there all by herself.

At first, the other young women visited her quite frequently, but when the holidays ended and there was pressing work in the garden, they stopped dropping in. Her mother-in-law rarely visited her and, when she did come, stayed only a short time. The old couple had not taken the two older grandchildren because they disturbed their mother. As for Havrylo, he remained in his own home, stopping by to see his wife only in the evening, on his way home from the estate where he worked as a day labourer.

Yivha also did not devote her entire day to her daughter—the infant took up a lot of her time, and she spent every free moment working in her garden.

She had no fears regarding her sick daughter. Her heart ached, of course, when Katrya began to groan more loudly, and her entire body went numb when she looked at her daughter's neck, all covered in festering abscesses. But she kept reassuring herself that it was only a burn, and not a fever or some other illness—the kind for which even a woman healer did not know a cure. And so, Yivha was confident that every day brought with it an easing of her daughter's pain.

"On the fifth day, the burnt flesh will start to heal," the woman healer said.

Yivha waited for this to happen on the fifth day, and on the seventh, the ninth, and the twelfth; constantly reassured by the healer, she tried to lift her husband's spirits. Besides, the very idea that her daughter—so comely, gentle, obedient, and the mother of three little children—might die from a strip of burned flesh on her neck was so preposterous that she simply did not consider it in the realm of the possible. Yivha dug her garden, planted it, and spent more time thinking about the rain than about her grief.

And so it was that Katrya was almost always alone in the house, lying on a new mat covered with a thick white linen cloth. The window was shut tight and draped to block the sun; Katrya could not see how profusely the cherry tree had come into bloom in the orchard. Nor did she see the sun, or the fluffy white clouds in the sky.

It was only the bright, star-filled spring sky that greeted her. Katrya waited impatiently for the moment when Yivha would uncover the window for the night. Exhausted by their heavy labour, the old couple quickly fell asleep, but Katrya did not take her eyes off the sky, the moon, the stars . . .

It was in this way that the twentieth night arrived. On this day, Yivha, seeing that Katrya seemed to be better, fell asleep by the cradle early in the evening. She awoke at midnight. It was like daylight in the house. The cherry tree, covered in blossoms, peeked through the window like a young bride coming to invite them to her wedding; in the other window, a full moon was suspended. Yivha took care of the infant and then, quietly walking up to Katrya, looked at her intently.

Katrya was not sleeping. She was gazing at the moon with widely opened eyes.

"Aren't you sleeping, my child?" Yivha asked as she sat down beside her. "Why aren't you sleeping? Is the pain worse?"

"No, nothing hurts; it's all so pleasantly numb . . . But I keep wondering—what's that 'other world' like, mother?"

"You don't even know this world very well yet, my child, and you're already beginning to talk about the next one!" Yivha said, yawning.

"And in your opinion, mother, what is this world like?"

"Well, you can see for yourself how bright and beautiful it is outdoors."

"But there's also much grief and falsehood in this world!" Katrya stated slowly, softly, and sorrowfully.

"It can't be any different, my daughter. There are evil people who do evil things, and life for them is bitter in this world, but for people who have no malicious thoughts, the world is pure and white—just like that cherry tree by the window. It grows, blooms, and then covers itself with berries; and it repeats this cycle as long as it was meant to . . ."

"But I'm always thinking about the other world," Katrya said after a slight pause. "I think it's much nicer there, mother, than it is here. No wonder dead people are always washed—everything there is so clean and bright. You should go there with a pure heart and a sinless soul. Oh, mother dear, how I yearn to be better than I am."

"What do you mean, better? My dearest, you're . . ."

"Oh, no, mother! If you only knew how mean I am, how spiteful I can be! Back then . . . that evening . . . I hated my mother-in-law so intensely, and I was so angry with Havrylo . . . I was so furious, I was so . . ." Her voice trembled, and she broke off what she was saying.

"You're only distressing yourself, my dear, agitating yourself," Yivha tried to calm her daughter.

"How I wish that the door would open this very instant, and that my mother-in-law and Havrylo would walk into the house."

"What would you do?"

"I'd confess to them," she said, after giving it some thought. "I'd admit how angry and unforgiving I was that evening. They didn't want to harm me in any way. Was it so bad that they wanted to live in this house? Their cottage is old and damp, while this house is new. And our garden is better, and our yard is bigger—and they just wanted to have something better.

"It's all so clear to me now . . . And it no longer seems so mean and ugly . . . Did you begrudge them the house? You didn't begrudge it, and daddy didn't, and neither did I . . .

"If only they would come, mother! If only someone would ask them to come, mother."

"Who would go to alarm people in the middle of the night, my child? And, as for the house, you haven't thought everything through clearly enough. Go to sleep now, and tomorrow God will give us a new day and advise us what to do."

IV

God brought the expected day, but along with it He brought unexpected grief—Kateryna died at dawn. No one heard her last groan, no one received her last look, no one heard her last behest.

Yivha awoke and got ready to go and milk the cow; it was only when she picked up the milking pail and her kerchief that she happened to glance at her daughter. And it seemed to her that Katrya was no longer breathing. Not believing her eyes, Yivha placed a hand on her daughter's forehead—it was cold. Like a madwoman, she flung herself at her daughter and began shaking her body with all her might.

"Katrya! Katrya!" she shouted at the top of her lungs, as if her shouting would determine whether her daughter awoke or died. Hearing her shouting, Ilko rushed into the room—and his hair stood on end. He caught hold of his wife's arms and shoved her away from their daughter's body. Yivha fell silent at once. But her eyes blazed so fiercely, with such an infernal fire, that they were unlike anything Ilko had ever seen before in his life.

"Yivha! Yivha, come to your senses! Yivha, don't look like that! Yivha, cross yourself and submit to the will of God," Ilko attempted to calm his wife, but he, too, could not control his feelings and burst into tears.

The women came over, seated Yivha off to one side, and started preparing the deceased for burial. All of them were crying, and they were crying very sincerely; it was only the mother who did not weep. She stared at her dead daughter as if she did not see her, as if she could not admit the truth. It was in vain that a few of the women, alarmed by such an unexpected turn of events, tried to move her heart with grief and make her cry—it was as if her soul, her heart, her thoughts, and her memory were all petrified.

It was dreadful to see her motionless figure next to Havrylo who, tearing at his hair and his shirt, covered his dead wife's hands and feet with kisses, and alongside old Ilko, who sat on a bench and wept inconsolably. The entire outward appearance of the bereft mother was dreadful, but it was most dreadful to look at her thin, even, and tightly clamped lips. It seemed that her lips were concealing a secret, and it was terrifying even to try and guess what they might reveal if ever they opened.

"It would be better if you prayed to God," Ilko approached her.

Yivha rose to her feet and, treading heavily, approached Kateryna. She adjusted her daughter's head-dress, kneeled down beside her, and hid her face in the sleeve of her daughter's blouse. The room became hushed as everyone fell silent.

"If only the poor dear could cry," Nastya whispered to Ustya.

But after some time had passed, Yivha stood up—her eyes were dry, her lips were sealed tight . . .

"She'll go mad! If only there were someone here to lament properly and movingly," Nastya said worriedly. "Perhaps if someone went to get Stekha . . . She might have come home from the market by now."

Onyska ran to fetch Stekha.

A few minutes later, Stekha walked into the room. She was a thin, tiny woman; it seemed as if her entire body was woven out of nerves, that her whole soul was composed of poetry, and her heart was nothing less than a wonderful harp—the strings of which had been broken by the hand of her drunkard-husband. This was the first she had heard of Katrya's death, and she had not yet seen her body—and so, under the fresh impression of her grief, she lamented for her friend so loudly, so sincerely, that the mother's frozen heart was moved, and she began to weep.

V

But the tears did not bring the longed-for ease to Yivha's soul; they only seemed to rupture the thread binding her soul to her body, to other people, to the entire world.

Now there no longer were people who were either dear or distant to her. There was nothing that was either appealing or disgusting. The whole world was a cold, empty wasteland, where her soul wandered in an endless expanse, without touching anything or stopping anywhere. And it seemed to Yivha that she had been wandering like this for centuries, and that she would wander this way forever.

Nastya reminded her that it was time to begin preparing the funeral dinner, with its *kanun [spiced diluted honey]*. As Yivha listened to her, she felt as if she were in a dream. She found it strange to hear people say that she should be doing something, that she had duties to perform. She unlocked the door to the storage room and handed over all her treasures to strangers.

Everything had lost its value, its meaning, its substance; everything seemed like some kind of a vision, a shadow. *Pyrohy [turnovers]* had to be baked? Noodles had to be cut? Someone was going to eat, to drink? Someone needed her wealth? That's fine, that's fine—let them drink, let them eat, let them take everything, let them drag it away, haul it off . . . Let them even take the house, for even if she had earned and saved ten times as much in her lifetime, it would still not be enough to fill the emptiness through which her soul now drifted.

And there was Ilko—worried about the whiskey, getting ready to go somewhere, hurriedly rushing away. She saw it all—she even got the bottles ready for him, but she could not get it through her head that he was her husband, her partner, the father of her Katrya. To her, he seemed to be as much of a stranger as all the other people; he was the same kind of illusion, a shadow, like everything else in the world. At least he was not there, where her soul was meandering. Of course, there was no one in that wasteland—not even Katrya was there.

In the past, when her neighbours died, it had seemed so clear, so obvious to her, that the soul of the deceased hovered near its blood-relatives, and that they could feel its presence. Now, however, she no longer was sure about this—she did not sense Katrya near her, nor did Katrya's soul make itself known to her.

Perhaps there was no soul?

One time, Tryndychenko had stated that there was no such thing as a soul. When she heard him say this, her hair froze on her head—but now she was not afraid to think the same thing herself. Now she had no fear of anything—she no longer feared sin, or God, or His punishment. In the desert where some kind of a rapacious power had cast her, there was nothing with which she could be punished.

And thus, overpowered by confused feelings and even more confusing thoughts, Yivha numbly did everyone's bidding, did everything that was asked of her. At first the women were only surprised by her behaviour, but gradually they began to condemn her. Their feminine hearts, so willing and eager to offer comfort, felt cheated. In the room where the deceased lay, there was no one to console, no one to soothe; it was even awkward to cry. But when could you cry to your heart's content, if you did not wail for a deceased woman who was your neighbour?

There was no time for a woman crushed by toil to dwell on her own misfortune. Just as it is not possible to tolerate a sliver that makes it difficult to knead dough, weave, or knit, so her grief had to be quickly plucked from her heart and thrown out of the house, out of the field. And only death, through its age-old traditions, gave her the right to minister to the needs of her soul. Whether it was a relative or a stranger who was laid out on a bench, everyone had the right to pause, to run in and look at the deceased, to think, to weep. At a time like that, no one asks why you are crying; no one pressures you to find out which tear is being shed for the fate of the deceased, and which one is flowing from the block of ice that has lain, perhaps for many years, in your heart.

A woman stands by the deceased and cries openly, without embarrassment, without concealing her tears, without hiding from either her mother-in-law or her brother-in-law. No one will condemn her, no one can guess if she is crying for a beloved who is not fated to be hers, if she is washing away her fatigue with her tears, if she is pouring out her heart over a terrible moral injustice, or if she is moved to weep by memories or hopes. She stands sobbing for a while, has a good cry, wipes away her tears with the hem of her apron, and returns home feeling heartened and stronger, as if she had rid herself of a heavy burden halfway up a steep mountain.

The death of Katrya, this unfortunate young woman, did not give them such an opportunity. The mother was not weeping, and the father was not at home. Havrylo, having cried himself out, was sitting silently, and the children did not fully understand the misfortune that had befallen them. There was no one to feel sorry for, and there was no opportunity, reason, or desire to weep. The women were just about to go home, when Odarka entered the room.

She instantly grasped the mood of the women.

"Aha! So was I wrong to be angry with her?" she asked the women. "Wasn't I right? What kind of a mother is she? What kind of a heart does she have? Her daughter is lying on the bench, and she's rummaging in the pantries and cellars. All she's interested in is money and wealth! She begrudged her own daughter a corner of her house, so now let her dance in it with her old man to her heart's content. Maybe she's looking forward to having the grandchildren? Let her forget about that! Let the little ones die sucking rye water, rather than drink so much as a drop of milk from her cow.

"And that cow isn't going to bring her any joy much longer. It's covered in abscesses, and now it's gone lame. It's all God's punishment! Let her not be cruel to poor people! Let her not be proud! She'll see—her sins won't make their presence felt only in her cow. You'll remember my words when hail destroys her fields, when her chickens drop dead, when a heavenly thunderbolt sets her house on fire." Odarka spewed out her rage with increasing intensity, elated that she had an audience for her rancour.

VI

The burial ceremony for Katrya was over. Yivha came home from the cemetery completely drained. "Rest, for at least a minute," her fatigued body told her, but it was not possible to think about resting. A large crowd of people was already assembled in their yard. The old couple had not invited anyone to come to the funeral meal, but despite this, more than enough people had gathered to eat what had been baked and boiled.

In the middle of the yard, three rows of white tablecloths were spread on the green grass; on the cloths lay sliced bread, *pyrohy, knyshi [stuffed bread],* and bowls filled with curdled milk. For the most part, the women sat together, while the men selected spots where they could be close to a neighbour or in-law. Behind the women sat the children. There were no bowls of milk or bread in front of them as yet, but they all had their spoons ready. While the people were still settling in, Nastya and Ustya placed tureens filled with noodles and borshch on the cloths.

Ilko started to make the rounds of the people with a shot glass.

"You, too, should treat the women at least once, auntie," Nastya said to Yivha, shoving a bottle and a shot glass into her hands.

Yivha did not argue; she went to offer the women a drink.

The abundant funeral dinner and the costly funeral—at which Yivha had wept copiously—succeeded in erasing the negative impression that Yivha had made initially on her fellow villagers. And now, having undeniable proof—in the liquor, the food, and the fine kerchiefs that were distributed—that the parents had truly loved their daughter, the people sympathised with them wholeheartedly.

As the guests accepted the shot glass from either the host or the hostess, they all crossed themselves in a dignified manner with a broad sweeping gesture, while pronouncing sadly and with great feeling: "May the Kingdom of Heaven be hers!"

After making the rounds of one row of tablecloths, Yivha stepped up to the second one. She poured some whiskey into the shot glass and extended her hand; however, at the very moment when another hand reached for it, she jerked her arm back. The glass fell into a tureen, knocking a large chunk out of it, and noodles spilled on the cloth.

A child, catching sight of the hostess, cried out in alarm. Yivha's face had darkened, her body was trembling, and her eyes blazed like those of a fierce, wild animal.

Before her stood Odarka; holding the smallest grandchild in her arms she said with a smirk: "If it breaks, it's for good luck."

The people watched them, but did not understand what was going on. Had the glass fallen accidentally from Yivha's hands, or had she dropped it on purpose, so as not to treat her in-law? Yivha herself did not know how it had happened.

"Did you stumble on this stick?" Nastya asked.

Yes! Yes! Nastya had guessed correctly—she had stumbled on a stick . . . Yes, she had "stumbled." And her soul, that had been wandering thus far in a boundless wasteland, also stumbled onto something now. . . Another second passed, and Yivha felt that a single emotion—a dreadful, burning hatred for Odarka—was binding her soul on all sides.

Ah! It was no wonder that her soul had been drifting aimlessly— but now it had finally found its enemy. Here she was, the one who had damned her to eternal suffering. Here she was, that enemy of her soul, that malicious enemy that had ruined her life. It was she, Odarka, who had successfully prayed to God, pleading for the fate that had befallen Katrya. She had boasted publicly about the power of her prayers, and she had composed a prayer in her evil heart, asking for the death of the daughter-in-law she detested. When all hope of laying hands on their house faded, she had decided it was better for Katrya to die, and have Havrylo marry Onyska.

And what could be done now? Who could swear that Odarka had accidentally raked those embers out of the stove? And had it really been impossible to save Katrya? After all, they had managed to put out the fire and save their hovel.

Ah yes! It was Odarka—this fiend, this snake—who had done it all on purpose, intentionally! Had she not threatened her with fire? And Yivha felt that her hands were forming fists of their own accord, that her eyes were filling with blood, and that her heart was engulfed in flames. She wanted to shout in Odarka's face: "Murderer!" It seemed to her that if she did this, the people would lunge at Odarka and tear her to pieces, crush her like a snake.

But then Yivha cast an eye at the assembled people, and they, too, became odious to her. There they sat, eating the noodles with such gusto and dipping their *pyrohy* in the sour cream. Of what concern was an unfortunate mother or a murderer to them? These were the same people who had drunk and danced at Katrya's wedding. Didn't they know Odarka back then? Didn't they know that an angel like Katrya could not have a life with such a mother-in-law? Why hadn't anyone said something then? Why hadn't they warned her?

Damn them! All they were interested in was eating and drinking. They drank when they initiated the evil pact, and they were drinking now, at the conclusion of the crime. There was the matchmaker, sitting right over there. And there was the girl who carried the candle at the marriage ceremony . . . They were all sidekicks of this serpent—they were all enemies of the unfortunate Katrya. Damn them! Damn them all to hell! Yivha bit her lips to stop herself from shouting these words.

"Auntie, dear, you don't look well! Go into the house and rest," Nastya, seeing the ferocious look in Yivha's eyes, exhorted her.

Yivha shoved her aside and, moving off a bit to one side, leaned against a ladder. Yes! This was the best place for her. Here, the people could not see her, but she could keep an eye on all of them. She needed people now the way a fire needs fuel. If she did not see the people, the flame of hatred in her soul might be extinguished, but it had to continue burning for a long, long time, so that she could scrutinise all her enemies in its red flames.

Yivha watched Odarka drink, eat, smile, and chat with the people; and it was with unmitigated joy that she sensed the feeling of vengeance that was sprouting in her heart. To take vengeance! To burn her cottage! To choke her daughter! To wreak fierce vengeance on her! It was only through such vengeance that it would be possible to extinguish the infernal fire of her grief.

"Look over there, at Yivha—do you think she's gone mad?" Nastya asked, tugging at Ustya's sleeve.

"Let's go into the house, auntie dear," she once again pleaded with Yivha. "You'll tell me what to do in the house."

"In the house? Why didn't she, the witch, burn the house and the entire farmstead? It would have been better if, instead of murdering my daughter, she had grappled my soul with an iron hook! It's she . . . she, the viper, who caused all this!"

"God be with you, Yivha!" Nastya stopped her. "No one is to blame for your misfortune; it was Katrya's fate to die like that!"

"Her fate? Everyone else is fated to live, to have children and grandchildren, and it is only she—such a young woman—who is fated to lie in the ground?"

"It can't be helped, if that was her fate!"

"Fate? There is no fate. It's all in the hands of people; it's all in their hands. It's snakes like her, fiends like her, that ruin our lives."

Nastya and Ustya took Yivha by the arms and forced her into the house.

"If only I could have a drink of fresh water," Yivha pleaded.

Ustya ran to fetch the water, while Nastya arranged some pillows on the bench and tried to convince Yivha to lie down.

Yivha agreed, for she truly did feel a great need to rest.

She lay down, but she did not fall asleep. Much of what was happening under the window or behind the door, either in the porch or in the yard, she did not hear; nor did she notice when the day drew to a close, and evening descended on the earth. At the same time, however, she did not fall asleep for even a minute—and she did not stop thinking about her grief.

At first her thoughts continually circled around Odarka, but then they moved on to Katrya. As Yivha reviewed Katrya's life from her childhood to her last days, she recalled that final night.

"O my dearest daughter! You knew you were going to die! Your soul foretold you; your soul was always ready to warn you. But why did my cursed soul remain quiet? Why did I go there that day? Why did I drag myself over there? And it was I who bought you those coral beads! I didn't begrudge the money to buy them—only to have them destroy you!

"You wanted to see us home, my little darling, and your father wanted you to come with us; it was I who made you go back—to your death. I'm blaming others, I'm searching for your enemies, but it was me—I'm your worst enemy. It was I who shortened your life, who heaped the earth on your chest. O my darling daughter! My daughter!"

Now she was shouting, wailing, beating herself on the chest.

Ilko walked in. "Calm down, Yivha; you'd do better to pray," he pleaded with her through his tears.

"Pray?" Yivha exclaimed, jumping to her feet. "Pray for whom? For my cursed soul? When my daughter was still alive, when there was someone to pray for—I didn't pray as others do; I didn't fast, I didn't go on pilgrimages, and I didn't know how to weep and plead with God to spare the life of our only daughter—and I'm to begin praying now? For whom? For what? God has punished me for my sins, and there's nothing left that he can punish me with; but he also has nothing to pardon me with, for he can't return my daughter to me. No, even if God himself were to come down from heaven and say that He punished me for my sins, I, Yivha, still would not pray."

Hearing his wife's terrible words, Ilko dropped to his knees before the icons . . .

The death of his daughter had wounded him, just as it had wounded his wife, but the two parents experienced their grief differently. Grief had enslaved the mother's soul entirely, without leaving any of it untouched; in the father's soul, however, there remained a corner that grief could not encompass; it belonged to him, the father, and, as long as he lived, no power and no misfortune could destroy his need to protect it.

Notwithstanding his immense grief, Ilko still felt hunger, and thirst, and the need for sleep. He was still concerned about his farmstead and could not bring himself to hate and curse that to which he had been devoted his entire life. The sun would not stand still because Katrya had died, and Ilko's tears would not make the sown earth produce.

Katrya was gone, but the whole wide world remained the way it always had been, and even though his obligations to Katrya had ended, his obligations to that wide world, to himself, his wife, other people, and his grandchildren had not disappeared. Especially to his grandchildren. At the time that Yivha's soul, seemingly torn by grief out of her body, was roving through space, pausing first over Odarka and then over the sins of Yivha herself, Ilko's eyes saw only the three grandchildren—those orphans that from this time on he would have to care for twice as much and work for twice as hard.

Ilko also could not change that part of his soul where his strong faith abided. He had always felt the need to pray, and this need was neither increased nor decreased by either grief or joy. Ilko had prayed daily for the health of his daughter, and now he prayed in the same way for the repose of her soul.

Ilko knelt before the icons and bowed his head deeply to the ground, but Yivha just watched him . . .

The days passed by, but they did not bring with them even a drop of relief. On the contrary, grief became more deeply rooted in the mother's heart and pressed relentlessly on her brain.

Yivha walked about aimlessly, roaming around for days on end without finding either a corner to sit in, or something to do. Her body and soul, as if severed from one another by grief, conducted their separate lives in hostility, without understanding one another. Her soul opposed any demands of her body, and her body did not want to submit to the will of her soul. And, caught in this unremitting conflict, Yivha lost her way completely. Now she had absolutely no idea what to do, what to think, how to live.

At times she sat motionless like a stone for an entire day in the orchard, holding her head in her hands; at other times, she fled from home and wandered through the village. There were times when she was happy to have someone come to visit her and, with tears flooding her face, she would talk about Katrya and complain about her unending grief; at other times she would hide, locking herself away from people, afraid to have them peer into her soul, to exacerbate her grief with their sympathy, advice, and distractions.

And every day she experienced periods of intense hatred for Odarka, an insatiable desire for vengeance, and an aching, all-consuming boundless jealousy of every mother who had a child to caress, and of every person who did not have to bear the grief that she was suffering. There were also times when she cursed herself, but these moments came and went, leaving her soul in the claws of grief.

She hardly spoke to her husband. It seemed to her that grief had stripped his soul naked, just as a hurricane rips off the roof from a dwelling, and she hated the starkness of his soul.

One time, when he was kneeling before the icons, bowing fervently to the ground, she could not restrain herself any longer.

"Why are you praying?" she asked him in a dull, choked voice. "Tell me the truth, why are you praying? So that God will give you a good crop of wheat? So that you'll live to a ripe old age? Or so He'll help you to find peace and forget that your daughter—your one and only daughter—is rotting in the ground?" Yivha lamented and wailed.

"I'm praying that the Lord may grant her the Kingdom of Heaven," Ilko replied, sighing softly.

Yivha fell silent, wiped her tears, and fixed her eyes on the corner of the room where the candles flickered before the icons.

"The Kingdom of Heaven!"

More than once she had heard Katrya's wish to be in the Kingdom of Heaven, and more than once she herself had whispered these words. But had she prayed sincerely even once, with deep bows, with her whole heart, with her whole soul, that the Lord might grant her daughter the Kingdom of Heaven? Never! But the Kingdom of Heaven was all that she could now ask for her daughter. And she had not done so up to now! To pray! Yes! To pray for the Kingdom of Heaven.

Up to now she had not known how to pray sincerely, and she had not succeeded in securing a good fate for her daughter, but now she would pray, and she would succeed in gaining, for her, the Kingdom of Heaven. For all her daughter's suffering on this earth, the Lord would grant her paradise in the other world.

Not only would she pray, she would make a vow, go on a pilgrimage to the Holy Monastery of the Caves of Lavra, take an oath not to eat meat to the day she died, pay for a remembrance service at the monastery on the fortieth day of her daughter's death, buy a silk cloth to be placed under the Holy Gospel, and give away everything that she had to beggars, so that they too would pray for the soul of her daughter.

To pray! To have everyone pray for her! Nothing pleased God like prayer. It did not matter if it was a sinner who prayed, or someone without sin, a good person or a bad one—it was still a prayer. The laws and the commandments—these were meant for people, for earthly judges; but for the Heavenly Judge, prayers and glorification were needed.

To pray! To pray for the Kingdom of Heaven—this was what she must do for her daughter. And in this infinite desire to find something to which she could dedicate her heart, she fell down before the icons, weeping profusely.

Ordinary, everyday prayers did not enter her mind now; her lips whispered words she had never uttered before. These words came effortlessly, flowing like a warm stream, like the blood from her heart, and her heart truly was eased—it seemed that it was growing smaller, and it no longer ached, distended her breast, or weighed on her like a stone.

Little by little, her tears stopped flowing. The final word of her prayer was uttered, and it felt as if there were no more thoughts in her head, and no more torment in her heart! She had told God everything, told it all sincerely—and He had heard her; He must have heard her, for He had eased her soul.

Oh, she felt much better now!

Yivha rose from her knees and looked over at her husband who was sleeping on the floor. It seemed to her that he was not comfortable, that he had not covered himself well, and she carefully adjusted the blanket on him. Then she recalled that, for a long time now, she had not given him any milk for his porridge or cooked him supper, and her heart stirred with pity for the neglected old man.

And then she recalled that she had not seen her grandchildren for some time, and that she had not packed away Katrya's clothes in a trunk. She also remembered that during all this time she had not checked the chickens for eggs, and that it was time to put some eggs under the speckled brood hen.

Completely preoccupied with her household duties, Yivha crawled up to the bed on top of the oven and fell into a sound sleep. And almost immediately, she had a wonderful, joyous dream. Katrya was still a girl. Katrya was dressing to go to church, and Yivha was braiding her hair, smoothing out her ribbons. Katrya was happy, but Yivha was even happier—she could not tear her eyes away from her beautiful daughter.

"And here I dreamed that you were dead," she said with a laugh, and at that very moment she felt that someone struck her with great force, right in her heart . . . Her heart wrenched loose, fell, and began beating violently.

She leapt up—and remembered everything.

"Katrya's gone! It was a dream! Katrya's gone, and I'll never ever see her again."

Her heart, once again drenched in blood, choked her chest. She felt confined, hot—she could not breathe. She tore off her shirt, wrung her hands. This house was repulsive to her, like an abscess, and her husband was also repulsive.

She wanted to wake him up, to yell right into his ear: "Katrya's gone. Katrya's in a grave! The worms are gnawing at her body! The raw earth is choking her breast, but you console your miserable soul with 'the Kingdom of Heaven,' and now you're fast asleep! What kind of Kingdom is it? Who has seen it? Here's where the kingdom is—here on earth. Where does the truth lie?"

Why must she suffer like this? Every criminal is told why he's being punished, but she did not know why such a heavy punishment had been meted out to her. For her sins? She did not know of any sin that she had committed that would have made even the fiercest judge punish her like this, for all eternity. For the sins of her grandfathers? Her ancestors? Punishment into the third or fourth generation?

Where, then, is the mercy of God?

Perhaps this grief had been sent her to perfect her soul amidst unending torment? But no! Her soul had grown more evil, blacker, and jealousy and hatred had fixed themselves in her heart.

And what about the children? Why had He condemned these orphans to perdition so early in life? Surely He knew how difficult it was for orphan children to save their souls from sin! Was it really necessary to increase the number of sinners on this earth, to ensure that there were more people to punish? Where is the justice of it all?

Having created heaven and earth, does He not want to give people a better chance for happiness, or is He unable to do so? Or did He perhaps create everything and then leave it all to its own will, like an indifferent farmer sometimes leaves his planted garden to destruction by cattle, to the will of the weeds? And if so, who could guarantee that the same injustice did not prevail in the Kingdom of Heaven?

Question after question flew into her soul, like ravenous rooks fly to a corpse, and her mind, unexpectedly awakened, could not answer any of them. But her soul could not be restrained. Driven by its impassioned and daring quest for answers, it flew to God himself. It was better to suffer a terrible punishment, a fierce punishment for this quest, for this greatest of all sins, than to bear the fate of a slave serving an unknown Master.

To die! To die right now! To go quickly either to Katrya, or to hell, or into an emptiness—anything to end this senseless suffering on earth.

She ran out into the yard, into the fresh air.

The new shed, the neatly piled rick of last year's straw, the stack of freshly raked hay, the airy, well-built white house . . . How gladly she would set all this on fire and cast herself into the very heart of the flames; but her husband was sleeping there . . . He still wanted to live. He wanted to live for his grandchildren; he still had hope. He believed that the children could live on this earth according to the truth, knowing the truth. He was mad! But let him live! Let him suffer for dozens of years yet—her suffering would come to an end right now.

To die! To die right now! To hang herself on this joist that the carpenter seemed to have intentionally left sticking out from under the roof in the shed.

Yivha rushed to the porch, pulled a length of rope from behind the kneading trough, and hurried to the shed.

But as she approached the joist, she suddenly stopped and turned off into the garden. She walked down the slope the length of the garden, found two bunches of mint and pulled them out by their roots, tossed some periwinkle into her apron, and, leaving the yard, walked down the street, through the pasture, and across the fields, until she came to the cemetery.

VII

Katrya's fresh grave, covered with thick grass, shimmered darkly in the middle of the cemetery. Yivha ran straight to it, swimming up to her knees in the damp grass, stumbling in the depressions of ancient graves, and climbing over recently heaped mounds.

The moon was shining brightly. The acacia bushes planted thickly by the ditch were in full bloom, and their sweet smell wafted in warm waves over the cemetery. Yivha shook the plants out of her apron and pressed herself briefly to the grave.

"O my dearest daughter! My darling little daughter, I'm coming to you right away."

Hurriedly, as if some enemy were chasing after her to rob her, she planted the two bunches of mint at the head of the grave, and then began sticking the periwinkle into the ground at random, all over the mound.

Her heart was pounding with impatience; her hands were trembling. Caught up in her hasty work, she was overcome with a single desire—to finish this work as quickly as possible. She dug in the damp soil without looking around, without raising her eyes. And it was only when she finished poking the last sprig of periwinkle into the earth that she straightened her back and took a look around.

She looked—and froze in awe.

Never before in her life had she seen such a grand, such a mighty tranquility. It was so quiet in the cemetery that you could almost hear the grass breathe.

It was so still on this patch of earth, where for countless years people had buried their suffering, and where every inch was sprinkled with tears; and the stillness was so powerful, so unshakeable, that the din, the turbulence, the groaning, and the laughter of life seemed, by comparison, to be some kind of temporary misunderstanding, and the clamorous bustle of work, of struggles, or of joyful pleasures, was like a chaotic, cacophonic prelude when the musicians are tuning their violins, tambourines, kettle-drums, and snare drums in preparation for a grand, harmonious symphony.

And the first chord of this harmony echoed in Yivha's soul. In this kingdom of death, among hundreds of its victims, there was nothing sad, nothing dreadful, nothing that would remind you of the confusion and the suffering that death brings with it to human dwellings.

Silence! There was a great silence, like a pause signalled by a single gesture of a master conductor and sustained by a whole legion of musicians in the middle of a turbulent symphony.

The moon, not wishing to startle this silence, seemed to be suspended in the sky; the stars, not wishing to disturb it, abandoned their smiles; and every leaf on every tree held its breath.

And the mother's despair—the protestations of her enervated intellect and the cries of her aching soul—drowned and dissolved in this magnificent tranquility.

The Tragedy of a True Friend
(1909)

If you are struck by a great misfortune—let's say your good old friend falls ill—withdraw some money post-haste from the bank if you have any there, or borrow some if you do not; seek out the very best doctor, nurse, and medical assistant; buy a thermometer, hot-water bottles, and ice bags; abandon your family, move in with him, and make yourself comfortable on the floor beside his bed on his fur coats and overcoats; go without food, and deprive yourself of sleep. You will be more than repaid for all of your sacrifices the moment that your unconscious friend finally recovers and fixes his clear, bright gaze upon you.

If you are struck by a great misfortune—let's say your good old friend dies of typhus, cholera, or pneumonia—buy wreaths, erect a tombstone, and do not begrudge money for an elegant funeral service. You will be more than repaid for all your sacrifices the moment your friend greets you on the threshold of that other, transcendental world and clasps your hands in his dematerialised ones.

If, may God forbid, you are struck by a third misfortune—let's say your friend falls in love—oh! take pity on all those who require your constant care: your little children, your wife, your father-in-law, and your dear old mother-in-law; recall post-haste all the civic responsibilities that weigh upon you; enrol in every philanthropic organisation; drink and be merry; in a word, expend the full treasure-house of your moral, physical, and material powers on whatever you desire, however you wish—but not on your friend.

I swear to you: any sacrifice on your part will not only be in vain, it will become, without fail, a fatal calamity that will bring with it a whole series of misfortunes to you, your dear ones, and all those who were imprudent enough to stand close to you during your friend's romance.

If you are amazed at the pale—almost green—face of your friend, his lacklustre grey (or, in the case of your friend, it may be brown) eyes, if your friend does not respond to your queries, refuses to partake of a baked delicacy at the dinner table notwithstanding the ingratiating words of your wife (I am emphasising the word 'notwithstanding' because wives ingratiate themselves only with those friends of ours who are leaving us forever, or who are going to die within a day or two), you would be better, if you are employed, to take a vacation, or if you are dependent on your family, to invent some kind of illness—refer specifically to your liver, lungs, heart, or neurasthenia—and flee far away as quickly as possible.

I know it will immediately occur to you that, instead of fleeing yourself, it would be better to distract your friend with a trip to Africa, or America, or even Australia.

Do not fall into this trap.

He will spend all your money and come back ranting like a madman. You will arrive to greet him at the train station and open wide your arms to embrace him, but he will scarcely touch your hand and, firmly refusing to go to your home for supper, will drag himself off to a hotel. And woe to you if you drag yourself after him. He will babble on about so many unpleasant things that, in the morning, you will arrive in your office feeling as if you have a hangover.

During the time that he was away, his ardour will not have cooled—it will have become enflamed, and it is only you who are to blame for this, because you set about trying to rescue an ailing person from an illness about which you, a complete ignoramus, know absolutely nothing.

"Every fool who has at least the heart of a frog is well aware," your friend will say, "that: 1) to part a man called, let's say, A, from a woman called, let's say, B, is the best way to increase the strength of that love tenfold, because the strength of that feeling is directly proportional to the number of tilled fields separating the lovers; 2) the number of steps on the illusory terraced hill, up which the enamoured A leads his beloved B by the hand, is directly proportional to the time of the separation."

If your friend shows you in such a simple mathematical formula the psychological law of a feeling that you recall rather vaguely, your conscience, forever besieged by distressing reproaches, will ensure that the second time that such bad luck strikes you—relapses occur quite frequently—you will once again do everything exactly opposite to what you should be doing.

You will go to your friend, seat yourself across from him, and after making a few desultory remarks about politics, you will take a look around and then boom firmly and resolutely—as from a pistol—that he simply cannot remain in these living quarters any longer because the dampness is already making your bones ache, and the wind is blowing through the cracks in the floor.

You will try to convince him that the windows are disproportionately small (or big), that the scales being played endlessly by the pianist on the top floor of the building would drive anyone out of his (her) mind, that there is an overpowering odour of wagon-grease and herrings from the store on the main floor, that the wallpaper in his study is poisoning the air with mouse droppings, and that his neighbour across the corridor is ill, it would appear, with smallpox.

Your enamoured friend, of course, will not heed your words: "Who the devil needs good health? What the deuce is this life worth? I'll just shoot myself . . ."

Ignoring these words, as if you had suddenly gone deaf, you return to the topic of politics and then, lighting up a cigarette, you suddenly recall a bit of news given to you by your friend—a very sympathetic, respectable lady who has her own home on Street "X," just happens to be looking for a tenant to occupy two of the rooms.

A faint blush flares up on your friend's pale cheeks. You casually add the address of the building—it is exactly opposite the one where "she" lives.

You can see only too well how the extinguished eyes of your friend light up. He casts a questioning glance around his living quarters, and you can see that it may also seem too big (or too small) to him.

Then you recall that there are two consecutive holidays this week, and you really have no idea how to occupy yourself during this time. If he (your friend, that is) were planning to move into new quarters at that time, you would be most willing to assist him in packing up his library. As for his clothes—Marko would do the best job of bundling everything up, and as for the glassware and other miscellaneous articles, Lukerka would do a wonderful job of moving them.

Your friend is silent, but he presses your hand firmly when you part with him.

You then rush off to the landlord in whose home he has been living thus far, and then to the new landlady where he will soon be taking up residence. You tearfully implore the old landlord not to take the case to the courts, and then you tearfully plead with the new landlady to find an excuse as quickly as possible for asking her long-term renters to move out of the two rooms and to prepare them for her new tenant. In the former place you rip up the old contract, and in the present one you sign a new one. You pay all sorts of "penalties" and surcharges both here and there; and, finally, you congratulate your friend, on the appointed day, on the occasion of his move into new quarters.

No more than an hour after moving into his new home, he has already managed to catch a glimpse of "her" three times in the window, and you can see how his appearance improves, and how he grows in stature and gains in strength before your very eyes. But . . . do not be in too big a hurry to rejoice; a week flies by and these formulae come into play:

1) Bringing A into closer contact with his beloved B is a tried and true method of increasing tenfold the strength of his love, because the degrees of love are directly proportional to the sum of moments in which A is fortunate enough to lay his eyes on B;

2) the strength of the feeling increases directly in proportion to the measure in which the image of his beloved descends from the empirical heights and assumes the real image of a flesh and blood person.

To put it more simply, you have done your friend a disservice. If he lived far away, if he did not see her every minute, if . . .

In a word, you are not a psychologist, and you have destroyed your dearest friend. And when he shoots himself in the heart, you will not dare to even cast a lump of soil on his coffin, because you are nothing more than his murderer.

It may well be that this is a lengthy preamble, but it was absolutely essential in order to characterise the position in which I found myself, and to elucidate clearly what suffering I had to endure when I discovered that my friend Kost had fallen in love.

"My final testament to you," he burst out one autumn evening when we were sitting together in my study, " is that you personally pack all my books and send them to the town library."

"What library? Why are you making a will?" I mumbled with a numb tongue.

"Surely you don't think that I'm about to continue playing out this comedy any longer?"

"What comedy?"

"Life. Here's a sketch of the tombstone that you'll place on my grave."

He pulled out a catalogue of monuments from Zeydelman's store and pointed at a tall, slender open-work cross enveloped in hops.

"But Kost, listen here . . ."

"What's there to listen to? What purpose do these comedies serve? Both you and I know that there's nothing left for you to say . . . and nothing left for me to listen to."

"But Kost!"

"Kost! Kost!" he mimicked me. "What, for example, can you say to your Kost with respect to a document like this?"

From his notebook he pulled a newspaper clipping with the following announcement: "Yesterday, a delightful party was held to celebrate the engagement of Captain P. with Miss H.A.B. At daybreak, he departed for a tour of navigational duty; the wedding will take place in the spring."

Upon hearing this, it took all the willpower that I had not to say the following: "But there's nothing surprising about this announcement—the romance between Captain Petrenko and Miss Bondarenko has been common knowledge for two years now, and only a person who is madly in love could have sought comfort in the hope that some preternatural forces would stop the marriage."

And so, instead of saying what I thought, I scoffed at the announcement: "Ha-ha-ha! What kind of a document is this? There are still seven whole months before the marriage ceremony. Aren't there any number of engagements that disintegrate into acrimony? My own sister fled from the altar . . ."

"She loves him," Kost mumbled.

"Did she tell you this? Are you sure? Can you swear that it is so? Or do you think, perhaps, that engagements are always a sign of love? Do you think that only those who are in love get married?

You're wrong, my friend! I can help you recall twenty couples who married for entirely different reasons. What's more, I have personal knowledge of one such case. My sister, for example, got married with the express purpose of getting even with the man she loved."

"You said she fled from the altar," Kost reminded me. "And it seems to me that you have only one sister."

"One sister and twenty cousin-sisters," I succeeded in extricating myself out of that one. "My aunt told me about it later . . . In general, notwithstanding the great number of economic, social, and ethical contracts, none of them is marked by so many complications, misunderstandings, and falsehoods as a marriage transaction. It is always the man who does the wooing—and this one custom alone is enough to ruin everything. If only our present day morality and ethics permitted women to do the courting, you would see how all of our acquaintances would sort themselves out into different couples.

"I, of course, do not know what Miss Halyna is thinking, nor have I peered into her heart, but for some reason I'm sure . . . it's my intuition, that if she could be assured that she would not remain an old maid, she would most certainly find herself a suitable young man, and if she had the right to do the wooing, under no circumstance would she choose that fat, black gypsy; instead, she would woo . . ."

"Who?" Kost interrupted me impatiently.

"I don't know who. Perhaps even you . . ."

Kost pushed his chair back and grabbed his hat.

"Wait! Where are you going?"

"I refuse to converse with comedians," he flung over his shoulder as he rushed down the corridor.

I hastened after him: "You've offended me for no reason at all, Kost! I would never have the nerve to contrive comedies . . . Perhaps I'm mistaken, and she never would marry you, but if I am mistaken, you have only yourself to blame; you confided in me, and I always thought that your courting of the young lady was only a trifling flirtation. I didn't know that you were actually wooing her."

"I didn't ever woo her."

"You didn't? So why did you offend me, scold me? If you didn't woo her, then you yourself don't know anything, and you don't have the right to judge whether life's worth living or not."

"I'm neither blind nor mad. Do you want me to experience the torment of shame in addition to my misery? To have them spit in my face? To have them shove me out the door?"

I clutched my sides, forced myself to recall an anecdote that I always relied on in such difficult moments, and burst out into loud laughter that rang through the corridor.

The effect was wonderful.

The black thread of Kost's thoughts broke off and, instead of keeping his eyes fixed downwards, he raised them to look at me.

"Ha-ha-ha!" I convulsed with laughter. "'To spit in my face! To shove me out the door!' A person who is getting prepared to leap below Hades, into the sunless abyss of Tartarus itself, is afraid of such inconsequential barbs!

"Listen, Kost," and I took the opportunity to slap him with all my might on the back, keeping in mind the physiological consequences of such a massage, "a few minutes ago I could have believed that death was your only way out, because I respect above anything else in the world that holy, great feeling of love, and I understand perfectly that life isn't worth living with a broken heart, without one's beloved. That's what I thought a few minutes ago. But listen to what I'm saying now. You do not have the right to commit suicide until you have a definite basis for it. To put it concisely, you have to win her hand in marriage."

"Now?" Kost shouted in a voice pitched a whole octave higher than usual. "Now, when the engagement has been announced in the newspapers?"

"Even if she were already married, before you fire a bullet into your heart, you have to recall the great law of nature which cannot be negated. I think that if you were convinced that a married woman was in love with you, platitudinous morality would not deter you from snatching her out of the arms of someone she did not love and fleeing with her to the ends of the earth. I'm advising you sincerely, as a friend—seek her hand in marriage."

Kost waved his hand and wiped the sweat off his brow.

"And if you do not have the courage to do so," I concluded, "be a patriot at least once in your life. Preserve the tradition of your ancestors and send a matchmaker. I will gladly assume this responsibility. Just give me your permission." I finished what I was saying and waited for a response.

Kost did not respond for a long time.

I do not know what he was thinking; my own thoughts, if the truth were to be told, were murky, because my proposal had caught even me by surprise, rolling off my tongue quite unexpectedly, as if of its own accord. Nevertheless, I deemed it necessary to become infuriated at my friend.

"Why aren't you saying anything? What's there to be hesitant about? It's all as clear as daylight . . ."

"It reeks of philistinism, of something vulgar . . ."Kost grimaced.

"We're talking about a life—and he's playing with words," I thundered. "I'm requesting your permission."

"Do as you see fit," he said with a despairing gesture.

"But you have to give me your word, that until such time as I return from her home . . ."

"I won't shoot myself? Rest assured. I myself am very much interested in seeing how this comedy will play itself out. It may be that I will have to assume the role of a nursing brother to you."

I glanced at him in surprise.

"Well, if I were the father of Halyna Andreyevna, I would shove a brazen matchmaker like you from the third floor."

There was no denying that there was more than just an element of truth in Kost's words. My supervisor, my uniform, my underage children, my faithful wife Marusya, and a host of other things flashed before my eyes—but I was Kost's friend, and I abandoned myself to fate.

II

The next day, at nine o'clock sharp, I was at the home of Halyna Andreyevna. Her family—consisting of an elderly father, a teacher of calligraphy at a girls' school, her mother, a stout, red-faced woman with a limp, and ten children in all—owned a home of their own on the outskirts of the city, and I had to spend the better part of an hour trying to find it.

I was very pleased, however, to note that it was a small, one-storey building, nestled in such a sheltered spot that I had no need to fear a rowdy end to my matchmaking.

I had seen Halyna Andreyevna only twice, and on both occasions it was in the street when she was wearing a veil, a cloak, and a hat. I could have sworn that she was a dark, robust young lady.

To my great surprise, a blond, light-eyed young woman with a dainty figure came out to meet me.

My first impression of her was very unpleasant. I did not like the expression in her shiny, almost metallic, eyes, nor her high-pitched, ringing voice; but most of all I did not like the way she moved. She introduced herself to me and plunged into a deep, ancient, well-worn armchair that swallowed her up completely.

"Oh my dear God," I thought angrily, "to pussyfoot around such a tiny kitten. To end one's life for such a trifle!"

And without further ado—without choosing my words carefully, or thinking about the tone of my voice, or my expressions—I told her everything.

"Poor Kostyantyn Pavlovych! Oh, the poor dear!" she responded in an unexpectedly low and deep contralto, and she sighed deeply. "I never would have suspected . . . It never occurred to me . . . He doesn't know me at all. I was certain that he knew about my romance with Petrenko a long time ago . . . What's to be done now? It never occurred to me, but perhaps I am to blame for it after all . . . Perhaps, at some time, I inadvertently, in some way, gave him some reason to hope . . . Perhaps I am somewhat to blame . . . And I'd be more than happy to rectify the wrong I've done him and more than happy to save him, but how? Advise me."

"This is my advice," I began rather boldly, but instantly stopped short. Halyna Andreyevna's eyes suddenly grew dark, the merry sparks in them faded, and her lips clamped shut severely. I understood in an instant that I would have to change both my tone and my manner.

"If you'll permit me, I'll give you some advice," I began anew, using a totally different approach. "You probably know, my dear Miss Halyna, the great significance of one particular human feeling—hope. You probably know, my dear young lady, that only hope gives people the power to endure the fate of a convict, to rot for decades in prisons . . . Even when one is in the hands of a hangman, standing before the scaffold with a rope around one's neck, a person still hopes for amnesty . . ."

"Yes, yes, I know," she interrupted impatiently.

"Extend to him, young lady, at least the tiniest hope," I pleaded.

"I fail to understand you," she drawled. "What kind of hope can I extend to him, given that my marriage date has been set?"

"Be merciful—tell him that you love him. One word from you will suffice to keep his hopes up, and you'll be saving a life at the same time."

"Do you think so?" she asked me after a pause.

"I'm certain of it."

"If it's a matter of saving a life . . ." The young lady fell deep into thought, and I fastened my eyes on her pensive face.

"But won't I end up making matters even worse?" she inquired after a lengthy pause.

"Nothing can be worse than a bullet."

"That's true," she agreed, "and it's worth telling a lie in order to save a life. Fine! I'll give him reason to hope," she added decisively. "Just tell me how and when this is to be done."

"Today, right now, as soon as possible."

"I can't do it right away. I first have to think about all this, to reflect on it. Moreover, I don't know Kostyantyn Pavlovych at all! What kind of a person is he? What does he like? What does he dislike? I never paid any attention to him."

"Oh! He's a person whose equal I've never seen," I eagerly seized upon this opportunity. "He's educated, intelligent, humane. And, most importantly, he's an aesthete—he loves music, poetry, sculptures . . ."

"I understand. It's how I always imagined him to be. And, it seems to me that he's also wealthy."

"He's a very rich man, the biggest landowner in the district."

"Wonderful! I'll go see him."

"Then I'll be on my way to forewarn him."

"No, no! Under no circumstances must you do that. He must not know that you were here to see me. If one is to engage in falsehood, then one should lie with an uninhibited imagination, of one's own initiative, according to one's own schemes, without involving anyone else, without paying heed to anyone else. Trust me—I'll think of something."

"Thank you! I trust you completely; there's only one thing that is bothering me—that your fiancé might prevent you from carrying out this act of mercy."

"But I'm not going to ask his permission about such a trifling matter. To say 'I love you' to a person that you never even think about is the same as saying to a maidservant: 'Bring me some water.' If you think that demonstrating my affection will give him more hope than my words, then I am more than willing to kiss him once, twice, three times or even ten times, because to kiss a person that you don't love is the same as kissing this album, this table, or some tree. This evening, without fail, I'll be at his place. By the way, where does he live?"

She opened an old, worn album and, at her request, I wrote Kost's address under the photograph of some great ancestor of hers.

III

I gave my word not to go and see Kost. But I had not gone more than a dozen steps when I began to chastise myself for placing my trust in a person who was not known to me, and for delivering up the life of my friend to the indulgence of her fantasy.

"But what if she lies? What if she changes her mind? Or doesn't want to? Or forgets, or doesn't find the time to go and see him today? If I also don't go to see him, he'll be sure that I've abandoned him, and he'll shoot himself . . . On whose soul will that sin then lie?"

I agonised over it all day, and when evening came, and a heavy rain pelted my windowpane with huge drops, I was at my wit's end. I kept grabbing my cap, turning out the light, running out into the street—and then racing back indoors again; and even today, when I recall all the feelings and thoughts that possessed me that evening, I still can't understand what power was able to make me keep my word until ten o'clock.

At ten o'clock on the dot, he came to see me.

"My friend! My brother! You didn't go to see her?"

"Forgive me, my dove! Forgive me, my friend!" I flinched like a true liar.

"My friend!"

He caught me in such a tight embrace that I almost screamed.

"You know what—she came to see me!"

"Who?" I asked, assuming the appropriate expression of an ignorant child on my face.

"She! Halyna . . ."

"Really?"

"She just drove away from my place. It was so unexpected. She came to ask about a room at my landlady's house, noticed my card on the door, and knocked. Do you understand? She did it so straightforwardly, as if she were visiting a friend, a relative, someone close to her . . ."

"But the poor thing! What a terrible tragedy she's living through. And I didn't know anything about it. You guessed it; you're a prophet—she doesn't love the captain. It's all the doing of the old despots, especially her mother—that damned, fat trader, that ugly philistine! Such parents should be hanged! Such mothers should be taken to court!"

His voice was raised a whole two octaves above his normal register.

Before this, I had not known that he had such a wide vocal range and, to tell the truth, this new characteristic of my friend made a negative impression on me.

"Quiet!" I hushed him. "The children are sleeping in the next room."

"Now, my dear friend, I have only one big, one great big request to make of you. Help me, my brother!"

He grabbed my hand and squeezed it in his.

His hands were hot, and his pulse was throbbing like that of a person ill with typhus.

"It's a big, a great big request—get a hold of a couple of thousand for me."

"At eleven o'clock at night? Come to your senses!"

"I'm begging you! I'm ready to fall on my knees . . ."

"What for? Why do you need the money so urgently?"

"I can't tell you,' he sighed. "I know this isn't how a friend should act, but I can't tell you. I'll tell you later, but right now, I can't. It isn't right to say anything before it happens—there's a saying to that effect. It's bad luck to do that; things won't work out. People have known this for ages . . ."

"Kost! Come to your senses! Do you now believe in superstitions, like old women?" I asked in alarm.

"It's absolutely none of your business what I believe in, or what I don't believe in. Let it be that I'm an old woman, that I'm insane; you must fulfil my request, because my destiny depends on that money."

"My dearest dove, I would be only too happy to do it, but how am I to . . . Where am I to get it in the middle of such a night?"

And I pointed at the ceiling to remind him of the rain clattering on the metal roof.

"I beg you!"

He put his hands together as if in prayer; tears flashed in his eyes.

I thought about it for a moment, and then I grabbed my hat.

I won't even begin to describe where I ran, where I ended up, where I knocked, what doorbells I rang, because this would be an epic poem filled with embarrassment, vexation, misunderstanding, laughter, and tears. I also won't mention the countless petty adventures that would be encountered by anyone who set out in a downpour in the middle of the night to scare up some money.

At three o'clock in the morning, I flung a package of banknotes on the table before him and collapsed on the couch, like a sagging sheaf of wheat.

"Andriy! My friend! My brother! I won't forget your sacrifice, your efforts on my behalf, your brotherly assistance, as long as I live, until the day I'm buried!" he flung himself at me and began kissing me.

"Perhaps you need more help from me? Perhaps I shouldn't go to the office tomorrow?" I asked, touched and moved by my friend's hearty, sincere kiss as we parted.

"No, thank you, my dear friend! Now I can manage without you."

And he truly did manage.

When I ran in to see him the following evening, not a single stick of his old possessions remained in his living quarters.

Instead of the wonderful couch that extended along one whole wall, and on which he liked to sit with a book in his hands, his feet tucked up under him, nestled an inconsequential, blue sofa. Instead of the ancient armchairs constructed out of redwood, there were some puny, bronze chairs perched on chicken legs. Instead of the expensive, huge clock that was as reliable as the sun itself, glimmered a shiny round bagatelle with a fidgety pendulum and a strident and hurried ring.

Everything was sprinkled with—or rather, doused with—attar of roses.

"You see, this is why I needed the money. I couldn't stand looking at those ponderous tables and armchairs. This is what she likes. She chose everything herself. Tomorrow, two mirrors will be delivered. We also bought a chandelier. We ran from store to store the whole day long.

"Tomorrow I'm travelling to Petersburg for some cabinets and books. There just aren't any stylish cabinets here. And my library has to be replenished with new publications. She rattled off dozens of books that I've never even seen. I'm leaving tonight. I'll take care of everything in four or five days.

"And as for you, I beg you by all that's holy, in the name of all that you hold dearest, write to me, telegraph me about everything that happens, about every, God forbid, misfortune."

What was I to do?

It was a waste of time appealing to reason in this lunatic's palace—so I ran to see her.

"Miss," I said. "Yesterday I exaggerated a trifle when I said that Kost was the biggest landowner in the entire district; I'm warning you that his fortune won't last for even a year if he continues spending it in this manner . . ."

"You begged me to save his life, not his wealth, and I've already assumed responsibility for it; and because of that, I beg you not to intrude any further into matters that are of concern only to me," she retorted sharply, haughtily giving me the once over with her greyish-green eyes.

I was forced to retreat.

In the morning, however, I sent Lukerka to inquire about the health of the young gentleman and to find out if a doctor had been called.

"The young gentleman has gone away someplace," Lukerka reported back to me.

"And it's wonderful that he's gone," I thought. "At least I'll be able to look after my own affairs."

And I telephoned the office and asked them to send me all the papers and accounts that I had neglected to take care of.

I was able, however, to enjoy this life of bliss for only one day. On the second day, I received a lengthy telegram. Kost was already cursing Petersburg; he had given up hope of finding suitable cabinets, complained that he could not sleep, and begged me "to write."

I understood, of course, that the bacilli responsible for his sleeplessness was most definitely not in the fogs of Petersburg, nor in the stagnant waters of its canals—but of what use is it to make a diagnosis if you don't know the cure for the ailment? I firmly resolved not to reply, especially since he was going to return home in four days, as soon as a carpenter could alter the encrustation on two cabinets. But my firm resolve turned into dust the very next day.

It was a holiday.

The first snow had fallen during the night—a wonderfully soft, clean white snow. And, at dawn, the first frost firmly stamped it with its seal.

At noon the young lady ran in to see me. In her tiny white hat and her little white fur coat, with a small white muff on her hands, she reminded me more of a lump of snow in the bright winter sun than a muddy bacillus of the ague, but then I suddenly recalled the senseless little stools, the mirrors, the cabinets.

"How can I be of assistance to you?" I asked, as severely as I could . . .

"I hate asking for advice or help, and I hate to have to bother you. I received a telegram from Kostyantyn Pavlovych—he's worried, bored, and he's begging me to come to him. I said that I would, but of course, I won't. Now it's your duty to detain him in Petersburg as long as possible; and, to do so, I'm giving you these . . ." And she threw on my table an entire bundle of telegrams that were ready to be sent.

"With these telegrams, you can keep him in Petersburg for an entire month."

I picked up one of them; on it was written: "Dear Halyna is a trifle ill. I'll tell you more about it tomorrow."

"What's all this about?" I asked.

"There's a date on every telegram—don't get them mixed up," she said, leaving my question unanswered. "So, for example, this telegram in which 'you order' him to send me some mineral water No. 1348 . . ."

"There is no such water."

"I know there isn't."

"What's all this for? What's the reason for this mystification? I respect my friend so highly that . . ."

"I knew it!" the young lady stamped her foot angrily. "Do I actually have to explain to you such a simple psychological principle—that if a person is fussing over the one he loves, then he doesn't think about himself; he doesn't root about in his own soul?"

Having said this, she turned on her heel and walked out.

I called in Marko and sent him to the post office with telegram No. 1.

In the morning there were two telegrams, one after the other, from Petersburg.

On the second day, I sent No. 2, and once again there were two replies.

On the third day, I sent two; and the same again on the fourth day. Then I sent one per day up to No. 20.

In reply to No. 20, in which I mentioned that the young lady had asked me to pass on a request for a red bodice trimmed with gold, I received eight telegrams. He implored, pleaded, adjured me to send him the size, but the size was hidden away in telegram No. 26.

Finally, after spending a week buying cabinets and books, frittering away several days searching for mineral water which, of course, he could not find anywhere; striking an entire week from the days of his life because of the bodice, which he also could not find; and having attended to countless trivial requests of the young lady, he bounded home.

To the great surprise of me and my Marusya, he came directly to our place.

"She was at your place, and your living quarters appealed to her so greatly that I'm tearfully begging you: let me have the spare room that you aren't using," he assaulted me with a stream of words even before he took off his coat.

We did not have any spare rooms, but Marusya and I did not protest, and he settled in at our place "for the time being," "for a while."

His lodgings in our home were cramped, and the Petersburg cabinets with the new books had to be stored in the shed; it was also not convenient from a romantic point of view, for it was a good *verst [kilometre]* from our building to her home. From an aesthetic point of view, his room was far worse than those palatial quarters in which he had formerly found all sorts of defects, but "it had appealed to her"—and that was enough for him to find, along with the lack of comfort, an idyll in our living quarters.

IV

I don't know with which adventure, or from what time, to begin my brief synopsis of those pages of Kost's romance that transpired in my home.

The young lady's starting point was to charm my wife, make her lose her powers of reason, fool her, and blind her. Marusya loved her as her own daughter. At every opportunity—and without the need for any opportunity if Kost happened to be nearby—she referred to her as "my sweet little daughter," "my dear little Halyna—Halynochka," "sweetheart," "my precious one."

Respecting the secrets of others, I never attempted to extract from my wife what topics she discussed with Kost in their conversations that lasted well past midnight. I did not inquire of Kost what hopes his beloved cheered him with, and I did not interfere with the way in which things were being done in our home.

In any event, the united, intimate, conspiratorial triumvirate at once decisively separated itself from me. The young lady appointed two days for her visits. At first she selected Tuesday and Friday, and these days were devoted completely to her. When she moved her days to Wednesday and Sunday, and made holidays of the other two working days, Tuesday and Friday were still respected in the old manner, and thus, there were only two days left in the week—Monday and Saturday—in which I could demand that even the slightest attention be paid to me.

Up to now, I had conducted the financial affairs of my friend, but now I was no longer informed about these matters.

My rights were limited to my study. Beyond its doors lay a kingdom where every foot of the floor, every inch of the walls, every atom of the air, belonged to the bright-eyed goddess and her passionate pagan priests.

"Don't smoke here—Halynochka's coming," "put the chair back where it belongs—Halynochka's coming," "wait for your tea until Halyna comes."

And in the meantime, life was bubbling in Kost's room. Judging by the people who hurried in and out of our porch from morning until late at night, I could see that Kost was up to his ears in some kind of hasty money operations that changed with every visit of the young lady, forced him to hold secret conversations with traders of large fortunes, to conduct affairs with vendors of salted and dried fish, to carry on a correspondence with agents in foreign offices, and to initiate relationships with both entrepreneurs and philanthropic societies.

The varied, intense life of my friend should have gladdened my heart, but I was not at all happy. In this phase of his life, Kost reminded me of a paper soldier that jerks its arms and legs at the bidding of a child. It was amusing to look at him, but just let a careless child jerk the rope even once, in anger, or as a merry joke, and the little soldier would disintegrate into little pieces.

Is it better to die of one's own free will, or to live and toe the line of someone else's will? I did not want to descend into such deeply philosophical questions. There was just one practical question that stood before me—what would happen when the young lady tired of dragging out this comedy and suddenly broke it off? This question began to plague me most after an incident when the young lady kissed him in my presence.

"Marusya! Don't cater to the young lady; don't talk to Kost so often about her; don't vouch for her in front of him—don't throw oil on the fire. Don't believe her—she doesn't love him," I said one time to my wife at seven o'clock in the morning, having picked, of course, one of the free days—Monday—and taking advantage of the fact that my wife was still luxuriating in bed.

"What's this? She doesn't love him?" Marusya instantly leapt up. "Is it possible that you've gone blind? Your heart must have turned to stone, your blood must have congealed if you can't see, if you can't feel, what is happening before your very eyes. She's too much in love with him; she's madly in love with him. She loves him ten times more than he loves her. In comparison to her, he's ice, a stone, a person without any temperament—a wad of tobacco leaves. All she thinks about, all she dreams about is getting married. Now her mother is ill, but as soon as she's better, they'll marry at once and flee from here, to India if need be, or to Korea."

"To India, to Korea . . . How do you know all this?"

"Oh, Lord! How do I know this? All our time is spent preparing for the trip. Look!"

Marusya jumped barefoot from the bed and pulled out from under the table in the icon corner a new and finely woven basket, filled with pastries for the trip. She uncovered a chest—it was packed to the hilt with women's lingerie.

"We've ordered travelling clothes for Kost as well. As for his financial matters, we decided that it was better to complete them abroad, and for this we've turned to a German firm that buys up Russian estates. All that's left is to arrange for an illegal passport for Halynochka because, of course, the police won't give her one without the consent of her father, but we decided that you would look after this matter yourself. In a few days, a certain person will come with a proposition, and we'll send him to you, to your office."

"In short," I thought, sorely tempted to summarise all those decisions with those vexing, annoying "we's", "we've decided to send you to Siberia for dealing in illegal passports." But I was first and foremost Kost's friend, and I squelched my egotistical feelings.

The planned trip and Marusya's assurances that the young lady "was madly in love with Kost" opened before me completely new pages of the romance, and a new uncertainty crept into my soul.

"The cunning little dear," I thought, "must deem Kost to be a much more favourable match than the captain, and she'll marry him for the sake of his wealth, but then my poor friend will be ruined forever."

"But perhaps the young lady is interested only in his wealth?" I suggested quietly to Marusya.

"Iceberg! Stone! Frog! Fish! All you think about is filthy lucre!"

Luckily for me, the sharp ringing of the doorbell interrupted this prelude to a domestic tempest.

"It's a telegram! My sister's died!" Marusya screamed.

"It's an investigation!" I shouted.

I threw on my jacket, Marusya—her peignoir, and we rushed to the porch.

I opened the door—it was the young lady who was ringing the doorbell.

"Dear God! How's the health of Kostyantyn Pavlovych? I had such a terrible dream—I could scarcely wait until morning."

"Kostyantyn Pavlovych! Kostyantyn Pavlovych!" Marusya rattled Kostyantyn Pavlovych's door and banged on it with both hands.

I remembered that I was without a vest, and so I fled without waiting to see the end of this incident, but my mistrust towards the young lady was completely swept away. Her troubled face, her anxious voice—all this was sincere, all of it reflected a feeling of great concern about the health of a very dear person.

"My Kost," I thought, "was born under a lucky star, and my idea to act as a matchmaker was a stroke of genius."

I was truly happy on this day as I worked in my office and, on my way home, I bought a bottle of good wine to honour fate.

To my great surprise, Kost did not have the appearance of a favoured child of fortune at the dinner table; on the contrary, he was much paler than usual, ate less than was his custom, and complained of a migraine headache.

I drew Marusya's attention to all of this.

"Happiness is found in one's heart—and not in one's stomach, or one's head," she flung reproachfully at me.

There was nothing more that I could say when confronted with such a truism. I just told the children not to make a lot of noise near the door of my fortunate friend and to let "uncle" catch up on the two hours of sleep he had missed.

It became quiet; everyone held their breath; everything in our home came to a standstill . . .

Kost had already begun to snore evenly and deliciously, when, once again, the doorbell rang shrilly, and she appeared, even more troubled.

"Dear God! What's happened? All the blinds are drawn!" she screamed in a voice that sounded as if she were being carved into a hundred strips.

Kost was already standing on the threshold of his widely opened door.

And, O God! what an unpoetical appearance, what a miserable image he projected at that moment! Dishevelled, with damp hair, sleepy, in a wrinkled jacket, an unbuttoned vest, and wearing only socks . . .

I glanced into his room—there was an even greater disorder in it. There were pillows lying on the floor; his shoes were lying askew by the couch; in front of the big table there was an overturned chair; and on the round table stood a dish with water and compresses.

"Dear God! What's wrong with you? The blinds in your room are lowered; you're deathly pale! Kostyk, my dear! Is it the ague? Typhus? Pneumonia? There's cholera in Saratov, and I know that you like baked roaches . . ."

Kost never ate fish at all, but even so, was he at all interested in roaches right now? With a terrified, crazed expression, his gaze wandered helplessly over our faces, seeking our help, pleading with us to rescue him.

Marusya seized the young lady by the arm and dragged her off into her room; but Halynochka did not want to take off her coat and, without waiting for Kost to freshen up his appearance, fled home to drink tea with her family.

Perhaps this incident ended happily for the young lady with a glass of tea and some tasty jam to sweeten it, but for Kost it triggered a whole series of unexpected consequences.

"If she ran in unexpectedly once, she might do so a second time, and a third one." This thought appeared to have been hammered into his head with ten nails and, still under the influence of his recently experienced shame, he rushed to the scullery to issue a stern request to Lukerka to tidy up his room as quickly as possible.

Our Lukerka was always an obedient girl. She nodded her head in agreement and, from that day on, she knocked on his door every day before sunrise with a brush, a rag, and a bucket of water in her hands. When he attempted to protest sleepily the first few times, she raised such a ruckus and so skilfully scared him with a possible visit from the young lady that, in the end, my friend became accustomed to leaping out of bed at the slightest sound, at every word, and to miss four hours of sleep a night on a regular basis.

He considered it even more dangerous to lie down and rest during the day than to sleep longer in the morning because, according to his theory, there was a 95.5 per cent chance, as opposed to 4.5 per cent, that she would dash in unexpectedly during the day. In the meantime, his nerves were going. He began to argue about the smallest details, got into a quarrel with his entrepreneurs, chased away the agents from the various bureaux, and began to pick fights with me.

I endured it, of course, for a long time, and I would have preferred to go on enduring it, but I'm no saint . . .

One day I intercepted the young lady in the street.

"Young lady," I said. "I'm sure that no one is happier about your good fortune that I am, but good fortune often makes egoists out of people."

She cast a glance at me as if I were stating God knows what kind of a new bit of information. Then I told her, without any embarrassment, what a hell had been created in our home because of her.

"The poor dear! He's afraid of me!" she sighed, lowering her eyes. "The poor dear! He's ruined his nerves, has he? I must cheer him up. Music is the best cure for nerves; that's the latest word from science."

And that very same evening she ran over to our place with a bundle of notes under her arm.

Without even entering Kost's room, she hurriedly greeted him, brushed Marusya with a kiss, scarcely touched my hand, and rushed to the piano; she uncovered it and placed her hands on the keys.

Kost chose the darkest corner, shut his eyes, and fell silent. The first chord was inaccurate from top to bottom. I coughed. Marusya, quite a good musician, crept surreptitiously out of the room.

"It seems that I didn't get it quite right," the young lady said.

"That's nothing, that's nothing. Please . . . I can't forgive myself that I've never asked you to play before. I didn't know you played the piano," Kost chirped in a little bird's voice.

"I would have acquainted you with my repertoire long ago if Andriy Semenovych had not forewarned me that you hate music."

"Who, me? When did I say that?" I jumped to my feet in amazement.

A second, equally false chord resounded in answer to my protests, and after it "flowed," as the poets say, "the sounds of a charming waltz."

I'm not at all musical. I have never been able to sing even the simplest melodies in tune, and so, even if angels from heaven came down to try and amuse me with a waltz, I would flee from them into hell. Without waiting to hear the first coda, I fled into my study out of embarrassment for the piano player, and out of sympathy for the listener.

As I walked past Kost, however, I did glance at him. My friend's face was covered with an expression of the greatest surprise, and his entire body was collapsed into a huge question mark—the kind that I once saw in an advertisement for third-rate cigarettes. After this waltz "flowed" similarly badly-played polkas, romances—for an entire two hours.

When the outside door shut behind the young lady, I walked out of my study to put out the light by the piano. Kost was running back and forth through the living room with a knotted forehead—evidently the final polka had not given him the answer to the question that the first waltz had posed.

"She's an idiot," I wanted to assist Kost. "That's what these waltzes and polkas have proven to you."

But . . . "Happiness is in the heart, not in the head," I recalled Marusya's words, and I did not say a word.

Did the tactfulness of a friend and the politeness of a host that I showed that evening indicate my readiness to listen to these same waltzes and polkas ten evenings in a row?

Did it give Kost either the legal or the moral right to demand that I listen to her scales, exercises, and false chords from eleven until three?

The trio of them worked out the following daily schedule: Lukerka went to his room before sunrise, tidied up in there, and cleaned and polished until eight o'clock. At half past eight we sat down to drink our tea in an unswept and unheated dining room; at nine I went to the office.

And at twelve, the young lady rang the doorbell. Kost let her in, and she went into his room for a moment so as not to greet him in public—but she kissed him so loudly that you could hear her in the entranceway. Then she took him by the hand, dragged him over to the piano, sat him down on a stool by the wall in such a way that it was not possible for him to walk out, uncovered the piano, and began practising her scales.

At three o'clock she hurried home, and at six she once again drove to our place in a carriage to play her waltzes.

Was I to concur that such a schedule was an appropriate one for an official who had to earn his daily bread? After all, my nerves are not made of rope . . .

I endured it for a week.

The second week, I put forward a brief proposal about the possibility of shortening the musical part of the evening and introducing diversions of a literary nature into their schedule.

"Ah!" Kost leapt up as if he had been stung. "Is this a hint that 'we' are disturbing you with our music? Is this a dig at us? But you must know, my dear little dove, that music critics such as you have been immortalised in Krylov's fable "The Donkey and the Nightingale."

"So you're saying that Miss Halyna is a nightingale?" I carefully suggested.

"She may or may not be a nightingale—what's it to you? What right do you have to interfere in my intimate affairs? What business do you have prying into my library? What right did you have to peek at the books that I packaged up and put in the shed?"

"I swear that I didn't peek at anything."

"I'm not a fool, nor a half-wit, nor an idiot—I know that you're ridiculing the idiotic romances I brought back from Petersburg. But what business is it of yours? Who gave you the right to do so? And who told you that Halyna Andreyevna takes pleasure in reading these romances?" his shouting echoed through all the rooms.

I endured it for another week.

On Wednesday of the third week, an incident occurred that made all the scales, exercises, waltzes and polkas seem trivial. The heroine of this incident and of this drama turned out to be—who would have suspected it?—our Lukerka, pockmarked, as uncouth as a recruit, fierce like a snake, always unkempt, barefooted, with her skirt hitched up crookedly on one side, and madly in love to the very tips of her curly hair with Marko.

She had forgotten a feather duster in Kost's room that morning. When she heard the young lady ringing the doorbell, she rushed liked mad to get it and bumped into Kost in the doorway. This was enough for the jealous heart of the young lady.

"A-a-a-ee-ee! And with a maidservant at that!" she shrieked, and, falling into a hysterical fit, the likes of which I had never seen in all my life, in either the theatre or my dreams, she attacked Kost with a cascade of sharp words unlike any I had ever heard a young lady utter.

I saw how grievously this offended my friend, who was always correct and proper in his speech; I saw how the veins bulged on his forehead.

It was my duty to prevent a catastrophe: "Halyna Andreyevna! My dear young lady! This is a misunderstanding that you'll laugh at tomorrow. Why, it's enough to take one look at this slovenly Lukerka . . ."

"Ah! So it's me she's jealous of, is it?" Lukerka fired her salvo like a stone aimed directly at a window.

I grabbed her by the shoulders and pushed her away, but the snake still managed to hiss from the threshold: "I'd spit at a lazy good-for-nothing like your young gentleman."

Marusya, of course, could not forgive the maidservant for these cutting words; she had to send her packing then and there—but this precipitated a new grief. The children latched on to Lukerka's skirt and would not let her get dressed or pack her miserable belongings. I had to slap one on the nape of his neck, pinch the other one's ear, and toss them both out of the scullery into the adjoining room. But my wife had completed the course of the German pedagogue Frebel with first class honours. She could not find it within her to forgive me for such a crude violation of the elementary principles of child rearing.

I grabbed my hat and fled into the street.

Our dark, narrow, and twisted street now appeared like a paradise to me, and the corpulent sausage maker, who for the past fifteen years had regularly poisoned me and my guests during the holidays, seemed like an angel. I would have preferred to walk interminably on this street, preferred to talk endlessly with the sausage maker than to see "him" and "her." I would have preferred to be poisoned by rotten sausages than to see this enamoured couple, even once a year.

I paced our street and some neighbouring ones for a long time, until I was exhausted. When I returned home, "she" was no longer there—she had gone home; "he" also was not there—he was walking her home.

In the scullery sat Marko, gloomy like a sreech-owl and doomed to misery for the rest of his life. But Marusya was kneeling in her night attire in front of the icons. Her face glowed with happiness, contentment . . . I felt I could safely assume that the cloud had passed.

"Praise God, everything has fallen into place, and here I was afraid that a few carelessly spoken words, a few sharp little words . . ." I began.

"'Words!' 'Little words!' He only thinks about 'words!' A terrible drama is unfolding before his eyes! A young heart is bleeding before his eyes, and he talks about 'words,' 'little words!'" Marusya flung at me with unspeakable scorn.

And then, demonstratively turning out the light, she added in a tone that I will never forget: "A bed has been made up for you in your study."

The foundation of my own happiness had cracked—I could see this quite clearly; but the hour was too late for protesting to fate or for making reparations.

Without saying a single word to my dear little wife, I made my way silently to my study.

I felt devasted and all alone. Reproaches from my conscience were shredding my soul, and thoughts, each one darker than the one that preceded it, crawled into my head. I was suffering hellishly, but my need for sleep was even greater.

Tearing off my clothes, I threw myself down on the couch and, with my eyes already shut tight, turned off the electric bulb that hung above it.

At that same moment, another light that hung over my desk flared.

"Two words, Andriy Semenovych."

Before me stood Kost.

"Only two words . . . Things can't continue like this—it's impossible. I suffered quietly (!), I endured it (!). But your antics today . . . (!!!)"

I stared at him; my mouth gaped like that of a deaf mute.

"Your capricious behaviour today . . ."

My brows leaped upwards, forming two question marks.

"You had no right to interfere in our intimate affairs; you had no right to turn into a farce the drama of my beloved's soul; you had no right to make us witness your wild, vulgar, and bourgeois relations with your servants; you had no right to slam the door, to put on public display your treatment of your children and their mother, Mariya Mykolayivna; and you especially did not have the right to flee histrionically from your home in the middle of the night.

"You were offended by a few careless words spoken by Halyna Andreyevna, but not all people are capable of hiding their natural emotions—like bureacrats in certain departments. I forgave you for you allusions concerning the music, I forgave you for mentioning the literary readings, but I am not able to forgive you for what you did today. You must apologize to the young lady tomorrow, and if you don't . . . we'll have to settle accounts."

"In the name of all that's holy—my wealth, my position, my personal happiness—I'm prepared to pay for my sin against you and against Halyna Andreyevna," I shouted sincerely and passionately in a voice that reverberated through the apartment. "No later than this week, I'll procure an illegal passport for the young lady, take care of your financial affairs, buy everything that you require for your trip—and may God help you in your flight! She loves you, you love her; don't waste any more time; take advantage of your moments of happiness—they are as uncertain and fleeting as are our lives."

"That's all true, only now a passport is required for the West, not for the East," Marusya spoke up from the other room. "I'll be dressed in a minute."

In two minutes she was at our side.

"A passport is needed for the West; she told me decisively that she wants to travel to Paris," she announced.

"To Paris?" Kost asked in surprise.

"Yes, to Paris. I advised her to do this, because the best conservatory is found in Paris."

"Conservatory?" Kost asked in even greater surprise.

"Why are you so surprised?" Marusya became angry. "She might not possess great talent, but if she practises for nine or ten hours every day . . ."

"Halyna Andreyevna never mentioned it," Kost smiled crookedly, as if he were close to tears.

"Because Halyna Andreyevna is not a person who casts all the jewels of her soul before people's eyes in a single evening. She has still another secret dream, even two of them."

"She never said anything to me," Kost groaned.

"She didn't say anything because you never asked her. She didn't have the nerve, she didn't dare to speak about it openly, because she felt in her heart that you, like all men, are an egoist, a despot."

"I never ever gave Halyna Andreyevna the occasion to view me as a despot or an egoist," Kost protested.

"You didn't? Really?"

Marusya pulled an absurd red-yellow-green-blue-card out of the pocket of her peignoir and gave it to Kost: "Read what she's written."

Kost ran his eyes over a few of the lines scribbled under the picture and blushed furiously. Then I took the card.

"My dear lady, Mariya Mykolayivna; I'm sending the children some candy. I'm terribly bored. In my dreams I see the opera, the theatre, and concerts. But don't tell him. Kiss him for me." I read this and shrugged my shoulders.

"Ah!' Marusya attacked us instantly. "I knew it would be like this. You don't like the peacock on the card? The flowers are too yellow for your taste, the sky is too blue, and with all your aesthetic whims you can't see what's most important—the golden words that are written on this card."

"No, no, how could you say such a thing? I have nothing against the card, I simply grimaced because of the perfume that's wafting from the card. You see, I simply hate, I simply cannot tolerate cheap perfume," Kost said hurriedly, like a guilty schoolboy.

"'I simply can't tolerate,' 'I hate,'" Marusya mimicked him.

"Unfortunately, all cards smell like that now," I hastened to add my bit to the conversation, which appeared to me to be getting somewhat dangerous. "All cards definitely smell like that, even those that are bought in the very best stores. It's truly unfortunate—this whole business of fashion! Let's take, for example, the newfangled hats that are six feet in height . . ."

"Hats follow fashion; as for perfume, it's something separate and individual. I know, of course, that this perfume," Kost touched the card with his finger, "is not from the toilette of the young lady, but I have to say that if my wife sprinkled her hair with such a perfume, I'd . . . I give my word . . ." Kost hesitated for a moment, obviously in order to state exactly what he was sure of, and he added decisvely: "I swear to you, I'd leave my wife."

"Don't swear, my good man! A woman is not an old boot that you can toss away at any moment. It's often much more difficlut to leave a wife than to marry her," Marusya observed.

"I know," Kost dragged out his words in a sepulchral tone.
The clock struck three.

"God! It's three o'clock, and the lights are still burning in the house!" my little housekeeper was aghast. "Tell me quickly, what should I write in response to Halyna's letter? Will you go to a concert, or to the theatre?"

"Oh, God! Anywhere, but not to a concert," my friend pleaded.
I recalled the waltzes.

V

I do not know if he went to bed that night. It must have been the tickets that prevented him from sleeping. At least, when I was putting on my coat in the porch to tend to the matter of the passport, he was no longer in the house, and the cook had gone off to the young lady's at still an earlier hour, with a letter from him.

Before breakfast was served, he returned all happy and joyful with the tickets, a dozen candy boxes, and a bundle of all sorts of treats; I came back home filled with a great hope that a passport could be obtained more quickly than I had expected.

Our dinner was exceptionally merry because, notwithstanding the fact that Marko spilled some cream on Kost's back and twice forgot to change his plate, no one mentioned either Lukerka or the sad incident connected with her name, or anything else that could have diminished our appetites.

Our conversation revolved exclusively around the topic of the need for diversions, from a psychological, physiological, and pedagogical point of view, for people in general—infants, toddlers, schoolchildren, youths, adults, the elderly, the aged—and the special need for diversions for people in their younger years.

I never thought that my friend had studied the role of the theatre in the history of culture so painstakingly, and I admit that I listened with great interest to his lengthy discourse. As for Marusya, she was so enormously delighted with his panegyrics in praise of theatrical practitioners, that she made me promise to escort her to the theatre twice a week.

We rose from the table in the best of all possible moods, and with the greatest friendly relations. A glass of black coffee savoured in comfort on soft armchairs around the table in the dining room strengthened our amicable bloc even more.

We parted at five o'clock.

At seven, Kost walked out of his room; he was all spiffed up— shaved, his hair trimmed, sprinkled with the most delicate perfume, and elegantly dressed in a long black evening jacket, a white collar, and white cuffs.

We were ready as well; our fur coats were lying on the chairs, and our boots, lined up in a row, glittered in the middle of the porch. We were momentarily expecting the arrival of the carriage that had been sent for Halyna.

She did not seem to be arriving.

At first Kost waited for her silently and patiently, then he became nervous; he kept pulling out his watch, and when the clock struck half past eight, he nervously began to predict calamities of such a great magnitude that I also became upset and sent Marko to look in on the young lady.

Finally, at half-past nine, the long-awaited guest arrived.

She was all wrapped up, covered from head to foot, and her face was tightly screened by a black veil.

"Oh, you have no conscience! We've missed the first act because of you, my little precious!" Marusya, her arms open wide, flung herself at Halyna.

"Just don't kiss me! Don't kiss me!" the young lady fluttered, waving her hands and pulling her downy veil still further over her eyes.

"What kind of a whim is this? Just like a princess! Is it possible that a sore throat or a cold has caught our princess unawares?" Marusya said jokingly.

"Perhaps it really has?" Kost asked anxiously.

"Oh, leave me alone, for heaven's sake!" the young lady stamped her foot angrily and jerked her right shoulder in a coarse gesture, like a chamber maid in a third class hotel.

Kost was aware of the social meaning attached to this movement, and a cloud of annoyance flitted across his face, but he mastered himself and, in a quiet and kind tone, asked the young lady to take off her warm cloak until everyone finished dressing.

"I won't take it off! I won't take it off for anything in the world!" she said, waving her hands for emphasis.

"Aha! Our princess is becoming peeved," Marusya laughed. "If she's going to be cross in the theatre as well, it would be better not to go."

"Do you think I want to go? I hate the theatre. It's ten times more pleasant to spend the evening among one's friends, chatting with those who are closest and dearest to you . . ."

"So maybe we won't go to the theatre?" Kost seized upon the young lady's words as if he were catching a star from the sky.

The unfortunate man, deluded as if with hashish by the single word "dearest," had already forgotten the yellow-red-green-blue card and a dozen or so words that posed a threat to the good name of his beloved: "Perhaps it would be better to sit here and have a quiet converation. What do you think, Mariya Mykolayivna?"

"My plans were, and are, to go to the theatre, but if you want to, you can sit here and talk," Marusya replied in an annoyed tone of voice.

But her permission came a trifle too late, because the cloak, the fur boa, veil, and hat were already dangling in the arms of the delighted Kost, and the young lady herself was adjusting her coiffure in front of the mirror in his room.

Marusya and I got dressed in a flash and turned out the light.

"Run in and tell our turtledoves that their supper is waiting for them on the buffet," my wife instructed me.

I went up to Kost's room and knocked—no one answered. I knocked a second time—there still was no reply; I knocked more loudly, and then still more loudly, and finally, I opened the door. And this is what I saw.

The young lady was standing by the mirror, calmly aranging a stack of tangled, matted hair stuck through with various combs and pins, while he, the poor man, all bruised, broken, and crushed, was standing against a wall; it seemed to me that he was writhing in convulsions of shame, grief, and despair.

I could not understand anything. I could not comprehend the meaning of what I was seeing, and I stopped in amazement in the middle of the room.

"So you're still going?" she spoke up, catching sight of me in the mirror. "I can't understand why! I hate the theatre, comedies, actors, the crush of people, the suffocating heat."

410 | The Tragedy of a True Friend

"That's not true!" Kost's voice cut off the young lady's words as if with a knife. "That's not true! You're bored without actors; you see the theatre, operas, concerts in your dreams. Yesterday I read your card to Mariya Mykolayivna. You're either not speaking truthfully today, or you were fooling us yesterday."

She turned around sharply to face me, and it was then that I understood everything. Powder from the lady's face was sifting down on her fashionable velvet dress, her eyes were lined, her eyebrows were darkened with grease.

I understood that this was a tragic moment for my friend. The blood in my heart seethed, but I simply did not know what to do, and so I rushed to get assistance from Marusya.

"Oh, how loathsome you've both become to me! Oh, how disgusted I am with your whims, your foolishness!" Marusya clapped her hands in annoyance.

"Halochka! Brush the powder off with a handkerchief, take some vaseline from the cupboard and wipe off those cosmetics. What fool advised you to put make-up on your pretty white face? Look at how you've alarmed these two fools . . . Just look, Kostyantyn Pavlovych has turned pale with fear. Ha-ha-ha! Kostyantyn Pavlovych, wake up! Come to your senses; you're frightening Halynochka . . . Andriy, bring him some water."

I dashed off for the water, but when I returned, I truly did not know to whom to pass the dipper—to Kost who was standing white as chalk by the window, or to the young lady who was wringing her hands in an affected pose in front of Mariya Mykolayivna and groaning: "Oh, forgive me! Oh, forgive me!" or to my dear wife who, caught up in the passion of a matchmaker, had lost all her tact and sense of proportion, and was shouting at Kost: "Her pure kisses, the jealousy of a faithful heart, the music of a child, the card, the perfume, her hair, and the powder—you've censured everything with your vile lips. Everything seems 'unaesthetical' to you, everything seems 'vulgar' to you," she mimicked him in closing.

"Yes, it is vulgar," Kost stated firmly and decisively. "But I have never betrayed my word, and I will keep it this time as well—I'll give the young lady my name, my wealth. But I simply cannot, it is beyond my powers, to love a wife who uses make-up on her body and on her soul."

He grabbed his head in his hands and sobbed like a little child.

"Halynochka! My daughter! My precious! Don't look at him, come away from him, don't pay any attention to his crocodile tears, and don't grieve," Marusya seized the young lady's head and pressed it to her bosom.

"Don't cry, don't grieve," she continued. "This is the day of your greatest good fortune, and not of sorrow. A person who insinuates his way into someone else's house uninvited, who stoops to playing around with the maidservant, who instructs his friend on how to punish children—this person is not a fit partner for you. He's not fit! He's an egoist, my daughter, the likes of which the world has not seen, a despot who would not permit you to take a step without his blessing. The cards, the music, the hair, the powder . . . My precious, he's not a fit partner for you!"

She embraced the young lady's hand with one arm, pressed her head to her shoulder with her other arm, and led her swiftly out of Kost's room.

It was then that I approached him: "Kost, come to your senses. This is going too far, my friend."

"'My friend!' You dare to say these words to me?" Kost leaped to his feet. "You're Lucifer himself in the guise of a friend! You're a devil in the guise of a friend! It's you who has caused all this. It's you who went to her as a matchmaker."

He no longer resembled a human being. He did not even resemble a monkey—he looked like a beast of some kind, a fierce, maddened being with bloody, bulging eyes, with two pincers that were ready to rip apart an angel itself, with ten claws ready to dig into the fleece of a lamb.

My whole body quaked.

It was impossible to hate anyone more than we hated each other at that moment.

We became fierce enemies for life.

Just one careless movement, one word—and both of us would most certainly end up lying in a pool of blood.

Fortunately, my infinite mercy did not fall asleep this time either—I recalled the other victim of this madman, a victim who was quivering, most certainly wronged, shamed, in bitter tears, in torments of despair on the breast of my wife.

Running towards her groans, I called out: "Miss! Young Lady! Miss Halynochka!"

My heart filled with the ether of pity, expanded with every word—caressing words of comfort and kindness were bursting from my chest; my knees were involuntarily bending before the pure image of the young martyr, my hands were reaching out of their own accord, to this tragic image of a young soul's first encounter with grief.

"Young lady! Halynochka!"

"Jesuit! Hypocrite! Judas! To destroy an unfortunate child! To bring her together with such a villain, with such a despot. It's all your doing! You're the one who went to her as a matchmaker," Marusya attacked me.

Heated, passionate tirades were taking shape in my innocent head and rushing to my pale lips, but the work of even the most famous defence lawyer is in vain when fate itself assumes the role of the prosecutor.

"Oh God!" I thought. "For what sin of my fathers have You given me the fate of a murderer? This enamoured kitten will drink some mouse poison or some sodium sulphate, and on whose soul will the sin then lie?" I asked myself.

And I clearly pictured the fresh little grave and, on it, the cross enveloped in hops. In my despair I cracked my knuckles so loudly that the sound echoed through the house.

"See Halynochka home!" Marusya screamed at me.

Lord! You show your mercy to even the most terrible sinners.

I almost clapped my hands in delight over such unexpected good fortune—I would be alone with her for a whole hour! I would have a whole hour to calm her, comfort her, assuage her. Oh Lord my God, that's what I wanted above all else in this world.

I dashed into the porch as fast as I could. I fastened her cloak myself, her fur boa, and her boots; I passed her kerchief to her, her gloves, took her under the arm and—weak and dejected as she was, with a thick veil over her tearstained eyes, I led her out into the porch

"My dear young lady!" I began saying sensitively, sincerely, in a trembling voice, as soon as the door of the carriage was shut.

"Well, what will you give me to drink for keeping my end of the bargain? Ha-ha-ha-ha-ha-ha!" She burst out laughing unexpectedly in a ringing and cheerful voice that resonated through the street and stung my soul like a billion fine, tiny, sharp barbs.

"Stop!" I shouted insanely to the carriage driver, and tore my way out of the carriage as if I had been scalded.

"Don't forget to order a requiem mass—tomorrow marks three months since your friend shot himself in the heart!" she yelled after me with frenzied laughter.

I came to my senses, but the carriage had already vanished from sight . . .

Now, every day, I practise shooting my pistol in the shed and spend half an hour perfecting my fencing skills with a rapier. I have to prepare myself just in case I am challenged to a duel by the captain.

In the meantime, the police are conducting an investigation to find out who purchased a foreign passport that was stolen in NN.

O Cross enveloped in hops! It is my grave you will be standing on . . .

No. 1001 and No. 17
(1909)

It was a quiet winter night.

On the corner of a dead-end street in a big city, two coachmen were standing abreast with their sleighs.

No. 1001, a tall, scrawny old man with a grey beard, was wearing a blue cloak, a leather belt, and a cap pulled down over his ears. No. 17, a blond, clean-shaven, and rather young man, was also clad in a blue cloak, but it was girded with a wide woollen sash.

They had dropped their reins a long time ago—giving their horses the freedom to doze, or to dream about tomorrow's ration of oats, or to let their thoughts wander into the realm of their earliest memories and the wide steppes of their native Orenburg— and, turning their backs to the sidewalk, on which only tramps and students, both male and female, wandered about at this late hour, they tucked their hands pessimistically into their sleeves.

"A sheep is stupid, and that's why it's sheared, and its fat is used for candles for the Sabbath; the horse ate hay from Christ's manger—and that's why he has to work day and night; a pig's a pig—a disgusting, filthy creature—it can't be eaten until it's cleansed with fire," the older coachman stated, continuing a zoological conversation they had started up quite some time ago.

"It seems that all creatures are bad in one way or another," the younger man commented sadly.

"Well, what did you think? Take a wolf, a snake, a beetle . . . and so on. One crushes people to death, the next one bites them, the third ruins grain, the fourth spoils fruits and vegetables . . . Or, take a sparrow—it's such a nothing—but even it dared to chirp by Christ's cross: *'zhyv-zhyv [alive-alive]'*. Or a butterfly!—it seems that there's nothing prettier—but just think how many worms it breeds. Or a bee? There's wax for a candle, but a sting for the eye . . ."

No. 1001 adjusted his apron and once again shoved his hands up his sleeves.

No. 17 sat without stirring. The words of his older companion had made a strong impression on him.

He had known for a long time that a sheep is stupid, a horse is damned, a pig is filthy, and a sparrow—a cheap liar, but these separate bits of information had never before entered his mind at the same time; now, No. 1001 had lined them all up and placed them one after the other as reliable material for constructing an entire philosophy. The world, established for the glory of God, for the common good, now seemed to be built for an entirely different purpose—for evil, for the obstruction of the highest ideals, of justice.

"What about a human being?" he turned to his neighbour.

"A human being? A human being is . . ." and No. 1001 chose the saltiest word in his lexicon to describe human beings.

No. 17 protested. As long as the discussion was about various insects and animals, the evil tendency of the universe did not affect him all that closely, but he could not deliver a human being into the claws of a malevolent spirit.

"People are sinful," he thought, "but to say that they're as filthy as pigs . . . Why? How?"

"Well, let's say that a pig is filthy because it eats all kinds of filth, but a human being . . ." No. 17 began his statement for the defence.

"But a human being thinks all sorts of filthy things," No. 1001 cut him off and then spit.

"People have all kinds of thoughts," No. 17 reminded him.

"Look over there!" No. 1001 pointed his finger at an immense grey prison. "See how huge that building is—it blocks half the horizon, and if you went into it to have a look, what is it filled with?"

"Of course, there are murderers, robbers, and all sorts of criminals there, but people who are free, not locked up . . ."

"They were all free at one time," the old man impatiently interrupted what the younger one was saying. "It matters little that these," he nodded his head at a group of young people who were walking past them on the sidewalk, "are still free, that their arms and legs are not bound in chains; but if you were to peek into their heads, you'd soon find out what kind of a conscience they have, what kind of thoughts. Arms and legs won't set fire to something, and they won't kill someone—if the head doesn't make them do it.

"And what's a head for? For thoughts. Well then, stop and figure out where sin thrives. You can see arms and legs, but you can't crawl into someone's head. You can put chains on arms and legs, cut out a tongue, but what are you going to do with the head? Even if you bound it in the tightest chains, you still can't shackle evil thoughts. And so they grow in freedom, and they always have a malicious purpose.

"I went to the market today to buy some oats. I purposely went very early, just as dawn was breaking. 'Our buyers in town are swindlers,' I said to myself. 'I'll be better off buying the oats from a simple peasant—those people have more of a conscience.'

"So I went. And I came across an old man with some oats. He looked honest, and he vowed, he swore by his oats . . . He untied one of his sacks—the oats were good and not too expensive. Well, I bought them. He hauled them to my home, and I paid him and told him to pour them into the bin in the stable.

"In the meantime, I quickly harnessed my horse and left, so I wouldn't miss the early morning train. I came home at noon and poured my horse some of the oats . . . Well, he wouldn't eat them. What the devil was going on? I took a better look at the oats—they were rotten."

"Of course, that's the way it is sometimes, that can happen," No. 17 said. "You can sometimes chance upon a bad person . . ."

"You can't avoid them anyplace, those damned swindlers! I've taken an oath now—I won't believe anyone again as long as I live. No matter if they vow to me, or swear to me, or if they fall on their knees and eat the ground in front of me . . . All people are thieves, all people are thugs . . ."

"Coachman!" the call resounded in the street.

No. 1001 jumped upon hearing the voice.

By a small, dingy hotel stood two gentlemen dressed smartly, even elegantly. One was still young, but the other was up in years.

They hopped into the sleigh without bargaining about the price.

"To the 'Paris'," the young man almost whispered in a hoarse, baritone voice.

"Not this way—go along Mykolsky street," the older man ordered in a sweet, but somewhat raspy, tenor voice.

"It's a long, roundabout way by means of Mykolsky street," the coachman observed to his passengers, "and there are a lot of potholes in that road."

"Get going!! Go where you're told to go," the younger man called out sternly.

"Oh sure!" No. 1001 thought. "He thinks he's some big shot! But if he doesn't give me a *poltynyk [a fifty-cent coin]* I won't drive them any farther."

And then he added out loud: "I can't do it for less than seventy *kopiyky [cents]*, gentlemen."

"Get going!" both passengers replied with one voice.

No. 1001 turned the horse around, cut across the wide street flooded with electric light, and turned right into a tight lane hemmed in by small old houses with three windows and narrow five-storey brick boxes crammed to the attic with factory workers. It was quiet here, like in a desert. There was no fear of bumping into a drunk man, or of running over a deaf one, or of getting in the way of a streetcar, but it was also dark, the holes were very deep, and the snowdrifts were so high that the coachman could not go faster than a trot.

"What if he's lying and doesn't bring 'that one'?" the older passenger spoke up after a moment's pause.

"Fedko won't lie; he'd never do such a thing as lie. I've known him for six years now; we've been through a lot. Besides, 'that one' has already arrived," the younger one said.

"Perhaps he's come empty-handed?"

"Oh, no—he was drinking champagne at the train station."

"That's a good sign! If so, we'll have a bountiful harvest. Let's hope your foolish Fedko doesn't get things in a muddle this time like he did with the ten-spot card. Or with the jack. Goodness me! How could he have lost that jack?"

"It was a king, not a jack," the younger man corrected him softly.

"A jack . . ."

"He said it was a king."

"And I'm telling you it was a jack; I reminded him twenty times, I warned him twenty times . . ."

"It was the king of spades."

"He shouldn't lie; it was the jack of spades. I'm prepared to swear that it was a jack."

The young man jabbed the older man with his elbow and nodded his head at the coachman's back.

The older man bit his tongue, then turned to address the coachman: "Granddad, do you have any children?"

"Yes, I do sir; I have two sons. Oleksiy, the older one, is working as a salesman, and Stepan, the younger one . . ."

"I call my son a jack, a jack of spades."

"So that's it! I was wondering why you were arguing about a jack. Does he play cards a lot?" the coachman queried carefully.

"Play cards? To have a son of mine play cards! Why, I'd have laid a curse on him long ago . . ."

"I'm just as unmerciful when it comes to cards," the coachman picked up happily on the gentleman's words. "In my opinion, there's nothing more disgusting than cards. A drunkard only harms himself, a disobedient child annoys only its parents, but a man who plays cards is no better than a thief."

"You're right, granddad, you're right," the gentleman agreed.

"He's worse than a thief," the coachman spoke more freely now, "because there's a lock to keep out a thief, and there's a prison for a thief, but a man who plays cards can't be caught, and even if you do catch him, he'll just slip right out of your hands."

"Like an eel," the older gentleman seized on his words.

"Like the unclean spirit," the coachman corrected him. "Cards have made their way into our parts here in Podol as well. We've been cursed by those cards too," he added after a slight pause, sighing heavily.

"How?"

"My own worthless brother gambled away my best horse a week ago."

"You don't say! How did he manage to do that, the poor fellow?" the gentleman asked, as if he were truly sympathising with him.

"He came back from the army, and we were so happy that we invited a lot of guests, laid on the liquor—and he repaid us for it. He got drunk and gambled away my finest horse to some young gentleman, as he called him. But it probably wasn't a young gentleman—just some trash in a suit coat."

"It must have been trash! And what is your brother's name, granddad?"

"Maksym. The soldier, Maksym Ryaboshapka."

The tenor poked the baritone, and the baritone jabbed the tenor.

"Maksym. The soldier Maksym? Yes, I recall it—there was something written in the newspaper about him. They cleaned him out but good, that time . . ."

"The swindlers! May they be damned!" the coachman sighed.

"Young gentlemen like that should be put behind bars without even a trial," the older gentleman proposed.

"Yes, they should be," the coachman agreed.

"And old ones should be shipped out to do hard labour," the young gentleman added.

"Yes, of course; there shouldn't be any mercy shown to an old one—if he hasn't learned anything about justice living in freedom, let him learn about it in captivity."

"And young ones should be sent straight to the gallows."

"Yes, they should be, because if you're a swindler at an early age . . ." Turning around as far as he could, the coachman faced the passengers to finish what he was saying and abruptly stopped talking—the young gentleman was rolling with laughter.

"The young gentleman is laughing at a foolish peasant," he said quietly and abashedly.

"Wait! Here's a *troyak [three dollars]* for a new horse."

Delighted and dazed by his unexpected good fortune, the coachman did not even notice how and where his passengers disappeared. With trembling hands, he knotted the gift from fate into a handkerchief and set out at a trot to his usual spot in the street.

In the meantime, No. 17 was back from his trip as well. In all that time, only one gentleman had hired him. He had come up to him, asked him to drive him—over the hills and through the ravines—to the outskirts of the city, and indicated that he would pay him a *chetvertak [a quarter]* for the trip, a payment that was a whole *hryvenyk [a dime]* less than the usual fee.

The coachman agreed eagerly at first—just to earn anything at all—and he was quite happy to drive right up to the sidewalk to pick up his passenger, but as soon as the latter lowered himself onto the velvet pillow on the sleigh, he felt something stab his heart, and anger pressed down on his chest like a stone.

"The devil's scarecrow!" he thought. "He's cheated me out of a whole *hryvenyk*! A *hryvenyk*! That's enough for ten pounds of hay! Just you wait, my good man!"

He slackened the reins, and the horse trudged along as if it were hauling milk.

"Perhaps you're going so slowly because you don't see too well, my friend? It's probably a blindness brought on by malnutrition, right? It's a common ailment of the poor," the gentleman spoke up gently and kindly.

"What kind of ailment are you talking about? I don't have any ailment!" No. 17 responded angrily, cracking the whip on the horse's back so hard that the sound resounded through the street.

"Don't beat the horse," the gentleman pleaded.

"If I don't beat it, then I'll get beaten. If you earn just a *chetvertak* for such a trip, you can't even make enough to pay a policeman's ticket."

"That's true," the gentleman agreed. "The earnings of coachmen are uncertain, and they work hard for them. The majority of them die young from colds, because staying outdoors all night in the freezing cold . . ."

"Well, it might be better not to live than to experience trips like this one," the coachman grumbled.

"The greatest percentage dies from pneumonia. My own thirty-year medical practice in the cellars and rented rooms of the pitiful wretches . . . Carefully, carefully, my friend!" the gentleman broke off what he was saying and grabbed on to the coachbox, as the sleigh, making a sharp turn, nearly tipped over.

"Well, we've arrived. Add at least a little something extra," the coachman asked more reproachfully than pleadingly.

"I can't, my friend, I simply can't."

"At least add on a *pyatak [a nickel]*."

The gentleman waved his hands, pulled five copper coins out of his coat pocket, hurriedly shoved them into the coachman's hand, shuffled down the sidewalk, and disappeared behind a door thickly covered with business cards, among which stood out a copper tablet with the inscription: "The physician's assistance is available at all hours; no fee for the indigent."

No. 17 looked around—there was not a soul to be seen, no one at all, and no hope of finding a passenger anywhere. He almost wept in anger. He would have taken great pleasure in throwing those copper coins in the gentleman's face if the *chetvertak* had not been given first.

"The devil's scarecrow! May you not live to drive around any more! May you choke on that *hryvenyk*!"

He raged, and the farther along he went, the more furious he became, because the later it got, the more his hopes for additional earnings faded. Instead of chasing after illusory fate through the dark, deserted lanes of the fourth division, he could have turned on to a better street, but he knew from experience that you cannot guess what fate has in store for you, and so he went back to his old spot. In the meantime, it had become darker and colder outside.

No. 17 turned up his collar and peered into the impenetrable darkness.

"My, but it's a cold night!" No. 1001 spoke up unexpectedly as he sharply turned his horse around.

"There'll be a heavy frost by morning," No. 17 said.

"Yes, there will be," No. 1001 agreed.

He pulled a stubby pipe out of his pocket—which always signalled that he was in the best of moods—leisurely filled it, lit it, and leaned back comfortably on his sleigh.

"You know, uncle, it's all true—what you said about people; you look at a gentleman, and he seems to be honest, but he turns out to be worse than a dog," No. 17 said after a lengthy pause.

"Of course, that can happen," No. 1001 agreed slowly, "but all the same, people can never be compared to cattle. A human being is made in God's image; a human being has a conscience."

No. 17 blinked in surprise at his neighbour, seized the reins with both hands, jerked the horses with all his might, and flew off like a madman—all the way down to the other end of the street.

The Attack
(1910)

September the first.

Fedir Lvovych stopped the coachman a few yards from the gate, stepped out of the carriage, took off his long hooded cloth coat, brushed the dust off his yellow shoes with his handkerchief, freshened himself with eau de cologne, and then drove up to the veranda, sparkling clean, as if he had not been on the road at all.

At that moment, the mistress of the house, Varvara Ivanivna, was transplanting flowers in a perennial bed under the window.

"You weren't expecting a guest?"

"No, I wasn't. But I'm delighted to see you. My, you're all dressed up as if it were Easter—you're shining from head to foot!"

"It seems to me that I've never walked around in tatters," the guest said in a slightly offended tone, but then he instantly regained his good spirits and added cheerfully: "I've come to see you for a minute today about a certain matter."

"Is it a very important matter?"

"Well, it's not all that important, but 'strike the iron,' as the saying goes 'while it's hot,' or, as I like to say, 'before it's burnt all the way through'. We'll go directly to the orchard."

It was sheltered and warm in the orchard.

The yellow leaves of the black maple were already drifting over the pathway, the wilted leaves of the acacia appeared to be covered with smoke, the elm had doffed the greater part of its bushy mop and turned grey, and the hawthorn bushes were covered with a crimson veil; the desolate orchard, however, was not yet filled with the scent of death. It was tranquil here, like in a country of memories, of quiet rest—but not of death.

The weary trees, exhausted by their summer assignment, drooped their branches but, having only recently revelled in the charms of spring and experienced happiness in all its beauty and strength, they were shedding their attire without grief, without protest, without asking the heavens: "Why blossom? Why expend so much sap, deplete one's strength? Have we, in truth, earned a rest?'"

"It's so peaceful in the orchard! Why do our souls never know such peace?" Varvara Ivanivna sighed expressively.

"What's so pleasant about all this? The apples and the pears are all picked, and even the plums have been shaken to the ground," the guest remarked.

"But the sun! I like the autumnal sun best of all. It has no responsibilities now, and it plays and frolics freely, like a child. Look over there—the sun has silvered the trunks of the poplars, and over here it has whimsically showered gold on a tangle of old, twisted plum trees—useless even for firewood . . . There's gold everywhere, everywhere . . ."

"Oh, the devil take it! It's fake gold. I wouldn't give a *shah [half a penny]* for it."

"It's true that the gleaming, but cold, rays of the autumn sun remind me at times of the brocade on a corpse . . ."

"Ha-ha-ha! There you have it—the 'beauty' in the orchard! 'Brocade,' 'corpse' . . . No, Varvara Ivanivna, this is not the time for pessimistic remarks. Kateryna Antonivna—your good friend—told me something interesting about you today."

"Something interesting?"

"Well, it's not really that interesting, for I've known it myself for some time now—I guessed it some time ago. Come, there's a bench over there—by that flaming cranberry bush."

The guest hurriedly pulled the hostess across the autumnal grass covered with shiny yellow leaves.

"I planted this cranberry myself. It has grown into a most delightful shrub!" Varvara Ivanivna commented as she sat down.

"The shrub is delightful, but against the background of these crimson berries and dark green leaves you look even more pale. But then, you normally are quite pale. But that's of no significance. You will quickly grow healthier and more vigorous. You have an iron constitution."

"I'm suffering from the ague."

"It's all in your imagination! You don't have any fever at all."

"I swear to you—I can't eat or sleep because of the ague."

"It's all in your imagination! You're simply in love, Varvara Ivanivna."

"What in God's name are you saying?"

"Yes, yes . . . You're in love. And this is completely natural. With such a constitution, such a temperament, such a nature . . ."

"What kind of nature? I have an ordinary nature."

"No, excuse me . . . Ordinary people of your age are but a step away from death."

"And that's true of me, as well."

"That's enough now, Varvara Ivanivna. A person who is still capable of falling in love . . ."

"But I'm not in love."

"Varvara Ivanivna, we're not children. I know for certain that you are in love . . . you only have to tell me with whom. I mentally went through a whole list of men—all of them your friends—but I could not find one who is worthy of you."

"But I'm telling you—I don't love anyone, and I'm incapable of loving anyone."

"Varvara Ivanivna! Haven't I earned your trust in the ten years I've known you? I can see . . . I can read your soul, and you're suffering. But it could well be that your suffering is in vain . . . I'm even convinced of this—your happiness lies right here, in your own hands. Admit to me that you are in love. I will not give up. I will stay here for a day, for two days, for a month—as long as it takes to get you to admit this to me."

"Fine, have it your way—I'm in love."

"With whom?"

"Well, that's something I may not tell you."

"I won't leave until I know. I must know. I have to know. I will not leave your home until I know. Kateryna Antonivna hinted that it might be Oleksander Mykhaylovych."

"So, let it be him."

"You're joking, aren't you? That miserable towhead? I'll never believe you as long as I live."

"Yes, it's him . . ."

"Ah! So that's how it is! You're in love with Oleksander Mykhaylovych. The poverty of that towhead is your ideal. That's how it is! Well, and in what way . . ."

"In no way. I'm in love with him, and that's all there's to it."

"But he, of course, does not love you."

"Perhaps he does."

"Has he told you that he loves you? He's lying. Tell him this to his face. He does not love you."

"I don't know."

"You don't know, but I know. He can't be in love with you."

"Why?"

"Because every man, above all, wants his beloved to have a striking appearance, but you . . . Well, what is this mantle that you're wearing? And does anyone wear a head-dress like this nowadays?"

"Perhaps some people do. But it seems to me that Oleksander Mykhaylovych knows how to distinguish a person from her head attire. He pays no attention to style himself."

"But all the same, our Oleksander Mykhaylovych is no saint and, like all men, he is not immune to beauty. But you . . . you've lost so much weight, become so gloomy, grown so unattractive, become so old . . . Truthfully speaking, you no longer look like a woman. You're like a splinter now, like half a splinter . . ."

"I look in the mirror every day."

"Ha-ha-ha! Your mirror! I saw your mirror. Three *karbovantsi* [dollars] were paid for it fifty years ago."

"Excuse me, Fedir Lvovych, I myself am not yet . . . "

"Oh, what's the point of haggling about it! A year more, a year less . . . I know you're only thirty-five. But when a woman is thirty-five, there's nothing left for her to do but sit and darn stockings—it's the end of her beauty, the end of her loveliness."

"There are those who look for spiritual beauty in a person."

"Throw even the most expensive diamond into a slough—no one will begin to drink water out of it, even then."

"Fedir Lvovych!"

"Forgive me, I may have spoken too coarsely and inappropriately, but I do not refute the thrust of what I just said. When the purest, brightest, and most ideal soul is wrapped in a frail, old body . . . "

"But you just said, Fedir Lvovych, that my constitution . . ."

"What does it matter what I said? You yourself know how old you are."

"Mazepa was older than I am. And, after all, there was Othello. And then there was George Sand . . ."

"But those were Mazepa, Othello."

"Well, they're the same kind of people as . . ."

"They're not the same at all. You and I are not at all like that. We do not have the right to compare ourselves to classical exemplars."

"But I compare myself confidently to all people."

"Well, in that case . . . If you truly do, then . . . then—forgive me for what I'm about to say—you're undeniably ill . . . Your psyche . . . You're beginning to experience some kind of mania."

"To put it more simply—I'm insane?"

"You may or may not be insane, but, in any event, such a symptom is often an indication of a progressive paralysis."

"Paralysis? What do you mean? From where would I have got it?"

"What do you mean, from where? That's a strange question. Sclerosis at your age—this is quite common, and on the basis of sclerosis . . ."

"Sclerosis! O Lord! Heaven forbid! I'm so frightened of this. I saw what it did to my father . . . I must quickly flee abroad to consult some doctors."

"You're going to go abroad on your income? Do you see yourself not only as a Mazepa and a George Sand, but also as a millionaire? Abroad! Do you have any idea how much a pound of meat costs there? Or are you planning to place the responsibility for your sclerosis on your lessees, thereby robbing your own people for the sake of foreign charlatans who have never cured anyone of anything? You would be betraying yourself, your principles."

"That's true, Fedir Lvovych, what you've said is the holy truth! My situation is hopeless! I don't know what to do."

"That's the reason I came—to assist you. There is help for you. Listen, I know a certain gentleman . . . He's middle-aged, completely healthy, a brunet, handsome, a bit of a poet, more of a musician, quite a good singer . . . He's an idealist, of course. A wealthy person with guaranteed sources of income. He has a solid position, a good reputation, the respect of the community—he's a respectable person . . . And he loves you."

"Me? Half a splinter? What an unfortunate fellow!"

"Why unfortunate? Does everyone marry only Rubenesque women? And, after all, he will order you velvet dresses, bring in a *coiffeur*—like all the other ladies have—to put curls in your hair.

He'll buy you gold-rimmed combs for your coiffure. He'll adorn your slender fingers with rings. And, in the meantime, his brother, who is a doctor, will return from abroad with various medicines, diets, iron pills . . ."

"So much expense and trouble—and for what?"

"For what? Isn't a lot of money spent foolishly? Aren't there all sorts of people in the world? There's an old adage: 'To each his own.' Perhaps he's attracted to your voice. Although it's true that your voice is not impressive—and it's getting worse every day. This year the range of your voice has decreased dramatically, and its timbre has become uneven. Another year or two—and your voice will disappear altogether, because it's very weak already."

"Nevertheless, my voice is still stronger than yours. At least the day before yesterday, when we were singing a duet together, my voice drowned out yours."

"Ha-ha-ha! You're joking."

"That's what everyone said . . ."

"It's your friends—the Oleksander Mykhaylovyches—who lied to you. They were making fun of you."

"It was Karl Karlovych himself who told me this."

"Your Karl Karlovych was either drunk or could not hear how loudly I sang the encore. I assure you—you could not be heard at all. Your voice was lost, completely lost; only a few notes of the upper register could be heard."

"O Lord! Everything that was attractive about me has disappeared, vanished. The unfortunate brunet who wants to marry me will curse his fate on his wedding day."

"Well, that's his business. He isn't buying a pig in a poke. But enough! Let's put an end to all this prattle. That brunet is me!"

The Truth
(1911)

Maryna kissed Mykyta's hand as she would kiss a father's, crossed herself devoutly before the icons, and began putting on her outdoor clothing.

"May God help you!" Mykyta said. "I can't go myself because my leg feels like a dead log, but you shouldn't have any qualms. Go to the village assembly and tell the people what we've decided. There's no need to be ashamed or afraid. We want everything to be done truthfully, without any deception or double-dealing. That's why we're asking the community for its advice. Tell them I'm permitting it.

"We've lived together fifteen years, but God hasn't blessed us with children, and there certainly won't be any in the future. When I die, my brothers will chase you out of this house, and you'll have to eke out a wretched existence as a servant. You'll curse me, and perhaps I too will be burdened with the sin of having ruined a poor orphan's life.

"I shouldn't have married you. I served in the army for seventeen years—and I wasted my youth and my health in that service. I never should have married at all. But people meddled in our affairs; they persuaded us, brought us together, and married us. And in doing so, they committed a sin. Well, there's no point talking about that now. What's done is done. It can't be changed. But we do have to concern ourselves about what we're going to do in the future.

"I can see that you've taken a liking to Opanas, and it appears that he likes you, as well. He's also all alone—a childless widower—so the two of you should get together, just as if I weren't living on this earth, or as if I were your father. If God sends you children, I'll accept them as my own. Let them be my heirs. And once you have those children, you'll be able to live out the rest of your life in my house without any problems.

"Tell the people everything just as I've said it. If we were better off, we could go wherever necessary to file for a divorce, and you two could get married, so that everything would be done according to the law. However, since it isn't possible to do things according to the law, let it at least be done according to the truth, so that we can live out our lives without quarrelling and recriminations; so that we can look at ourselves, at God, and at the whole world with clear eyes."

Maryna listened attentively to everything her husband said, crossed herself once again, and left the house. She set out for the meeting in a dignified manner, without haste, reflecting on the words she was to utter publicly in a short while and assembling them in her thoughts in such a way that they might have a greater impact on the people.

In the meantime, Mykyta tried once again to go over all his thoughts, to mull over in his mind all the feelings and impressions of the last half year, from the day when he first called Opanas to to fix the porch door. The complicated, stubborn, and often heavy thoughts, that used to get all tangled up, were now obediently taking their places and proceeding in an orderly fashion, submissive to a single idea.

"No!" Mykyta said abruptly to himself. "No matter which way you look at it, no matter how much you think about it, there is no other solution. My young wife still doesn't grasp the situation herself. She doesn't have a single evil thought in her head. She has faith in herself, but often it's easier to see how things are by looking in from the outside. I watched her through the window yesterday, and I saw how long she stood by the well with Opanas.

"I've seen for a long time that she's sad. The only thing she takes pleasure in is her needlework, and even that falls from her hands. There's no denying the truth—she's young and strong. She wants to live as all people do, but this old man is like a log blocking her path. It's better that she not trip on it and break her leg. Let her step over it!"

Winding his thoughts up like a ball of wool for the last time, he tugged firmly at the ends, so they could not unravel again. Then he pulled the sieve with the peas closer to himself and calmly began to cull the wild oats and tiny lumps of dirt.

According to ancient village custom, women did not have the right to intrude into the conversation of men during a meeting. And so Maryna did not dare to go directly into the middle of the gathering; instead, she stood by the well and signalled with her hand to the elderly Harasym.

"I have something to tell the community on behalf of Mykyta, grandsire. His leg is inflamed, so he sent me in his stead."

"Step forward," the old man said.

The young woman's heart began to race, the colour drained from her face and, white as chalk, she drew nearer to stand before the men.

This village community—the assembly to which she was about to entrust her future, right up to the very day of her death—was comprised of only fourteen men, the householders of the village. All these men were either related to her through christenings or marriage, or were her close neighbours. She had worked alongside them for fifteen years. She drank with them, socialised with them, and quarrelled with them. She knew every one of them as well as she knew herself. She knew what each had eaten for dinner that day, what sin each could be reminded of, and what to say to annoy each and every one of them.

And yet, she was now trembling before all of these Ivans, Stepans, and Maksyms. Yesterday she may have scolded them to their faces, and tomorrow, perhaps, she might be making fun of them again. But now, her large, dark eyes flashed with fear.

She bowed to them silently and respectfully, pressed her right hand to her wildly beating heart, and stood absolutely still, waiting for permission from them to speak.

No one knew what it was Maryna had come to say, but from the moment the men laid eyes on her, they understood that she had not come with idle words, that she was turning to them as to some great, wise authority, bowing to them as one bows to judges—and all their private little discussions ceased at once. The community, as the defender of the pure, great truth, prepared itself to judge according to the truth.

"Tell us what you have come to say," Petro Vorona spoke up first—the same Vorona who only recently had stolen two ducks from Maryna—and the young woman rejoiced at hearing his words, just as if her own father had spoken to her from the other world.

"My good people, I will tell you everything without any deception, without any lies, as if I were under oath. I won't hide even a kernel of it, and I won't lie about anything. And if you don't believe me, then let any good Christian harness a horse and go fetch my husband. Let him tell the whole community that this is what he desires," Maryna began emotionally, glancing about uneasily and addressing each of the men in turn.

"We'll believe you. Speak freely," replied Harasym.

"As you all know, my good people, God has not blessed us with children," she continued what she was saying in a high, clear, and even voice. "My husband and I have never had any joy, any help, or any hope, and we have none now. We've been living together for fifteen years. We respect each other and look after each other. We don't scold each other, and we don't quarrel. Nevertheless, we're always sad and grieving, because we have no one to work for, no one to look after, and no one to live with in our old age. If I should die first, there won't be anyone to fetch my husband even a drink of water. If he should die first, I won't have even so much as a corner of my own in which to lay down my head . . ."

"No you won't, because Mykyta's brothers won't take pity on you, especially the middle one. He doesn't have a house, and his family is large, so as soon as Mykyta dies, he'll pounce on you," Danylo supported the words of the young woman.

"There you have it, my good people. You can see for yourselves—cold and hunger await my husband if he should be widowed. And, as for me, his family is cursing me even now. My husband instructed me to come to the assembly and ask the community for advice.

"'Go, wife,' he said, 'and ask the people to think about this matter and discuss it. Tell the people it is my will that you give me an heir, even if it's out of wedlock. I'll have that little child baptised and registered in my name. If God grants me enough years, I'll raise it properly.' My good people, it will be as you say, as you wish, as you advise."

"What kind of advice is needed here?" laughed Savka, a fair-haired young householder, who did not have any whiskers yet. "If the husband himself is telling his wife to find a lover . . ."

"Don't be in a hurry to show off your teeth—this isn't the marketplace," Danylo cut him off. "Whether Mykyta is ordering his wife to take a lover, or whether he isn't, it's no business of ours. Our business is to discuss what we are to do next, since he wants to present the community with a child that isn't his, as his heir."

"Well, let him do that—even if there are ten such heirs. If Maryna can't handle them all by herself, we'll hire them to graze the communal geese and pigs," Savka attempted to turn things into a joke once again.

Maryna blushed furiously.

"Shut up!" Savka was interrupted by Ivan, a tall, thin, red-haired man.

He could never speak while seated, so he rose to his feet and stretched himself to his full height.

The people had to crane their necks to catch everything he was saying.

"What business is it of ours? We're looking for trouble. What happens in another man's house is his business. Let the child first see the light of day," he stated harshly and abruptly in a blunt, hoarse voice, and then sat down again.

"That's true," Danylo supported him.

"It's true; what a man does in his house is his own business," Vorona added. No one argued with that.

Maryna understood that one part of the matter, the first question—whether the entire community would rise up against her if she had a child out of wedlock—had been resolved in the manner that Mykyta had expected.

"But will your child be Mykyta's heir?" Nechypir inquired.

"It will be the church register that will show that," responded Spyrydon, an elderly man who was still robust and sturdy. "Go home, young woman, and tell Mykyta all of this. Let him live as he sees fit. He is his own boss, his own man. And his house, his land, and all of his possessions will be inherited by the child who bears his name."

Feeling as if she had sprouted wings, the young woman flew home.

Only now, after looking fearlessly into her own heart for the first time, did she see that she truly loved Opanas, that she desired to become his wife for life. Only now, after finding the courage to sort out her thoughts, did she realise how sad, desolate, and cold her life had been . . .

And so, that very same day, something wonderful happened. Three hitherto lonely, unfortunate people, using the single word of truth as if it were a knife, cut through the chains of their misfortune, turned their faces boldly towards happiness, and unexpectedly saw that it still had a lot to offer each of them from its treasure chest.

Having given up his rights as a husband, Mykyta claimed the right of a human being to respect, care, and peace. All of these rights were gladly accorded him by Maryna and Opanas. Having rid himself of the terrible, burning fear that he would become the victim of his young wife's secret betrayal, that he would be abetting a great sin, and that he would be made the laughing-stock of the whole village in his old age, Mykyta felt an intense, secure contentment in the peace and self-esteem that his clear conscience gave him, and in the joy brought him by the happiness of the two people whom he had united.

Within the year, Maryna had a child—a daughter, Olena. Mykyta sold a boar and spent the money on the christening. All the villagers celebrated noisily for two days, as if they were at a wedding. No one even mentioned the fact that the infant was Opanas's daughter. Two more years went by, and God gave Maryna a son, Yakiv. The entire village celebrated in the same way as before, and the godparents, with a clear conscience, told the priest that Yakiv was Mykyta's son.

The two children thrived in the warm, tender care of three happy people, all of whom, even though they were constantly besieged by endless work, were contented and at peace in their own way. Raised under the vigilant eye of old Mykyta, the children matured, grew in beauty and in strength, and artlessly radiated happiness— just as the sun sends forth its rays—making their parents feel stronger and more enthusiastic about their heavy work, and warming Mykyta's old heart with the hope of remaining on this earth long enough to see still more little ones.

And the old man lived to see a wonderful day—the day Olena was married.

And he lived to see a second wonderful day—the day Yakiv was married.

And he lived to see a third one.

The villagers, as a commune, bought a small, but very good, low-lying hayfield. And they did this without paying a single kopeck for it, because they immediately rented it out as a melon patch for five years. In that way, the land was to pay for itself.

"That's how it's done, my son! That's how it's done, my children! What a great village this is! What a great community! To figure out how to do something like that! To make such a good deal! To parcel out land to everyone without spending a single kopeck! More than an acre of the hayfield will go to you, my son. Now you'll have a place to graze your cow, and you'll have milk for your little ones. What a great village this is! What a great community!"

The old man rejoiced and laughed, but he sensed that he would not live to see either the cow or the milk. He was only awaiting the springtime, so he could walk on his own hayfield at least once.

The old man did live to see spring arrive. It came and melted the snow, and chased the rivers of water from the hayfield. Mykyta took his cane and cut across an embankment to the lowland. When he came to the hayfield, he saw that the elderly Spyrydon was already there, standing on a hillock. Neatly girded with a belt and wearing a cap made of lamb's fur, he was leaning on his cane, deep in thought.

"Good health to you! I've come to take a look as well. I don't know yet where my acre will be," Mykyta greeted the elderly man.

Spyrydon touched his cap lightly as a sign of greeting, but he did not say anything in reply.

"I haven't been in the village for a long time, and I don't attend the assemblies. You're out among the people more often than I am, so do you know exactly where my acre will be?" Mykyta asked him, gazing with infinite tenderness from the hillock at the small, round patch of hayfield that was already turning green.

"It appears it won't be anywhere," Spyrydon retorted, without turning around.

"Did the deal fall through?" Mykyta asked in alarm.

"The deal didn't fall through. They're taking the deposit to the landlord tomorrow."

"Well then, why are you saying it won't be anywhere?"

"Because, you see, you won't be named in the purchase," Spyrydon replied, avoiding Mykyta's eyes. "If I were you, I would withdraw from the hayfield. You'll be dead any day now. Why trouble yourself on behalf of others!"

"Do you think I'm doing it for the others?" Mykyta was surprised. "Why should I be worried about the others when I have my own son?"

"You have a son?" Spyrydon asked him slowly and, moving his cane to another spot, he once again leaned on it and fell silent.

"Of course I have a son. Have you forgotten about Yakiv?"

Spyrydon just adjusted the cap on his head . . .

"Let the others live in good health as they see fit. But I have my own problems. I'm troubling myself about my son."

Spyrydon poked his cane into the ground a few times, remained silent for a while, and then, turning to face Mykyta, stated resolutely: "You have to withdraw from the hayfield, or else you'll be in trouble."

"What kind of trouble?"

"This kind of trouble—that Yakiv is not your heir."

"What do you mean, he's not my heir?" Mykyta began to shake all over.

"It happened a long time ago, and his old head is like a sieve. He's forgotten that Yakiv is Opanas's son. He's forgotten," Spyrydon flung out insultingly.

"So?" Mykyta still could not gather his thoughts together.

"So, the truth of the matter is—he's not your heir," Spyrydon stated calmly.

"But what about the church register?"

"What good are church registers? Many things can be scribbled on paper."

"And what about the meeting? With the entire village? With the entire community? And what the people told Maryna? And me as well?" babbled the old man, terrified out of his wits.

"So what about that meeting? What was it the people said there? I was at the meeting myself, and I heard it all. At the meeting, there was talk only about your house and your land. But now, you see, there's also a hayfield . . ."

"The same thing goes for the hayfield."

"The same, and not the same," Spyrydon said abruptly and, in his anger, drove his cane almost a quarter of the way into the ground.

"How isn't it the same?"

"It isn't the same, because in our village there isn't anyone who wants your house or your land. However, in the case of the hayfield, Yakiv is sticking in everybody's craw. We bought this hayfield for our village only. Opanas is not from our village. Yet now we'll have to take land away from our own children, in order to give his son a portion of it."

"May you be portioned into quarters!" Mykyta boiled over. He was shaking with rage.

"Why are you yelling?"

"I'm yelling because it's not the truth. You don't want to act truthfully."

"Well then, you swear that Yakiv is your son, and everything will be done according to the truth," Spyrydon retorted.

"You want me to swear? What do you take me for? Do you think I'm a gypsy? The community . . . the village . . . everyone will swear that Yakiv is my heir."

"We'll see about that," Spyrydon interrupted Mykyta. "The community elected me as its spokesman, and I'm just on my way to see the lawyer concerning your Yakiv . . ."

Mykyta could barely make his way home. His legs felt as if they were bound; they simply would not obey him. He could not see—it was as if he were in darkness, not in the bright light of the spring sun. Time and again, his cane slipped from his grasp and fell to the ground. He had been attacked and robbed in broad daylight. He had been stripped to his very shirt. And it was the village that had done this!

"Maryna! Maryna!" he called his wife, barely able to breathe. "Did you ever think—did you ever dream that such evil would befall us?" he asked her as she came running up from the garden where she and Opanas were planting beets. "They're ordering me to swear that Yakiv is my son, and if I don't, they're threatening that they won't let him come into his inheritance after me. They're saying he's not my heir."

Maryna collapsed on the threshold and began to wail. Yakiv heard her and came running. His wife followed after him. And then they called Opanas from the garden.

They went into the house and sat down.

No one offered any advice or voiced a clear thought. Like birds deafened and blinded by thunder and lighting in an ash tree, five people sat silently in their home, and they all had their own understanding of the truth. Feeling as if they were being crushed under a wall of earth, they were waiting for the village community to finish weaving a trap for them out of that truth.

"What will the lawyer say?" all five were thinking and grieving.

"And where is the great truth of the village assembly? Does it lie in the fact that this assembly concealed a falsehood for twenty years, or in the fact that it now wants to reveal it?" Mykyta asked himself.

And he felt death squeezing his heart ever more tightly with its icy hand.

A Spring Night
(1911)

A thunderbolt crashed, the church burst into flames . . .

Kateryna knew that Petro was inside, and she threw herself into the heart of the flames to rescue him . . .

Beams and joists cracked, gigantic red tongues engulfed the walls . . . The air was filled with noise, clamour, the shouts of people . . .

Kateryna did not see or hear any of it; frantic with fear, she raced from corner to corner, wringing her hands and shouting: "Petro, Petro!"

Finally she spotted him, found him . . . Lifting him up in her arms like a little child, she clutched him to her breast and hurried to the spacious, green town square: "Petro! Petro! Oh, what good fortune—you're alive!"

"Kateryna! Kateryna! Wake up!"

The girl's eyes opened wide, and she sprang to her feet.

The house was flooded with moonlight, and her mother, barefoot and wearing just a shirt, was standing in front of her. "Cross yourself. What were you dreaming about?"

Kateryna covered her face with her hands, trying to retain the enchanting dream for at least a moment in her memory; her heart was beating violently, fuelled by the intense happiness she had experienced in her dream.

"Mother! Why did you wake me up?" she said reproachfully, after a moment.

"Why did I wake her? She's blaming me! Tell me, why did you wake me? What Petro were you calling out to in your sleep? It wasn't Kalynchenko by any chance, was it? Maybe you went to order a fourth pair of shoes from that good-for-nothing!"

"Oh, mother, if you only knew how sick and tired I am of hearing about those shoes. I ripped them, gashed them on a rock.

Is the cobbler to blame for that? Leave me alone . . . You don't give me a moment's peace."

"You don't have a moment's peace because of me?" her mother was so offended and incensed that she jumped with fury. "Oh, you have no conscience! I've signed the house over to her already, and I've put away such fine feather ticks for her . . ."

"That's enough! For God's sake, mother, that's enough. Don't say that, don't talk about it all the time, don't count everything up over and over again . . . I don't need anything," the daughter responded with infinite suffering in her voice.

"You're lying—you do so! If it weren't for the cottage and the land, Ivan Danylovych wouldn't have asked for your hand in marriage . . ."

"That's enough, mother, enough! I beg you—that's enough!"

"What's 'enough'?"

"Enough talking. It's not the land, nor the cottage, nor the feather ticks, nor Ivan Danylovych that's on my mind just now."

"Huh, so that's it! Well, my dear young lady, what is it that's on your mind? Might it be princes from beyond the sea?"

"I won't tell you what's on my mind as long as I live, because I'm sick and tired of your reproaches and curses. We'd do better to go back to sleep," Kateryna said, and she resolutely placed her head on her pillow.

The pillow was drenched with tears.

"I was crying, I was actually crying!" the girl thought in alarm. "I weep during the day, and I weep at night . . . And I'll go on weeping like this for the rest of my life; I'll cry my eyes out . . . and all because of my mother . . ."

"Cross yourself, so that you won't dream about an enemy," the mother said, and she yawned contentedly.

Kateryna did not reply.

The ancient wooden bed creaked once under her mother's heavy body, and then a second time; and a moment later, the calm, even snoring of the huckstress resounded through the house.

But Kateryna could not fall asleep.

She could see in front of her the living image of Petro, dressed in the same way as in her dream; his dark eyes seemed to be peering into her heart, which was breaking with despair and sorrow.

"There is no escape from evil misfortune," Kateryna thought. "There is no power that can overcome the will of my mother; there is no sorcerer who could succeed in making the detested fishmonger renounce me; there is no path I could take to avoid the fate God has given me. I must submit to that fate; I must submit, fortify my heart, and die a slow death the rest of my life, for such is the will of God . . ." she concluded.

But her longing, her senseless longing did not hear, nor did it want to listen to, her wise words; it continued growing, increasing in intensity, and her heart felt stifled.

Kateryna could not lie still any longer; she leaped out of bed, threw on a skirt and kerchief, and went out into the open veranda.

She went out and, overcome by wonderment and boundless astonishment, stood transfixed by the door . . .

Oh, how fortunate she was!

It must be God who had chosen this spring night to finally inform people of His will, to reply to their eternal question—how were they to live on this earth? Gathering together all the clouds, He had chased them beyond the horizon; He had hushed the laughter of the excited stars, raised the full moon high in the sky so that all could see it and, with His own hand, had cast a single word over the wide, clear sky. And the birds had immediately read this word.

"Love!" The word rang out in a host of voices.

All the plants understood this word, and from even the tiniest flowers wafted waves of dizzying fragrances, as from a censer in church on a great holy day; and the frogs understood this word as well, and responded in a joyous chorus.

And fortunate people, who, despite the lateness of the hour, had not yet retired behind stone walls, also read this word. Nearby, beyond the fence, young lovers were whispering softly, a duet echoed from the river and, from the town park, came the sound of an orchestra playing a serenade.

"Petro! I'm coming to you!" The words burst out unexpectedly and joyfully from the girl's breast.

She rushed into the house, reached for her shoes under the bed, pulled on a jacket, and sped, as if on wings, to her Petro.

He lived far away. She had to run through almost the entire suburb. At every step, she was in danger of chancing up with a neighbour or an acquaintance, who, as early as tomorrow, could pass judgement on her and ruin her maidenly reputation. Dogs might attack her and, at such an hour, thieves, drunkards, and all manner of evil people roam the streets. And tomorrow, her mother might beat her to death, curse her forever, and, perhaps, even throw her out of the house.

It did not matter! Nothing mattered! She was obeying the will of God; she was in love, and she was flying, like the birds and insects, to her mate. He most certainly was not sleeping either.

And if he was sleeping, she would awaken him; she would knock at the window and cry out: "Dearest, get up! It's the month of May! The moon is shining, songs are resounding . . . The boat on the shore awaits us. . . The joys of love beckon us."

The little white hut was visible now. A light flickered in the small window; he was not sleeping yet. Kateryna quickened her pace. Her kerchief fell from her head, a light breeze tossed her blond hair, and her eyes were shining. Colour flooded her face.

Joyful as happiness and strong as truth, she hastened boldly, like a colossus of the spirit, to the small window. She reached it and pressed her hot forehead to the tiny pane . . .

Her dearest was not sleeping.

Her dearest was sitting on a bench in the middle of the room. Pale and weary, his head was bent down low, and his dark hair was falling over his eyes. Dressed in a white shirt, an old vest, and a large leather apron, he was holding on his knees a gaping, tattered, old red boot that had no sole.

"He has to cobble the sole before dawn . . . His mother is old, feeble . . . Bought grain . . . a place that's not one's own . . . fuel to heat the house," flashed through Kateryna's head, and she jumped from the window as if scalded, as if she were a thief caught in the act.

 Oh! She had been duped.

It was not "love," but "work," that was written across the sky, and it was she—a foolish, wanton, lie-abed—who had misread it.

Kateryna fled.

She ran home as fast as she could, and it seemed to her that the silvery, moonlit streets were laughing in her wake.

From Earth to Orion
An Easter Story
(1911)

"Passport! Visa!

The pale ray of light grew still paler—it had not expected this at all. It had fled from the earth to distant Orion to enjoy some freedom, but here, too, it heard the same words: "Passport! Visa!"

The cunning secret observer was not accustomed to giving up without a fight.

"I'm a messenger from Earth," it said haughtily to the guard.

On Orion, the inhabitants do not yet know how to lie, and so the guard believed the ray of light; he spun a small wheel, and the news immediately resounded through the constellation: "A messenger from Earth has arrived."

And, in a moment, thousands of tall, slender, bright-eyed beings in pink shirts surrounded the liar, and thousands of slim white hands extended bouquets of lilies to the dear guest.

Beautiful Queen Hede stood on a rosebush and passed the foreigner a chalice of mead.

Oh! The mead was more nutritious than the sighs of those who are in love, and, after drinking it, the ray of light was instantly emboldened.

"I'm a messenger from Earth," it said. "I'm a messenger from Earth, and I've come to invite all of you for a visit. Come to visit us. Earth is celebrating a holiday.

"It's our springtime, and it's like paradise. The cold snow is gone, and the ground is steaming. The ice on the rivers has melted, and fish are splashing about in the water. All the yards are filled with the cacophonous cries of geese, ducks, and turkeys. The calves and lambs are gambolling. Songs reverberate in the air. Everything is caught up in the throes of love, in a great, powerful thirst for life."

The Orionites did not know any of the creatures whose virtues the ray of light was extolling, but its concluding words touched a responsive chord in their hearts.

"Oh, it's wonderful there!"

"And what do people do?" asked the beautiful queen, enraptured by the stirring words.

"They love each other," the ray of light responded impudently, with a sly wink.

"They love each other? And that is all?" the beautiful queen asked slowly, in a saddened tone.

"Oh, no! That's not all . . . Of course, that's not all," the wonderful psychologist caught on immediately. "That wouldn't be possible. There's more to life than being in love. They love each other only some of the time, on holidays . . ."

"And on ordinary days?" the queen inquired.

"And on ordinary days . . ." the braggart stopped short for a moment. But then, recalling a certain conversation on which he had eavesdropped, he continued: "They fight for the truth."

"They fight for the truth?" the queen repeated, her blue eyes widening and gleaming like translucent jewels. "But is it possible for truth to have enemies?"

"Of course! Do you suppose, oh beautiful queen, that the most exquisite terrestrial pearl comes easily to people? Oh, no! It comes only with heavy sacrifices, painful struggles. We fight . . . We fight constantly . . . Christ himself came to us and gave us his commandments of truth and love; He gave us His holy banner and requested that truth prevail. But since that time, His followers have fought incessantly. His banner is pierced with bullets, covered with dust, and soaked with tears."

"Send a correspondent!" the agitated beautiful queen cried out.

And, in a flash, the beautiful Above—the pride and glory of Orion—obediently picked up his briefcase.

A moment later, his first report flew back: "I'm on Earth, staying at a hotel. It's neither cold, nor warm here. The planet is rich in animal life. In the square, about six hundred feet from my window, there are one hundred and twenty-two carts, with all sorts of fowl and animals. There are some fine specimens here, but they all belong to a vicious, dangerous breed, and, for this reason, they are tied up securely, or kept in cages. People take them away one at a time and cart them home, where they tame them.

"Anatomy is greatly respected on Earth. There is a vast amount of material here for anatomical dissections—mostly the heads of huge animals, their feet, livers, and intestines. Surgeons, clad in white aprons, willingly give them away—usually to women. The bloody material is thrown into baskets, taken home, and dissected there.

"I haven't witnessed a battle yet, but I have seen its victims and those exhausted by the stuggle—some of them wallow under fences, while others lie drenched in dirty water in the middle of the street . . ."

In a short while, a second report flew in: "There is some kind of danger—faces are anxious. The city will definitely be under siege. Huge amounts of bread, hats, boots, ties, and bottles of alcohol are being procured and stored."

In another little while, there was a third report: "It's clear—they're preparing for battle. Knives are being sharpened, and young ladies are concealing stilettoes in their hair."

And then, there was a fourth report: "The level of activity is increasing. People are walking about in alarm. I would say that the Christians are fearing a catastrophe, but it is not appropriate to use the word 'catastrophe' with respect to knights, fighters for an ideal . . ."

The fifth report: "The enemy must be close by; the Christians, sweaty, agitated, and upset, are running around threateningly. They're shoving one another and continually running to and fro, some barefoot, and some in boots. They have huge parcels under their arms—these must contain their weapons. There's a great outcry and much cursing—it must be against the enemy. Children are crying—it may be that they are the victims. Animals are bawling."

The sixth report: "The activity increases hourly. I don't see the enemy, but the Christians must see them, because their eyes are fierce, their nerves are taut. The most demonstrative among them are clenching their fists and preparing to do battle. They are hurriedly learning how to box—I saw two respectable women conducting such a lesson, and hundreds of pupils looked on without taking their eyes off them . . ."

The seventh report: "The enemy must be on its way—there's an evil odour in the air, and the level of activity is increasing, intensifying. . ."

The eighth report: "There's the smell of sizzling blood. It's night. I can't see anything, but I can hear people racing about, horses galloping, and there is so much activity and such determination, that the final battle must be at hand."

The ninth report flew in at dawn. "The struggle has ended—the Christians were victorious. The last battle took place in their homes. All the enemies of Christ's ideals—various fowl and four-legged animals—have been slain. Most of them are small, but their numbers are countless. There are several of them for every family of Christ's followers, and it goes without saying that the struggle was difficult. Now, all the foes have been slaughtered, killed, and, like trophies of a glorious victory, they lie preserved and adorned with flowers in Christians' parlours.

"Such a magnificent victory over the foes of truth immediately altered the general mood of the Knights of the Holy Truth, whose conviction that they have done their great Christian duty is reflected in all the minutiae of their lives.

"Candles and lamps are lit everywhere, and bells ring without ceasing.

"Throngs of Christians, dressed in holiday attire and with cheerful songs on their lips, walk about and greet each other with kisses, exclaiming: 'Christ is risen!'"

Verhuny: Sweet Pastries
(1913)

New Year's Day!

It was a holiday for Vadym Vadymovych as well. His landlady had considerately taken her entire brood to visit her sister, leaving her household in the care of a deaf-mute serving girl. And not one New Year's caroller, nor one New Year's well-wisher, nor the watchman, nor the chimney-sweeper had gained access to him, no matter how long they rang the doorbell, or how hard they knocked on the door.

There had been no other visitors, nor could there have been any. Seven years ago, Vadym Vadymovych had sold his property, chosen a town where no one knew him, settled on the fourth floor, and from that time on had not seen a single soul, except for the landlady's servant, in his living quarters.

Today, he had not gone out into the street, nor had he glanced out of the window even once. There could be nothing of interest out in the street. The big red, white, and blue commonplace box-like buildings had not grown one whit more attractive from having stood out there for another 365 days. And, even though they were thoroughly scraped, freshly whitewashed, and decorated for the holidays with new curtains and white blinds, they remained the same reservoirs of hatred, spitefulness, betrayal, and stuffy, unhealthy air that they had been for all the days of all the past years.

The tightly-laced, wild-haired young ladies in their high heels and huge hats resembled foolish turkey hens on this day even more than usually. The shiny mugs of the young bucks, enlivened by flasks of whiskey, appeared even more cynical. Mournful figures in dark clothing—dignified, well-bred, silent figures with lowered eyes—appeared hypocritical to him. Visiting officials, all out of breath and wearing new uniforms, were irritating—like comedians, buffoons, harlequins. Poor people, their slicked down hair and their clothes carefully patched, and genteel cripples, draped and gilded for the holiday, their hair powdered and their faces painted, evoked disgust.

Vadym Vadymovych did not want to see any of that, and he felt a true satisfaction, a great joy at the thought that he had the right and the wherewithal not to see any of it, that he clearly had no need of anyone, that he himself most definitely was of no use to anyone, that fate had already exploited all of his wealth—both material and spiritual—to the nth degree, and that people could not derive any benefit from him in any way.

A hundred steps lower in the same building, in one of the smaller rooms on the first floor, Motrona Karpivna had been sitting at the window almost the entire day. She had risen early, hurriedly dressed herself for the holiday in an attractive, shiny dress, gone to church, stood through the entire liturgy, returned home, and eaten her breakfast. Then she seated herself at the window and looked out into the street, unable to turn her eyes away.

During the night, snow had fallen, and it covered the street like white, fluffy down; the frost had woven a resilient carpet out of it, and the sun had adorned it with tiny silver stars. The buildings, gates, and streetcars were also sprinkled with silver dust; everything was shining and gleaming, while the large panes of the display windows flamed in the sun.

The carriage drivers' well-groomed horses, given an extra measure of oats because of the holiday, did not seem to be touching the ground with their feet as they raced over the street, vying to get ahead of one another. On the sidewalks, people wandered back and forth incessantly . . .

Just now, a townsman passed by the window with his wife and three little boys. Motrona Karpivna was concerned that the woman had only boys, that she did not have a daughter-confidante, no one to help her with the cooking or with other household chores.

And she asked herself: "Where are they going? Where is the townsman taking his wife and children—to his own mother, or to his mother-in-law's home?"

And now, a young lady rushed by, pulling on her gloves as she walked. Motrona Karpivna, noticing that she was in light galoshes, became upset with thoughtless young people who did not take care of their health. Then it occurred to her that the young lady might be an orphan and might have no one to give her good advice.

A young student strolled by; Motrona Karpivna let him go by without paying attention to him—his shaggy hair did not appeal to her. In his wake ran three little boys with worn shoes on their bare feet.

"Well, these are accustomed to it," she thought, "nothing will happen to them, even though they are barefooted."

Behind the boys, an elderly man in an expensive fur coat slowly came into view. He was walking carefully, leaning on a thick cane with a silver head. Motrona Karpivna recalled how much her pepper whiskey had helped Father Halaktion when his hipbone ached.

And now a constable ran by, followed by a whole crowd of people! They were all hurrying somewhere, looking fixedly at the same spot—there must be a fire. More than likely the soot had not been cleaned out of a chimney, and stoves were in constant use before the holidays.

"Or could it be that some drunk people are brawling?" Motrona Karpivna conjectured.

Just then, a pair of raven-black trotters tore past the window like swift bullets, and Motrona Karpivna's blood turned cold—a coach driver must have had too much holiday cheer to drink; more than likely, his eyes were bleary from alcohol and he could crash into people, run over them, cripple them—perhaps, the young lady who had just walked by, or the gentleman with the cane . . .

Across the street, there was a small, single-story building with five windows. The door leading into it had been opening and closing all morning. An attractive chamber maid, wearing a pink dress and a white pinafore, had been kept busy the whole time, admitting guests and seeing them off. Fifteen or more coach drivers had driven up to the veranda, and ever so many people had gone into that residence! The visitors were all men—old, young, middle-aged—and all of them were officials.

Just now, farther up the street, another sleigh drove up. There were two people in it. The first one, a young gentleman, hopped out, but what about the second figure? It was someone all bundled up, wrapped in shawls . . .

Motrona Karpivna ran quickly to her chest of drawers and found her big, black, horn-rimmed glasses. In the meantime, a door had opened wide, and five people poured out to greet the bundled up guest: a grey-haired gentleman, a university student, two high school students, and a lady. They surrounded the sleigh on all sides, kissed the guest, and raised her to a sitting position.

"It's an old mother, and that's her daughter, son-in-law, and grandchildren," Motrona Karpivna surmised.

The plaid throws and furs were tossed aside, and a stout old lady was lifted out of the sleigh. The lady was wearing an old-fashioned cloak. Motrona Karpivna's heart constricted in pain—she used to have an identical cloak.

"Where is it now?" she tried to remember.

Oh, yes—back home, in Vyshkvarky, hanging on a nail in a closet. Vyshkvarky! Her own Vyshkvarky! A small farmstead by a river. A lush orchard, a green yard, a well with a tall crane, and an old pantry overgrown with hop vines. The dogs—Barbos, Rudko, Zhuchka . . .

A curtain seemed to descend over the window—she could no longer see the street, nor the people, nor the streetcars; the hand holding her eyeglasses fell into her lap, and images of her former neighbors rose before her eyes—petty bourgeois, the priest, his wife, villagers, old men, girls, young women, children; the familiar melodies of Christmas carols and New Year's carols filled the air; there was the aroma of sausages, fried fatty bacon, the fresh, frosty air that the crowds of well-wishers brought with them into the house as they scattered grain and wished everyone good fortune.

A very familiar feeling, nurtured since childhood, seized the heart of the hospitable mistress—her hand reached out to pour the whiskey, to pass the *pyrizhky [turnovers]*, to greet the dear guests with the tastiest pastries, so they would not forget about her and pass by her house. And out there, in the veranda, more guests were stamping the snow off their feet.

Where had it all disappeared? A blizzard had driven it all away, some kind of a revo . . . a revo . . . a terrible judgement to which she had been forced to submit. She had not given in for a long time; she had not wanted to give up her patrimony. She would have preferred to lie down and die in her own yard, rather than give it up to strangers. And so, when the old woman Khymka said that the strikers were twisting the tails of the cattle, she imagined her dear little cow Manka and her horse Vorony with twisted tails— and, at her wits end, she sent a letter to her son in Petersburg.

"Sell off everything, take your money, and move to the city," her son instructed her—and cast her into a cold well.

Alone, completely alone, like a blade of grass.

There were no kinsfolk, no in-laws, no family . . . the holiday came—and she knew that not a soul would visit her, and there was no one she could greet with the holiday. She had bought and prepared so much for the holiday—but there was no one to host with the delicacies she had baked. Especially the *verhuny [deep fried sweet pastries]*!

She had gone to so much trouble, so much fuss and bother—preparing and frying them in the communal kitchen! But they had turned out wonderfully well—full, pink, and curly—and she had a heaping platter of them. What was she to do with them? Oh, how enthusiastically she would host anyone—anyone at all—with them! How eagerly she would share them!

And suddenly Motrona Karpivna thought of the old man who lived on the fourth floor in the same building. He was always alone, always gloomy, as if he, like she, had been forgotten by the whole world. Wasn't he the very one who should be greeted on this great holiday? Shouldn't he be the one to be feted with a special treat?

Motrona Karpivna jumped to her feet, ran to the cupboard, selected the prettiest plate, piled it high with *verhuny*, covered them with a clean cloth, and ran up the stairs—where had her old legs found the strength to do so?—hardly noticing the hundred or more steps that she was climbing. As luck would have it, the deaf servant was in the hallway at the time.

Motrona Karpivna had never communicated with a deaf-mute in all her life, and she could not even imagine how you should talk to one; however, her desire to pass the treat to the old man was so great, that her heart found its own way of getting her message across to the deaf-mute servant. She made a few gestures with her hands and her fingers, and the deaf-mute nodded her head, took the sweet pastries, and carried them off.

A couple of minutes later, Vadym Vadymovych, pale and furious, was pacing swiftly through his rooms, cursing the nasty old woman who had crawled like a snake under his locked door, and, through her kindness, placed him under an obligation of some kind.

But Motrona Karpivna, feeling contented and happy, was selecting the softest candies as a treat for the old man, so that the second day of the holiday might also be properly celebrated.

The Mercy of God
(1913)

Not a drop of rain had fallen all month.

The sky was grey, and clouds of dust filled the air. The grass and the weeds were completely withered. Parched, shrivelled crops jutted out on fields like the shaggy, unkempt hair of a feeble old man who lives alone. The cracked earth, hard as a rock, looked dead, incapable of growing anything. The sun, beating down fiercely, unmercifully, as if it were angry at all of God's world, scorched every stalk, gripped trees in a hellishly hot current of air, stretched its searing claws over the earth, and baked the roots in the ground.

The villagers, weary of praying, of paying for services of supplication, of having water blessed, gave up all hope . . .

Clouds drifted over their parcels of land as if over an enemy encampment and then descended to pour rain on muddy fields elsewhere. The people accepted the drought as God's punishment for sins that could not be expiated through prayer.

There was no hunger yet, but the first signs of its coming reign were approaching; the village property-owners—the recent despots of their small kingdoms, the omnipotent rulers of the chickens, ducks, pigs, cows, calves, and all that lived in their farm-yards—dropped the insignia of their power, and a time of anarchy and chaos ensued . . .

Granny Sokhviya's chickens were scratching in the garden, Ivan's calves were straying in the orchard, pigs were rooting in the pasture, and cows were stripping the willow trees. But these subjects were forgiven for everything—as long as they did not ask to be fed, as long as they took care of themselves and managed to stay alive one way or another.

It was only in the farm-yard of Onyska Holovchenko that everything was in order. The regimen for all the animals—the pigs, piglets and chicks—did not change. Every morning, the young mistress took handfuls of barley from the grain bins for the ducks, and set out a dish of millet for the chickens; she boiled potatoes for the piglets and added coarsely ground flour to the drink she prepared for the cows. The angry protests of her father-in-law, mother-in-law, husband, and brother-in-law were of no avail; neither rebukes nor pleading could persuade her to desist.

"You're crazy! Where are you taking the grain? May those chickens of yours drop dead! We'll soon be swelling from hunger ourselves!" her father-in-law thundered at her.

"We won't swell," the young mistress said, and, breaking off a chunk of *palyanytsa [flatbread]*, she went to feed the cow.

"Where are you taking the bread, you fool? Don't you have so much as a shred of conscience? You're taking away the last of our bread!"

"For priests, a first wife is the last one, but we'll have more bread," Onyska retorted. "The cattle shouldn't have to perish."

"Well, we shouldn't have to perish either!"

"You'll live," Onyska flung out, smiling, as she ran to the garden with a hoe.

"Do you want to raise the dust, so that more of it gets into our eyes?" her husband attacked her.

"God help you!" a passer-by called out in derision as he walked past the garden.

"Thank you," Onyska replied, and her tone made it clear that she had to keep on weeding and had no time to look up.

The strange behaviour of the young woman finally attracted even the attention of strangers.

"She's a fool! She's never known hunger, and so she's acting stupidly," some of the people said.

"She lacks a conscience!" others grumbled.

"She's not a fool, and she doesn't lack a conscience; she's smart," still others said. "She knows she won't die of hunger— she'll send her husband, father-in-law, and mother-in-law to work for others, and she'll stay at home and not have to do anything."

But they were all wrong.

There was only one person who guessed the truth.

"She knows something," Granny Sokhviya said.

Onyska truly did know something. She was absolutely confident that God is *merciful*. And the villagers' tears of despair could not extinguish the bright light of her deep faith. Moreover, she also knew that "if the women do penance, dig a well in three days when there's a new moon, and bless it, using the money they earn selling their homespun cloth, God would revive the withered stalks."

She had been told this by a woman passer-by who had been on seventeen pilgrimages to the Monastery of the Caves in Kyiv. And so Onyska waited impatiently for the new moon, concealing the joyful secret in her heart. As soon as the slender golden horn flashed in the evening sky, she hurried to tell the women about the pilgrim's advice, and the hearts of even the most sceptical ones leapt in hope.

In three days, a well was dug in the lowland. The men, doing a penance of their own, carried oak logs on their shoulders from the forest to build the curb around the well. The priest was invited to bless the well on Sunday, and so, on Saturday, Onyska told the women to sweep up the area around the well and spread it with fresh maple shavings, and ordered the men to cut boughs and stick them in the ground around the curb.

On Sunday morning, Onyska brought in a table, decorated it with *rushnyky [embroidered linen ceremonial cloths]*, set up icons on it, spread a *plakhta [a coarse hempen cloth]* on the ground in front of it for the priest, and placed new wooden buckets in all four corners of the clearing. She borrowed an ornamental dish for the holy water and procured a sprinkler for it made of lush, fragrant grasses.

Then she called the children together, washed them, and, having instilled the fear of hunger in them, told them to stay on their knees throughout the entire prayer service. Finally, she selected the liveliest little girl, gave her a white handkerchief to wave, and sent her to the nearest mound to keep an eye out for the priest.

By the time she finished all the preparations, the young woman was completely worn-out and perspiring profusely, but, through her efforts, she had created a festive day, the likes of which people had never seen before. And she had resurrected, in their hearts, their lost faith in God's infinite mercy.

The prayer service was over; the water was blessed. The villagers, carrying crosses and church banners, moved in a procession into the fields. And, by the time they finished sprinkling the sown fields with holy water, a samovar was bubbling on a bench in Onyska's home, and tea that her generous hand had made as black as tar, was boiling in a sleek teapot. A table was spread for the honoured guests—the priest and the deacon—and on it were placed convex glasses and a huge frying pan brimming with an omelette and fried, fatty bacon. The priest blessed the food on the table and seated himself in the place of honour under the icons, while the deacon sat down on a bench next to him. The father-in-law offered the guests drinks, and Onyska passed them some tea.

"If it's possible, give the priest a teaspoon," the deacon whispered to Onyska.

"A teaspoon! Oh, my God!" Onyska grabbed her head in despair and ran as fast as she could to Granny Chayka's home.

"Quick, give me a teaspoon, that silver one," she cried.

"What teaspoon? I don't have a teaspoon!" the old woman fired back angrily.

"It's for the priest . . . I saw it in your trunk."

"Where would it have come from? You must have seen it in your dreams . . ."

"It's lying in the trunk drawer, wrapped in an embroidered cloth. Give me the keys to the trunk, and I'll find it myself."

"Well, just listen to her—give her the keys to the trunk! So, you want to comb through my things and rob me?" the old woman screamed.

"I'm begging you—everyone's begging you. It's for the priest! You didn't give any money or any cloth to have the water blessed; so at least give us your teaspoon."

"I don't have a teaspoon! I don't have one, and I never had one," the old woman shouted, emphatically waving her arms.

"May your fields never yield, as long as you live! May they never see rain, as long as you live! May that teaspoon stop the sun's light from shining on you!" the young woman swore at the old woman and, cursing her one final time, ran off to Mariya's house. She grabbed a small wooden teaspoon from a shelf and dashed home.

Thank God, the teaspoon fit in the glass, and the priest even liked it. There's no need to say anything else about all the rest, of course, because Onyska had seen to everything and prepared it in the best possible manner.

The Mercy of God | 455

In the evening, a cloud moved in menacingly; the rooks grew restless, a wind blew in from the south, and there was a scent of rain in the air.

Onyska should have been overjoyed! But, no! She felt as if someone had ploughed on her side of the boundary, as if someone had poured boiling tar into her heart. Questions whirled in her head, and her thoughts buzzed around her like flies in the autumn.

"She didn't give so much as a *shah [half a penny]* or any cloth, and she didn't do anything," she thought. "And she even begrudged the teaspoon. God can see all this. How will he punish her? Will He have the rain bypass her field? Will He let the rain fall only on her garden that's dry as a rock? Or will He, perhaps, disperse all the clouds from her land and prevent her from seeding any buckwheat and hemp?"

All day long, she could not get Granny Chayka out of her mind. All day long, her questions and worries did not cease, and she lay down to sleep with an uneasy heart.

At midnight, thunder crashed. Everyone in the house woke up. Onyska also jumped to her feet.

The orchard was rustling, a humming sound—the precursor of a violent storm—filled the air, and the thunder rumbled. The father-in-law went outdoors, and Onyska ran out after him.

Half the sky was overcast with a black cloud, and fiery snakes were leaping horizontally and vertically across the cloud. A sudden flash of lightning flooded the farmstead with a brilliant light, and Granny Chayka's cottage shimmered like a white flower on a black tapestry.

"There will be rain, praise God," the father-in-law stated, as he crossed himself.

"Please, God! Pass by her house, pass over it!" And the young woman also crossed herself.

A few drops of rain splashed down.

"It's raining," said the father-in-law, crossing himself a second time.

"Look, father—it seems to me that there isn't any rain falling on Granny Chayka's cottage," Onyska remarked.

"Yes, there is, my daughter. It's raining the same all over."

After a few moments, the wind abated, and the rain poured down in buckets.

456 | The Mercy of God

"Glory to You, O God!" the father-in-law crossed himself a third time. "The rain is falling on the entire district. Merciful God has taken pity on us sinners after all."

"Merciful . . . Oh!" the young woman sighed heavily and dejectedly dragged herself back into the house.

No one was sleeping in the house; it did not even occur to anyone to lie down. The long awaited rain that had finally come so suddenly brought great joy to everyone, and every new drop of rain increased that joy, filled empty granaries with more and more grain, and generously poured hope into people's hearts. Every fresh streamlet carved an increasingly deep road to good fortune for the people who had been freed unexpectedly from the claws of hunger, maybe even death. And it seemed to them that it would be a great sin to sleep through or miss even a single moment of nature's great resurrection from death.

Even though Onyska knew and understood all this, her anger was greater than her understanding, greater than her will. She was losing all hope of seeing God's wrath. The Lord had not willed the rain to bypass Granny Chayka's yard, fields, or meadows. It had poured down on her beets, potatoes, and hemp, just as it had on those of all the other people.

Onyska was offended by God—to the point of tears—for not putting any boundaries or limits on His mercy, for condoning such a great wrong. Her heart felt heavy, as if the weighty sacks of rye, wheat, and potatoes that Granny Chayka's fields would yield this summer were pressing down on her chest . . .

Onyska silently entered the house, as silently lay down on the floor, and pulled a blanket over her head. She did not want to see or hear her father-in-law, mother-in-law, brother-in-law, and husband rejoicing in the mercy of God.

The Coffin
A Sketch
(1913)

Heavy autumnal clouds had hovered overhead for an entire week.

Mykhaylo, away on a military mission during this time, had not written how he was getting along; Annet, Halya, and Nyusya—also known as Nyuta—were living through days of heavy sorrow.

On days such as these, one's soul is shuttered behind three locks, and it is not easy to strike a chord that could make its way into it.

At least, not Beethoven, nor Mozart, nor Bach, nor even Liszt could evoke a response.

Halya gathered up their works—Sonata in A Minor, Fugue in B Minor, Polonaise in E Minor, Minuet in D Minor—put the scores away, and glanced at the clock.

It would be twilight in half an hour, and it would be terrifying to go to the store by herself, but, God forbid, if there was no interesting music for the evening—her soul, saddened by autumnal thoughts and confused by all manner of questions, would not be easily calmed. Yearning, pleading, begging for comfort and consolation, it would not fall asleep until the sun rose.

Her only hope lay in music. More precisely, in the music of modern composers . . . the most modern ones of all. The famous classical composers had lived and experienced life in a too simple and elementary fashion; they did not appreciate the fine nuances of human emotions. Their melodies were transparent and clear; their chords, always harmonious, could not reverberate on the countless rusty, broken, tangled strings in the heart of a person living in the twentieth century.

One's heart demanded something indistinct, foggy, confused, and incomprehensible, both in form and content, but it had to be bold, definitive, with strange cadencies, unusual dissonancies, unexpected consonancies, and a finale . . . that did not bring a resolution.

Within two minutes, Halya was on the veranda. It was drizzling outside; the sidewalks were covered with sticky, autumnal mud, and dirty water flowed swiftly in all the gutters.

Halya stopped on the steps to unfurl her umbrella.

"He was so young and healthy . . ." sighed someone close by.

"A student. He came from far away."

"He died, they say, from hunger."

"No, he came down with a fever."

"What kind of fever? He poisoned himself. Money was being gathered for his coffin, and I gave two *kopiyky [pennies]* as well."

"You're lying!"

"You're lying yourself, you infidel dog!"

The quarrel gained momentum, and the air was filled with the most colourful words found in the repertoire of the street.

Halya turned her head to where the voices were coming from; three old beggarwomen and a barefoot vagabond were sitting in a row against the wall.

She hurried past them and, constrained by her fashionable skirt, minced her way down the sidewalk; she was heading for the small platform at which the streetcar stopped. There was no one there, and no streetcar was in sight. Halya sat down on a small bench. The endlessly long street—disproportionately wide, newly paved, and not yet properly enclosed—was completely deserted and overcast with the grey mist of the drizzle; it was only far off in the distance—several field lengths away—that a spot showed up darkly in the very middle of the street. The spot was slowly moving forward, but its contours could not be discerned because of the mist, and so it was impossible to determine what was moving down the street until it was almost even with the platform.

A catafalque! A pair of muddy, raven-black horses hauled a catafalque on which a yellow coffin rested. There was not a soul nearby, except for the drivers of the hearse—two dark and dreadful looking men in tattered clothes and crumpled, faded felt hats with ripped brims. There was no sound except for the even, rhythmical pounding of the horses' hooves on the cobblestones . . .

"It's that student!" Halya immediately recalled. "The unfortunate student that the old beggarwomen were talking about. The one who came here and poisoned himself . . . Probably in the wake of a tragic love affair . . .

"Oh, God! Will there ever appear on this earth the great genius who will finally uncover the pattern in the labyrinth of the human soul, discover the laws of the psyche, and formulate the principles governing sympathy, antipathy, and the union of souls? Will human happiness ever be secured? Will there ever be an end to the eternal tragedy of love and the shattered hopes of a heart in love?

"But perhaps he really did die of hunger? He came from distant parts . . . He arrived here full of strength and hopes, with a sincere desire to work. Perhaps he rushed around, searched for work, pleaded for it as one pleads for alms, but was given nothing. He didn't find any. There wasn't any to be found. 'Even without you, there are more than enough people who want work. There are ten times as many workers as needed by capitalism,' they replied to him. And so, he committed suicide . . .

"Oh, God! Will there ever be an end to this social disorder, the injustice and capriciousness—so plainly evident to everyone—of capitalism? And where was pity? A worker dies of hunger, a human being commits suicide—and everyone is indifferent. They don't even pay their last respects to the victim; not a single soul accompanies the body . . . All alone in life, and all alone in death. Oh, people have no conscience!"

The young lady leapt from the sidewalk into the thick mud and walked behind the coffin . . .

At the same moment, an old woman appeared before her, as if she had risen out of the ground: "Give to the poor, for Christ's sake."

"May the departed one enter the kingdom of heaven!" another elderly voice spoke up on her other side.

The young lady opened her wallet, took out two *pyataky [nickels]* and gave them to the old beggarwomen.

The old women bowed down low before her, and it was as if this bow served as a signal for their companions . . .

From the sidewalks on both sides of the street, ragged, tattered beggars, cripples, tramps, and children moved towards her. They all stretched out their hands to her, prayed for the soul of the newly departed one, and then, satisfied by her generosity, walked beside her as a sign of their gratitude—or, perhaps, in the hope of cajoling another mite.

A little while later, a few curious young boys joined the group; and when they drew up alongside a small church where an evening service had just started, two townswomen came out of the cemetery and headed towards the coffin as well.

Halya heard the old beggarwomen tell the townswomen that she, Halya, was a relative of the deceased, and then they continued whispering as they walked along. What they were saying—Halya did not hear. Her thoughts, her heart, her soul, and her body were with the coffin, beside the coffin.

It had all happened too strangely. It was not possible to view this event as a simple, ordinary, chance occurrence—it contained elements of a transcendental nature. Everything that had happened in this particular episode must have been set in motion, long ago, in some other sphere; it was subject to other laws, had its own logic, its own goal. And the most minute detail of the deceased's life, and the most insignificant fact in her life most certainly formed links in a chain that, in the end, joined them together on this day.

There were no physiological, or physical, or economic, or social laws that could explain the fact that she was destined to pay the last respects to the deceased, that she had been successful in forming a small cortege to walk after the body of a completely unknown stranger . . .

No, most certainly *not a stranger*. A stranger in body, perhaps, but not in soul.

Her eyes could not see this student, but her soul could; it sympathised with his suffering, and it had ached because of him for a long time now; it just had not known how to express its pain. It did not know how to say it; instead, it had done what it wanted to do. It had made her turn against the classical composers, forced her to go to the store, sent the beggars to sit near her veranda, delayed the streetcar, willed the coffin with the deceased to come by just at the right moment, and gathered together the tramps and beggars around her, so that the unfortunate stranger would be remembered in at least the most rudimentary fashion.

The catafalque was passing a flower shop.

"Ah! There should be a wreath! And, as luck would have it— there's a shop right along the way."

Halya dashed into the shop, selected an exquisite wreath made of flowers from the steppes, threw some money on the counter, and raced off to the catafalque.

But the catafalque no longer held a coffin.

"Where is it? Where's the coffin?" Halya, alarmed and astonished, asked a townswoman.

The townswoman did not reply immediately—she gazed at Halya and the wreath as if she were seeing an apparition.

"Where has the coffin gone?" Halya asked again.

"The coffin? They carried it into the house, of course—a tradeswoman has died in there. But aren't you a relative of hers?"

Halya blushed furiously and leaped into the first streetcar that came along.

But when the conductor walked up to her, and she reached for her wallet—it was not in her pocket.

A lady on the streetcar offered her a cold coin: "Don't be embarrassed, Miss; please, take it for the ticket. When a person is in distress, you can lose not only your money, but your mind."

Halya jerked away from the lady, bolted out of the moving streetcar, and almost fell under the wheels of an automobile.

The Coin
(1913)

There is a tradition, handed down to us by our ancestors, of borrowing a plot from fantasy for a story for the festive season. There was a period when I was similarly indebted.

At the time, I was living on the eleventh floor, and the entire city, along with its great culture—its street cars, night clubs, schools, and churches, and its riches, poverty, and great sins—as well as the wonderful panorama of the countryside, with its forests, hills, steppes, and farmsteads were spread before me.

It was easy for me to open my window and say: "Fly away!"

And my fantasy would instantly stretch her thin little wings and soar into the boundless sky.

I never gave my fantasy any instructions, for I did not know where to send her. She was the one that chose the direction in which she wanted to set out. At times, she would fly to the heavens, warm herself near the sun, exchange smiles with the stars, bathe in dark clouds, transform herself into the shiny baubles of a blizzard, or stretch the skein of a rainbow before my eyes. At other times, she would plunge to the earth, race beside streetcars and automobiles, participate in expropriations, fly into palaces as an uninvited guest, descend into dungeons, study the encylopaedia of Brockhaus, steal rhymes, or, after attiring a beautiful duchess in velvet, mend threadbare shirts.

Whenever she tired of the present, she turned to the past or roamed through the future. And, after gathering impressions, thoughts, and moods, she would return, and then I could take as much as I desired from her storehouse of treasures.

And I could do so best of all when she returned with at least a tiny bit of hope on her wings, a small spark of warmth . . . At such a time . . . Oh! Then I felt myself to be a king above all kings, a giant above all giants, and a man wealthier than all others. At times like that, I heedlessly and unstintingly poured out entire handfuls of riches that I wanted to bestow upon you.

But now I live in a basement. There are three rows of stakes in front of my window. Yes, three rows of sharply hewed stakes, with thirty-two stakes in every row—thirty-two stakes nailed with very long pegs to oak laths.

I am no longer a king; I am a prisoner, a captive, a beggar, because my fantasy is incapacitated. Wounded, covered in scratches and bloody sores, and with her tiny wings mutilated by the sharp stakes, she became weak and enervated, and so I said to her: "Sleep!"

And I began to live in the real world—in the reality that was brought to me by the letter carrier dressed in his dirty cap made of Russian leather, or by the constable, or the watchman; in the reality that forces its way in through the doorway along with the fumes from the bakery, the stench of the air, and the song of a drunkard . . .

I live in the real world, and I remember holidays only when the vesper bell finds its way through my open window.

But today, just before the greatest of all holidays, all the bells, all ordinary sounds, are being drowned in a clamouring that is issuing from beneath the earth. There is much shouting there, a deafening uproar, because the chief devil, Mr. Beelzebub, has disappeared; the honourable gentleman went off somewhere in the morning, and he still has not shown up . . . and it's midnight already.

Mrs. Beelzebub is shouting; she is no longer able to hide her feelings; she no longer takes the time to put on the airs of a well-bred lady—she is yelling like a huckstress, so loudly that my wooden floor is vibrating with her shouts and curses: "Where has he disappeared? Where is he carousing? Where is he gadding about? Has he fallen asleep? Has he forgotten that on this day every master bestows his largesse on his vassals? Has he forgotten that he is Satan, cursed by God, and that all his power, might, and significance lie in his great talent to lure people with the most beautiful gifts?

"Can it be that he has become angry at the earth and no longer wishes to have anything to do with people? But, if so, what will he do in this world? And who will serve the devils? Even the way things are now, the number of slaves is growing smaller every year, and there have been times when Beelzebub himself feared there would be a strike.

"Not too long ago, for example, he did not know what kind of wages he should be paying to entice souls to hell. He took glory and power to them, but he brought it all back home: 'Souls have no need of all of this!' What, then, do they want? What kind of payment will satisfy them now? What kind of treats are needed to attract them? What kind of treasures are needed to bribe them? Does Beelzebub know? Where is he? Where the devil is he?"

And Lucifer's wife sent off messengers, one after the other. And it seemed as if all the devils had been dispatched, because I could hear echoes in the deserted corridors of hell, the clicking of the mistress's heels, the rattling of the souls scattered throughout hell, the slaps that the tsarina of the powers of darkness angrily administered to her children, and the wailing of Death . . .

It was this violent, harsh sound of Death's boundless despair that was the worst, the most terrifying. All the souls that Death had brought to hell were rejected by the mistress there. And Death swore in vain that all the souls, to the very last one, were mature and ripe, that they had all belonged to reputable people who had committed every possible sin.

The wife of Lucifer, refusing to believe Death, shook her as if she were a liar and shouted: "These souls are not yet ripe; they've fallen prematurely. These are the souls of infants! They're parodies of souls! They're all empty, without a grain of greed! They're all dried up and shrivelled like mushrooms, and as easily digestible as potatoes!

"Can love and jealousy, hate and betrayal be punished properly in them? How much pride is there in them—an ounce or two? Not even honour can be accommodated in them. Who the devil needs souls like these? What benefit, pleasure, or beauty is there in them? Is it worth the trouble to kindle a fire for such trash? To contrive paroxysms and payments for these dried up mushrooms? To sign agreements with such riffraff, or give them demand loans of all kinds? You, O Death, are just a provocateur! You're a traitor! You transport souls to heaven."

Death groaned, as if she had been stabbed in the heart, and burst into tears . . .

Then, suddenly, everything fell silent . . .

I fell to the floor and peeked through a crack. Beelzebub had arrived.

"Were you anxious? Were you worried, my darling, my little black dove?" his baritone voice, velvety-soft, and as sweet as the most seductive warbling, undulated through the air. "I was slightly detained in a village in the middle of the sea; I frolicked there with the waves and played with the pebbles. But I did not forget about the earth, nor about the holiday. No, I do have a present. I'm tossing it out now . . ."

Something knocked against one of my stakes.

I rushed up to the spot—there was a dark object on the snow. I bent over and picked it up. It was a counterfeit coin, a fifty-cent piece painstakingly fashioned out of lead.

"Our devil has gone mad," I thought. "Hell will soon be bankrupt. It won't be possible to find a single villain who will sell his soul for a mere fifty-cent coin. There's a fire burning in the stove, so I'll throw it in there—let his evil intentions melt like wax. But still . . . it would be interesting . . ."

I became very curious—even though I am no Eve . . .

It would be so interesting to see the humiliation of the devil, that I couldn't resist . . . I succumbed to temptation. Closing my eyes, I swung my right arm, and flung the coin with all my strength.

But as to where it fell, and who picked it up, and what happened, and who lost his soul, and where it happened, and what I heard— I'll tell you all about it another time.